FAMILY NURSING AND CHILD CARE

C. LUISE RIEHL
Night Supervisor
Assistant Administrator
  of Nursing Services
San Jose Hospital,
  San Jose, California

CHAS. A. BENNETT CO., INC.,
  Peoria, Illinois

Copyright 1961
BY CARMELLA LUISE RIEHL, R.N.

Library of Cong. Cat. No. 61-6566
PRINTED IN THE UNITED STATES OF AMERICA
Second Printing
26VH120

IN MEMORY OF MY HUSBAND, WILLIAM

C.L.R.

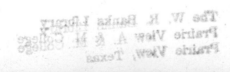

AUTHOR'S NOTE

It is a great human privilege to be able to take care of those you love when they are ill. Also, to know the reasons for good and bad health in your younger brothers and sisters makes it possible for you to contribute wonderfully to your own health habits as well as to theirs.

You may think of nursing as something too "intimate" for words! Yet it has as much true dignity as any other profession. When someone you love is ill, he depends on your mercy for many of the routine acts we think of as strictly private under normal conditions. Only in an emergency will you be called upon to assist in personal matters. At such times, the patient is depending upon you for inspirational, as well as physical help. So you must know how to give him the most aid possible.

There is nothing "wrong" with any natural human function. You can certainly be proud of your knowledge when the time comes that it is needed!

CONTENTS

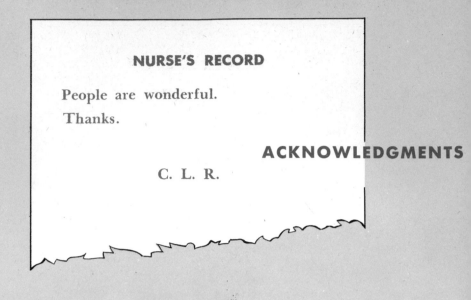

NURSE'S RECORD

People are wonderful.

Thanks.

ACKNOWLEDGMENTS

C. L. R.

The author is deeply grateful to the many persons who helped make this book possible. To the people who read and reread, to the many schools that opened their classrooms for trial runs of the various chapters, to the students who posed patiently—the author is deeply grateful.

My acknowledgment to Mrs. Jean Holbrook, Dean of Girls, Los Gatos High School, for consultation on the over-all manuscript and for the chapters on nursing arts; to Mrs. Mary F. Faverty, R.N., for consultation on nursing procedures; to Mrs. Martha Durham, physical education instructor, Sunnyvale High School, for reviewing the chapters on health and physical fitness; to Mrs. Helen Howard, Libby-McNeill-Libby Food Laboratories, for reviewing the chapters on nutrition, health and child growth; to Mrs. Mary Welton, Public Relations Specialist, for reading and condensing the chapters concerning health organization; to Mrs. Phyllis Kaufman, homemaking instructor, Sunnyvale High School, for reviewing the chapters on food and nutrition; to Drs. Richard P. Alexander and Coy L. Purcell for consultation and instruction on the sections concerning motherhood, child care, and anatomy, and to Mr. Jack Figareida for his photographic talents.

C. Luise Riehl, R.N.

1: NURSING AND YOU

Character of a Home Nurse . . .

There are probably many reasons why you are taking this course in Home Nursing. One reason is that you want to care for other people; another, perhaps, is to become familiar with certain facts that will show you how to live a more useful life.

When you work with other people, you have to know how to get along with them. People are often hard to understand, but you must accept them as you find them. Why is it that some people succeed and others do not? Perhaps it is because the successful know how to make people feel comfortable and the others do not. Your personality will help you or hinder you in getting along with other people.

Most hospitals have been established primarily to care for the short-term patient; thus, some patients, when they are discharged, still need care. Many communities have a home care program which is a partial answer to this need. Under this plan, visiting nursing and social agents supervise and instruct others to care for members of their families. The agency's work becomes easier if someone in the home can help.

What Affects Personality . . .

Let us look at the girl who gets along with other people. She fits in with those her own age, knows how to act with younger people, and knows how to be tactful with adults. First, she knows what she is doing and why; second, she enjoys her life and the people in it; third, she wants people to like and trust her— and they do.

Personality has its beginning when a baby is conceived; parents pass on to their children certain mental abilities as well as physical traits. As soon as a baby is born, his personality begins to appear; food, health, playmates, and other persons affect him. His personality will show how successfully he handles his adjustments. His home life and the personalities of his parents affect him more than anything else. He needs to be with people who care about him, and each other, who try to keep him happy and comfortable in a pleasant, friendly place.

A very reliable measure of your family's success and stability is the way its members feel and behave toward one another. Below is a quiz on family relationships used at the University of Pennsylvania. Read each question; think it through carefully before answering "yes" or "no."

As a rule, do you:
1. Have pride in one another?
2. Act considerately and generously?
3. Talk over family problems freely?
4. Strive for a pleasant, cheerful home?
5. Work and play together as a family?

Work and play together as a family.

Take an interest in religious activities.

6. Share the car without squabbling?
7. All usually eat at the same time?
8. Celebrate each person's birthday?
9. Take an interest in religious activities?
10. Respect one another's privacy?
11. All do your share of household tasks?
12. Notice and praise each member's accomplishments?
13. Encourage every member's special interests?
14. Co-operate when the going is tough?

These simple questions deal with the character and heart of your family. If your "yes" answers total 12 or more, it is almost certain that you have a united family. The average family scores 9 or 10. If your score is less than 7, something is wrong. The first approach is to help develop more understanding and better co-operation within your family.

We must go on from this to consider all other possible influences on our lives. By understanding these influences we are better able to understand personality traits. Sometimes we adopt the wrong traits, ones that actually irritate and antagonize others. We all need to be loved, to have success, and to feel safe. Because we need these things so much we try to get them, first one way and, if that doesn't work, another. Finally, each of us works out a pattern of behavior. Your personality is *expressed in* your behavior, your ability, successes, and failures.

It consists of your appearance, character traits, habits, and manners; it is the way you behave toward other people and how you react to things and events. It is the character of your spirit.

Self-check . . .

Let's see if your personality will help or hinder you in your desire to help others. Will you be successful and happy?

Ask yourself these questions to see if you show promise of developing the characteristics needed in nursing:

1. Are you reliable? A patient's welfare depends on your faithfulness in carrying out the doctor's orders.

2. Do you reach out for responsibility? The girl who volunteers to help at home shows the willingness and capacity for teamwork that a nurse must have.

3. Are you a good student? You must learn skills.

4. Have you an inquiring mind? A good nurse constantly asks "Why?" Is a crying child in pain? Is he frightened? Is he hungry, lonesome, too warm or too cold? You must be part "mother" as well as nurse.

5. Are you adaptable? You must have that sympathy and willingness to adjust that come from understanding and liking other people.

6. Have you a good sense of humor; are you cheerful?

All members of the family should be encouraged to follow their special interests.

The Public Health Nurse leaves instructions for your patient's diet.

Humor is like an air cushion. It eases the jolts. You must be able to see the ridiculous and laugh at it; see the heartbreaking and still smile for your patient's sake.

7. Are you tolerant? Pain, or helpless inactivity, often does not give a *patient* much *patience!*

8. Are you unselfish? You must often put the special needs of your patient before your own well-earned pleasure and convenience.

9. Are you in good health, physically and emotionally?

10. Do you have courage of the kind that helps you through unpleasant emergencies?

Perhaps this course will lead you to think of nursing as a career. If you can give the qualities of mind, heart, and spirit that nursing asks of you, it will give you, in return, rewards that can't be counted in dollars—rewards that can never be stolen or lost—and the satisfaction of knowing that the working hours of your life are of special use to others.

All signs indicate that the need for nurses will become greater, rather than less. Our population is not simply increasing; it is "exploding," as the sociologists say. Health education programs and free clinics inspire more people each year to seek early aid for illness. The growth of insurance protection makes it possible for more people to use the hospitals. Over 59 per cent of our population is now protected by some form of medical and hospital insurance, and this ratio is increasing. Hospital admissions have doubled since 1935. Although the average hospital stay used to be nearly sixteen days, new drugs and medical techniques have cut this average to about eight days. This very fact means that more nurses and nursing care are required to speed up patients' recovery.

"IN OTHER WORDS . . ."

A nurse must be liked. People do not necessarily like us because we are neat, honest, and dress well. People like us for the feelings we arouse in them. If you help people feel smart and happy, they will like you. Because you have to work at this, you may find you haven't as much time to think of yourself.

"Do's" for making people like you: Listen to them; be easy and friendly; give them credit for doing good work; appreciate their help; notice what they do. "Don'ts": Don't act bored or interrupt; don't always be airing your own troubles; don't boast about yourself; don't pry into things that do not concern you; don't give away "secrets."

You get along with people better, and care for them better, when you understand them and know how to make them feel comfortable. You learn how by understanding yourself. Perhaps you have been wondering why the subject is treated so informally here—why formal psychological terms are not used. It is because you are *primarily* learning how to care for others better, rather than taking a course in psychology. Opportunity to serve others is sometimes overlooked because of our inability to see ourselves in the proper light. There are simple values in life to direct you and remind you to do the right thing, if you take time to think about them. There are courtesies that you are expected to know. They will eventually affect your success. You will have opportunities to study psychology; meanwhile, you are in a period of concentrated special learning; what is learned here will stay with you and serve you all your life. You can be a more useful, more expert member of your family; eventually, whether you choose to follow nursing as a career or not, it will make you a better person because you will have learned the value of health care, good habits, neatness, perseverance, loyalty, careful planning, and skill. This knowledge may prove a key to success in every life venture for you.

● Think about your character traits that have helped you up to now. Make a list of them.

● Make a point of talking to classmates that you do not know very well.

● Make a list of your good habits. Have you been told at any time that you have an annoying habit? How can you do something about it?

14

NURSE'S RECORD

Your health is an obligation.

Achieving the physical fitness required of a good nurse.

Health and heredity.

Health and emotions.

Health and environment.

What is meant by good health? You can understand *illness* only if you know (1) what *wellness* is, and (2) the *service* you can do yourself and others by staying well.

Your Health Is an Obligation . . .

Much has been written about health obligations. You have an obligation to be healthy, first of all, because health makes life worth living. It has its own rewards: sound sleep, good appetite, strength to do the day's tasks with enough energy left over for fun and recreation—these are beyond price.

Secondly, the need to keep healthy stems from a social obligation. To burden others with concern for your welfare, to force additional work on them, is to become a social liability. On the other hand, an abundance of physical well-being means that others depend upon you for extra help, which is a great personal satisfaction to all of us.

The heart of the obligation to be healthy rests in the fact that health makes all responsibility easier; activity becomes fun. Poor health, low vitality, and weakness in body functions lead to a lack of desire to be successful. Furthermore, good health saves money, and that is certainly a worthwhile duty.

15

Health is a state of physical, mental, and social well-being, as well as the absence of disease and illness.

The effects of food shortages and poor food habits on the "health" of a country are shown in Red China, India, and others. Bad health attitudes lead to suicides and mental illness in our country.

Achieving the Physical Fitness Required of a Good Nurse . . .

We must keep in mind that "fitness is total." It is the quality of the whole person. It is as much a state of mind as a state of body. It is impossible to think of the one without the other. The human body is like a machine in many ways; health depends upon understanding how it is put together and how to keep each part in order.

A truly healthy person uses his mind effectively. He applies it to health as well as to other life problems. To hold onto physical fitness, it must be constantly re-won. Results of exercise soon wear off; vacations readily lose their tonic effect; rest is succeeded by fatigue. The solution is to anticipate this cycle and learn to make up every day for the resources that are used. Besides the regular demands, we must be ready for unexpected trials. Only by knowing what the body requires can we have confidence in meeting the day's emergencies.

Physical fitness gives us muscles that are always ready to go into action. This readiness is called *muscle tone*. When muscle tone is good, you feel springy and alive; poor muscle tone makes you feel "dragged out." Using muscles is the only way to maintain them. Massage helps a bedridden person. Always remember that if a patient does not use certain muscles, or uses them very little, they will lose tone.

The term *body mechanics* means co-ordinating the movements of the body. With proper body mechanics, you handle your bones and muscles efficiently, easily, and gracefully. *Posture* comes in here because it is related to bones and muscles. Good posture allows the body to work smoothly with the least amount of strain. It also makes us look better. Good posture depends upon good body mechanics, general health, healthy muscles, and good habits.

How to check on your posture: (1) Stand in front of a full-length mirror and line your body in this manner: head erect, chest up and forward, abdomen flat but not tense, feet parallel, one slightly ahead of the other. You should feel relaxed. (2) Now, let yourself stand in a normal position. Is your posture still good? If so, your chest allows room for heart and lungs, your diaphragm is free to move, and your circulation is superior; your pelvic and abdominal organs have room and support; ligaments are not strained; you stand firmly, look well poised, and feel sure of yourself.

With good standing posture as the basis for all exercises, you now must strive for good muscle control. Study the pictured stances and practice the following exercises. You will find that proper positioning and strengthening of certain groups of muscles will benefit you in lifting, turning, and serving a patient. Muscle conditioning will help you face each day cheerfully and zestfully.

Stand straight with feet apart.

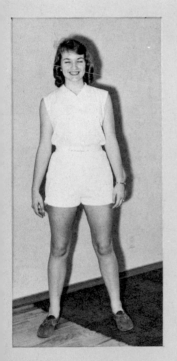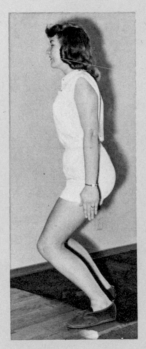

To the count of four, bend knees, sink to a semi-squatting position. Keep back straight. To the count of four, slowly rise to a standing position.

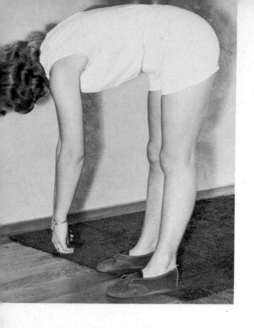 

Bend forward from hips; let arms hang, relaxed. Grasp inside calves of legs. Hold firmly and pull, stretching shoulder muscles. Relax.

Start from squatting position with both arms extended back on left side. Rise, twisting to opposite side as far as possible; fling arms overhead, reaching backwards. Relax.

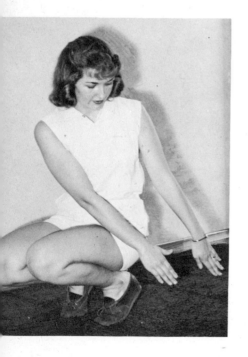 

Stand erect; hold arms straight up. To the count of four, stretch one hand as high as possible until you feel muscle over ribs strain. Relax. Repeat with other hand.

Health and Heredity . . .

Your original health equipment is given to you by your Creator through your parents. They pass on to you traits received from their fathers and mothers. In the father and mother cells that you came from were the *genes,* or determiners, that influenced your development. These genes are in bundles called *chromosomes;* you received 24 chromosomes from your mother and 24 from your father. The genes from one parent were paired with similar ones from the other. The stronger gene takes over and is called the dominant gene; the other, called the recessive gene, has little or no effect on your development, although it may dominate in your children.

Only in rare cases are malformations or disorders of the

body inherited. Most deformative genes are recessive; a person would have to inherit two of them to be defective. (You might inherit a quick temper, however, from a strong gene!) A good inheritance starts you off on a good path of life, but you can see why possibilities for health are not alike for everybody. The best condition you are capable of reaching may be less or better than that of a classmate, or other children in your family. That is why you should learn and remember your "health capacity." For instance, you may need nine hours of sleep to carry on your daily living routine, while your sister may get along very well on eight hours of sleep. You must know yourself and how far you can go; in other words—know your limitations and try to make the most of your outstanding talents.

Health and Emotions . . .

If we are to remember that health and fitness mean considering the body as a whole, we should break this down a little further. There are three "centers" involved in health—the *body organs,* the *mind* or "thinking brain," and the *emotions* or "primitive brain." Emotional health and mental health are hard to separate. The emotions meant here are not feelings such as pain and hunger, but rather the way we respond to people and events. Sometimes, guided by habit patterns or attitudes, they affect the body functions. For instance, you come to class unprepared for an examination; after you take it you worry all day whether you passed it, at dinner you are unable to eat, and later that night you are unable to sleep. You see how it goes: The emotions affect the body, the body affects the mind, the mind affects the emotions, etc. One worries, fears, hates, or loves with his whole body.

Good health means that your body organs, mind, and emotions are all working in proper balance, with none of them predominating the others harmfully. Medical science has been giving more and more attention to the effects of emotional and mental attitudes upon the body. Many physical pains may be traced to emotional difficulties. A doctor's business is to keep the body in working order, but first, in order to correct a physical defect, he must discover the cause. This means he must consider everything about the patient.

Health and Environment . . .

Proper food and clothes, good homes, fine school or work

Poorly tended garbage areas invite disease. Cleanliness is just as easy.

conditions, opportunities for fun and new interests, all make it easier to have good health. You may associate most of these things with money, and feel that poor people will be less healthy. This is not necessarily true. The wealthy person who disregards rules of proper nutrition can be more undernourished than a product of the slums. The *atmosphere* of the home affects health; quarrels, criticism, and lack of affection have a bad physical effect.

By setting an example for you, your parents teach you about health from your birth; also they shelter you, feed you, and dress you according to climate and weather. Later, when you enter school, this health teaching through habit and example is picked up and carried on by your doctor, teachers, school nurse, physical education leader, and friends.

"IN OTHER WORDS . . ."

Health habits are closely related to body traits and functions. Your inherited qualities, your family circumstances, your studies, your ambitions, illnesses, and injuries all tend to mold them. As you progress in life, you will understand them better. Now is the time to begin in earnest.

- Do you have a health problem? Do you know why?
- List your father's and mother's physical traits. Now have a classmate

21

list yours and compare them to see which are predominant. Do the same for her.

• Why is physical fitness necessary for a nurse? List three answers on a separate sheet of paper.

• Choose a partner and check each other on exercises to strengthen the shoulders; lower back; thighs.

• Make a list of your health habits that could stand improvement.

• Discuss the effects of various emotions on the ill person. How will worrying affect his recovery?

• Is there a mental health center in your neighborhood or city? If so, discuss with your instructor the possibilities of having a representative visit your class and give a short talk on mental and body health relationship.

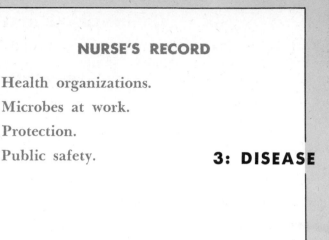

NURSE'S RECORD

Health organizations.

Microbes at work.

Protection.

Public safety.

3: DISEASE

The health of the people in the United States has improved greatly in the last 50 years. Improvement began when we realized that it was important to prevent disease—that this is partly the responsibility of national, state, and local agencies.

Civic health protection means keeping the city clean, setting standards for safe water; inspecting foods and buildings; providing health services and health education in the schools.

HEALTH ORGANIZATIONS

Federal agencies that carry on work relating to health are the Children's Bureau, the Office of Education and the Home Economics Division of the Department of Agriculture, the Office of Civilian Defense, and the United States Public Health Service in the Department of the Treasury, which is more extensive in range than any other federal health agency. Its functions are to prevent the spread of disease from other countries into this country and from one state to another; to study the cause and prevention of diseases that menace the public health; to assist other federal and private agencies to set up laws governing the use and control of drugs; to give aid to state and local health departments with their public health problems; and to give medical and hospital care to war veterans.

In working with state departments, our government is offering and urging the use of special programs in the fields of maternal and child health and in the control of social diseases.

Administrative Plan, Chief U.S. Health Agencies.

PRESIDENT
Chief Executive

CONGRESS	SUPREME COURT
DEPARTMENT OF AGRICULTURE	DEPARTMENT OF THE NAVY

BUREAU OF ANIMAL INDUSTRY
  HOME ECONOMICS
  CHEMISTRY AND SOILS
  PLANT INDUSTRY
  DAIRY INDUSTRY
	BUREAU OF MEDICINE AND SURGERY

DEPARTMENT OF COMMERCE	DEPARTMENT OF TREASURY
BUREAU OF CENSUS, STANDARDS, FISHERIES	DEPARTMENT OF NARCOTICS FEDERAL BOARD OF HOSPITALIZATION

DEPARTMENT OF THE INTERIOR	DEPARTMENT OF DEFENSE
	  SURGEON-GENERAL OF ARMY, NAVY,
	  AIR FORCE

COMMISSIONER OF THE OFFICE OF
  INSTITUTIONS IN THE DISTRICT
  OF COLUMBIA
	DEPARTMENT OF VETERANS' AFFAIRS

EDUCATION
INDIAN AFFAIRS
	EXTRA DEPARTMENTAL AGENCIES
	  MEDICAL HOMES
	  CONSTRUCTION SUPPLIES

DEPARTMENT OF LABOR
  CHILDREN'S BUREAU
  WOMEN'S BUREAU
	AMERICAN RED CROSS
	  AMERICAN PRINTING HOUSE FOR
	  BLIND
	  COLUMBIA INSTITUTION FOR THE
	  DEAF

DEPARTMENT OF HEALTH, EDUCATION AND WELFARE

SURGEON-GENERAL PUBLIC HEALTH SERVICE	COMMISSIONER OF EDUCATION
DIRECTOR OFFICE OF REHABILITATION	DIRECTOR SOCIAL SECURITY

State Health Department . . .

Every state has a department that works with local agencies to promote health and prevent disease. For example, in the use of the Salk vaccine against poliomyelitis, under the guidance and planned program of the federal health service, the state and local health departments working together were able to reach people in all sections of the population, including rural areas.

Administrative Plan, State Health Department.

GOVERNOR

Chief Executive

COMMISSIONER OF HEALTH

BOARD OF HEALTH

BOARD OF SUPERVISORS
DIRECTOR

DIRECTOR
DIVISION OF CANCER CONTROL

DIVISION OF PUBLIC HEALTH
     EDUCATION
     SCHOOL NURSING
     MATERNAL-CHILD HEALTH

DIRECTOR
DIVISION OF COMMUNICABLE
     DISEASES
     TUBERCULOSIS
     SOCIAL HYGIENE

DIRECTOR
DIVISION OF PUBLIC HEALTH
     NURSING
     SCHOOL HEALTH SUPERVISION

DIRECTOR
DIVISION OF LABORATORIES
     AND RESEARCH

DIRECTOR
DIVISION OF SANITATION

DIRECTOR
DIVISION OF ORTHOPEDICS

DIRECTOR
DIVISION OF MATERNITY, INFANT,
     AND CHILD HYGIENE

DIRECTOR
DIVISION OF PSYCHIATRY

DIRECTOR
DIVISION OF CHRONIC DISEASE

DIRECTOR
DIVISION OF VITAL STATISTICS

ADMINISTRATION OF STATE-TO-COUNTY LAW

OFFICERS IN CHARGE OF STATE HEALTH DISTRICTS
IN COUNTY, CITY, OR COUNTY-CITY DEPARTMENTS

HEALTH OFFICERS

Federal and state laws work together to protect us. The Federal Food, Drug, and Cosmetic Act controls the purity, safety, and labeling of foods and cosmetics that are sent from one state to another. State and local laws help control sanitation, communicable disease, and mother and child health.

Local Health Agencies . . .

Health problems are not exactly the same in all communities. They are related to the country, the climate, the food habits, and the living standards of the people who live there. Some groups live in crowded housing conditions; others will eat only certain types of foods. Often, superstitions and fears lead to poor health habits and little or no medical care. In the city, industrial lay-offs and plant shut-downs increase health problems. Depressions, wars, housing shortages, and rising costs of living also affect health.

States and local areas have the right to make their own health laws, but these laws vary, with some states having better

Administrative Plan, County Health Department.

STATE HEALTH DEPARTMENT

COUNTY COMMISSIONER OF HEALTH

COUNTY BOARD OF HEALTH	COUNTY BOARD OF SUPERVISORS
DIRECTOR—DIVISION OF ADMINISTRATION	DIRECTOR—DIVISION OF PUBLIC HEALTH NURSING
DIRECTOR—DIVISION OF COMMUNICABLE DISEASES	DIRECTOR—DIVISION OF SCHOOL HEALTH SUPERVISION AND PUBLIC HEALTH EDUCATION
DIRECTOR—DIVISION OF LABORATORIES	DIRECTOR—DIVISION OF SANITATION
DIRECTOR—DIVISION OF MATERNITY, INFANT AND CHILD HYGIENE	DIRECTOR—DIVISION OF VITAL STATISTICS

OFFICERS IN CHARGE OF HEALTH SERVICES
IN CITIES AND TOWNS OF THE COUNTY
(INCLUDES CIVIL DEFENSE)

HEALTH OFFICERS

health protection than others. Federal laws protect you, no matter where you live; state laws protect you if you are a resident of the state; local laws protect you if you are within the area. They must conform to federal laws as well as state. State laws must conform to federal laws. This means that even if the local community has inadequate health regulations, its residents still have a certain amount of protection.

Health organizations accomplish, on a large scale, what individuals could never do alone. Under this arrangement we have milk protection, meat protection, and protection of canned and packaged foods. We can use our water supply without fear of contamination, and put out our garbage knowing that it will be disposed of in such a manner as not to infect our community.

MICROBES AT WORK

Some of health's deadliest enemies are so small that they can be seen only under the strongest, most powerful microscope. These are called the disease-producing micro-organisms (microbes).

Illness comes from the disruption of body operations and from harmful organisms that enter it from the outside, although this was not discovered until the middle of the nineteenth century. Louis Pasteur, a French scientist, found that organisms from the air made milk spoil; he also discovered that these organisms grew and multipled but could be killed by heat and certain chemicals. Pasteurization of milk to destroy harmful organisms is one result of his studies.

Another researcher, Robert Koch, believed that an organism was the cause of tuberculosis, then went on to prove that it was found in the body of the person who had the disease. Such discoveries encouraged other scientists to look for specific organisms as the cause of other diseases.

Micro-organisms feed upon living things; they grow best in dark, moist, warm places, so most of them die if they are exposed to sunlight. (This is why we put sickroom furnishings out in the sun.) Although some organisms are harmful, others are useful to us. They are everywhere—in the air, the soil, in waste material, on the skin, and inside the body. Some organisms are so small that they cannot be seen even with the most powerful electronic microscope. Because technicians failed to isolate them even in the finest laboratory filters, they named them the "filtrable viruses."

Nose and Throat Infections . . .

Do you know how you catch a cold? The organisms occupy tiny drops of moisture which spread as people who have colds talk, laugh, cough, or sneeze. The cold-causing organisms get into your body through your mouth or nose. Some other diseases that enter this way are scarlet fever, whooping cough, pneumonia, tuberculosis, chicken pox, measles, mumps, and smallpox.

Digestive Tract Infections . . .

Organisms which cause diseases of the digestive tract—as well as poisons—enter the body mostly in food and water. To help avoid contamination, we have water, food, and drug laws. Garbage and body wastes that go into sewage are carriers of disease and must be disposed of safely. Food handlers with infectious diseases transfer organisms to food, so are required to take health examinations before and periodically during their employment. See why you, too, should wash your hands carefully before preparing meals.

Skin and Mucous Membrane Infections . . .

Some organisms penetrate and irritate the surface of the skin. Ringworm, impetigo, and athlete's foot are examples. Others cause diseases that affect the whole body or attack specific parts; they multiply and produce poisons. Some of these will be discussed in another chapter.

Once they enter the body, disease organisms try to grow and multiply by feeding on body tissues. They cause pain; damage and destroy tissues. This process is called infection. It may be confined to one place (local) or spread throughout the body (general).

PROTECTION

We are almost constantly exposed to infection of some sort. The body puts up its own defenses. If disease organisms succeed in establishing an infection, the body goes to work immediately to overcome it. In some cases, it builds up such a resistance during this fight that the disease may never occur again—for example, whooping cough and chicken pox.

Naturally all lines of defense are strongest when a person is in good physical condition. This is always the best protection against diseases such as colds and pneumonia, which a person can have many times in his life. Body resistance can be strengthened by eating the right kinds of food; having regular meals and proper elimination; getting enough sleep, rest, and recreation; spending some time each day in outdoor activity; and wearing adequate and suitable clothing for weather conditions of all kinds.

Scientific discoveries have also made it possible to increase resistance to disease. When organisms get past the body defenses and enter the blood stream, the white blood cells and lymph cells go into action and attempt to destroy them. The blood and body tissues also make other weapons, the "antibodies," that keep organisms from multiplying, dissolve them, and counteract their poisons. By studying these activities, man has learned how to make the defenses stronger by vaccines, toxoids, and serums. *Vaccines* contain weakened organisms that stimulate the body to make more antibodies against a disease; this is how smallpox vaccine protects you. *Toxoids* contain weakened poisons from organisms, thereby stimulating the body to make antitoxins; this is how diphtheria toxoid protects you. *Serums* contain antibodies made in the body of an animal or another human being. They neutralize the poisons made by the organisms; this is why serum is used to treat tetanus, meningitis, and other diseases.

Tests . . .

Tests show whether a person is susceptible to a certain disease. For the Schick test, the doctor injects a small amount of diphtheria toxin under the skin; if the skin around this spot becomes red, the person is susceptible to diphtheria. The Mantoux test, conducted the same way, shows whether or not a person has ever had active tuberculosis. The doctor usually recommends follow-up chest X-ray examination, if the test is positive.

Drugs . . .

Drugs are used mostly to fight disease after it begins in the body. Some modern drugs have a powerful effect on disease-producing organisms. Penicillin, sulfonamides, and the mycins will be discussed more completely in Chapter 18.

Controlling Communicable Diseases . . .

As long as people do get sick and communicable diseases (diseases spread by person-to-person contact) affect large numbers of the population, health authorities have another responsibility—they must keep disease from spreading. This is how the communicable diseases are controlled: (1) State laws require doctors to report specific cases to the local health department. (2) The health department sees that persons with a communicable disease are isolated. It also puts the sick person under restrictions for the length of time that it takes the disease to develop. "Quarantine" means that no one may enter or leave a house where there is a communicable disease; "isolation" means that no one enters the room of the sick person except those taking care of him. Regulations are not the same for every disease nor in every state.

Some diseases affect many "innocent bystanders" because contagious persons do not take precautions, do not recognize the symptoms, or fail to have treatment. Examples of such diseases are the common cold, "flu," and tuberculosis. The United States Public Health Service allots about $6,000,000 every year to local and state health departments and supplies consultants to states to help combat tuberculosis. The National Tuberculosis Association has fought this disease since 1904, raising money, as you know, through the sale of Christmas seals. Local sanitariums receive support from Association funds.

Social Diseases . . .

The most common social diseases, syphilis and gonorrhea, disable many people every year and cost the taxpayer thousands of dollars. Usually acquired through sexual relations, these are called the hidden diseases, because they act on the body quietly, then suddenly break out. When infected persons do not have treatment soon enough to protect their own health, they continue to infect others.

Full early treatment cures syphilis and gonorrhea, but if allowed to progress without treatment, they may affect both the body and mind of the victims, who become disabled and may require so much care that they have to be placed in institutions. The United States Public Health Service and the state and local health agencies make social diseases reportable, provide laboratory and consultant services, set up treatment centers, and distribute information explaining the symptoms and dangers. They urge the blood test as a part of every health examination, for every hospitalized patient, and for every expectant mother. Some states now require a physical examination and a blood test before granting a marriage license. The only real safeguard against these social invaders is a responsible and well-informed people.

Mother and Baby . . .

Proper care of mothers before, during, and after childbirth protects their and their babies' health. As the babies grow up, they, in turn, need protection against disease and other conditions that harm growth; they need a chance to become strong, healthy persons, with a good health heritage to pass on to their children. Governmental and private health agencies provide information about baby care before birth and after. Classes for expectant mothers and fathers teach prospective parents how to get ready for their baby and how to take care of him after he is born.

Schools and the Child . . .

The community is interested in protecting the child's health before he goes to school. Care in nurseries and nursery schools,

The audiometer is used to test the hearing of children in school.

DELAWARE STATE BOARD OF HEALTH

Form sent home by school with child who has been exposed to a communicable disease.

To Parents or Guardians:

Your child may have been exposed to the disease marked below. Please keep the child under close observation. If symptoms of the disease develop, keep the child at home and notify the school at once. Your co-operation in this matter is strongly urged to prevent the further spread of the disease.

Other family members may continue normal activities, but at appropriate time should be closely observed for symptoms.

Respectfully,
John Smith
Superintendent

WE SUGGEST THAT YOU PRESERVE THIS INFORMATION FOR FUTURE REFERENCE.

☐ *Chickenpox:* Two to three weeks from time of exposure to first symptoms, usually 14 to 16 days. Early symptoms include small water blisters which break easily; more numerous on trunk, often in hair. Disease is communicable one day before to six days after blisters appear. Child must be excluded from school and contact with all other people for seven days after blisters first appear; all crusts must be dry.

☐ *German Measles:* Ten to 21 days from time of exposure to first symptoms, usually 18 days. Early symptoms include slight illness, sudden onset, usually cold in head, rash which resembles measles. Disease is communicable for four days after beginning of nasal discharge. Child must be excluded from school and contact with all other people until rash and nasal discharge have disappeared. (Female contacts in the first four months of pregnancy should contact physician immediately.)

☐ *Measles:* Ten days from time of exposure to onset of fever, 13 to 15 days until rash. Early symptoms include cough, cold in head, sneezing, watery eyes, fever; blotchy rash about the fourth day. Disease is communicable for four days before rash to five days after rash. Child must be excluded from school and contact with all other people until end of fever and until all other symptoms are gone. This must be at least seven days after appearance of rash.

☐ *Mumps:* Twelve to 26 days from time of exposure to first symptoms. Early symptoms include sudden swelling and tenderness below ear and over angle of jawbone. Disease is communicable from two days before symptoms until swelling disappears. Child must be excluded from school and contact with all other people until all swelling is gone.

☐ *Whooping Cough* If child has not had a booster within the last year, consult family physician at once. Seven to 10 days from time of exposure to first symptoms. Early symptoms include tight dry cough which becomes progressively more severe and is worse at night; may cause vomiting. Disease is communicable from a few days before cough appears to three weeks after cough appears. Child must be excluded from school and contact with all other people until three weeks after beginning of cough.

—————————————

Date of exposure

immunization programs, and training in good health habits lay some of the foundation for healthful growth.

    In most states, the law requires or encourages health exami-

If the audiometer test shows that the child needs further help, he is examined by an ear, nose, and throat specialist.

DELAWARE STATE BOARD OF HEALTH
NATIONAL SAFETY COUNCIL

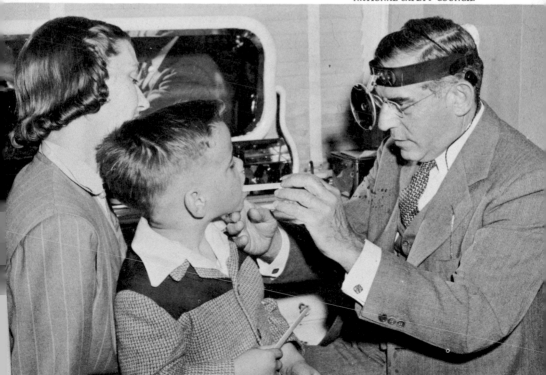

nations for school children to discover defects or conditions that need correction and to call their parents' attention to them. In some states, the school health department provides special classroom examinations of ears, eyes, and teeth, accompanied by education on these subjects. The community helps by finding ways to provide nutritional advice, medical attention, glasses, and similar health aids if the parents cannot afford them.

The health of children is affected by ventilation, heating, lighting, seating arrangements, toilet and handwashing facilities, gymnasiums, and playgrounds. Educators know that physical and mental deficiencies interfere with education: a child may have academic difficulty because he cannot hear well, see well, or because he is poorly sheltered or nourished at home.

PUBLIC SAFETY

The National Safety Council—with its state councils—and the Red Cross promote safety by studying the causes of accidents and suggesting ways to prevent them. They distribute information in print and colorful posters concerning accident prevention in industry, in the home, and on the highways. *Building inspection* and standard regulations reduce fires, accidents, and health hazards. *Vehicle laws* protect us with a bicycle code, by requiring inspection of automobiles and driving licenses, and by traffic regulation and road markings. *Educational programs,* such as offered by the Red Cross, teach people how to face emergencies, care for sick members, and how to prevent injuries in the home. The American Heart Association, the National Foundation, the Society for Muscular Dystrophy, and the American Tuberculosis Association are examples of other organizations. The class might wish to investigate the work of such groups.

Hospitals and Health . . .

Hospitals not only provide care for the sick; they go further by supervising health recovery and teaching how to prevent illness. Hospitals have greatly increased their facilities through the aid of federal funds matched by money raised in local communities. In recent years, some hospitals offer home care and instruction to their patients through their outpatient department and Public Health Planning Program.

Most hospitals orient personnel in public relations; total patient care is stressed. The patient needs to feel secure and happy, to feel that the hospital is made a pleasant home away

CHILDREN
FORGET

from home by the small courtesies and attentions shown him.

Hospitals are supported by public and private funds (endowments) and by patients' fees; they are classed as general and special hospitals. General hospitals take care of many kinds and types of patients. Special hospitals take care of mental cases, tuberculosis, or patients with highly contagious diseases. Other

Los Angeles County General Hospital, showing the Acute Unit (center) Communicable Disease Building (front left), and Psychiatric Unit (front right). The new Osteopathic Unit is not shown.

PHOTO BY DAL HARRIS

St. Luke's in the Desert is typical of the low, spread out tuberculosis sanatorium common in western states.

institutions take care of convalescents, old people, mothers, and children. Various religious groups have their own hospitals which offer spiritual comfort along with physical therapy.

The country needs more hospitals for people with long-term (chronic) illnesses. The Philadelphia *home care plan* has opened new possibilities in the care of patients with long-term illnesses. The primary purpose of health planning is to help the patient attain the fullest possible physical, social, and economic *usefulness* and—most important—*personal satisfaction.* Under this plan, all the community resources that are available to serve the patient are brought together and, using the teamwork approach, the patient and his family are in the central position on the team. It lessens the need to admit or readmit some patients to the hospital, and shortens the stay of those already there. Each patient is under the care of his private physician, from whom the visiting nurse receives her orders; she in turn instructs and supervises the family.

The decision to admit a patient to the plan is influenced by the readiness of the patient and his family to work with the team in a "think-ahead" manner. Patients and families who recognize the team's sincere interest can and do take their full share of responsibility even when the best conditions seem lacking in the home.

The Blood Bank . . .

Blood is so important that doctors, hospitals, and health officials consider blood banks a public health necessity. In 1958, the Red Cross blood program celebrated its tenth anniversary. Until the plan was established, blood sources were unorganized. Now a blood bank is available to everyone. The call for blood is unending, in community emergencies and for certain illnesses.

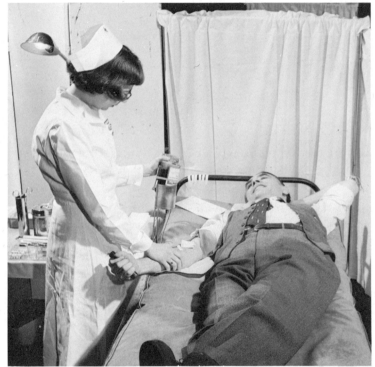

AMERICAN RED CROSS

Persons receiving blood often arrange to have their family and friends donate blood to replace what they have used.

"IN OTHER WORDS . . ."

Perhaps you feel that you will never be an expert on health agencies and their work. It is not necessary to be an expert, as long as you recognize the importance of such groups and learn how to co-operate with them. The more interest we have in them, the more their services will improve. Future success depends on the younger generation.

Health information is given at request—by federal, state, and local agencies, and by other organizations interested in special illnesses. Remember that public health means the health of all people—yours, your family's, your friends' and your neighbors'. You have an important place in this cycle of health.

- What is a health agency? Name three in your state.

- What diseases are reportable in your state?

- How is the National Foundation supported? What great discovery has helped in the fight of this disease? What does your doctor tell you about its success?

- If you planned to get a part-time job as a waitress in the school cafeteria or some other eating place, what would you do to protect yourself and others?

- What are the premarital legal requirements in your state?

- If you read the paper yesterday, tell of an accident reported and how it could have been prevented.

- How are we protected from accidents by the federal government? By your state? By your county? Check your home for any hazards; make a list of any noted and compare them in class.

- What is the local blood bank? Do you have a responsibility there? Seek out two individuals who are willing to donate to your local blood bank.

- When you do the family shopping for meat, how do you know you are buying government inspected meat? Would you buy meat that is dark red if it were cheaper? Why or why not?

- Does your community have a home care nursing plan? Where is your nearest nursing service organization? How does one seek needed service?

- What is meant by the social diseases? Are they curable? Why is syphilis called the invader?

NURSE'S RECORD

The cell.

Body systems and their common disturbances.

The special senses.

4: THE BODY AT WORK

Your nursing course is meant to teach you, within limits, (1) the nature of the human body, and (2) principles that will help you to maintain the health of yourself and members of your family—including home nursing procedures. It would be a waste of time to memorize terms of no use to you. For example, you need not memorize every muscle in the body, but you should know what the muscles do; this is called "function." With the help of anatomical plates functions of the body systems may be studied so you may know what to expect from them.

THE CELL

One reason why the body functions so automatically is because it is well organized. The primary part of this organization is the cell, the building unit of the body. Cells of the same kind join together to form tissues. There are as many tissues as there are kinds of cells, and every tissue has a special function. The different types are:

Epithelial (upon the skin)—covers surfaces and lines body cavities—skin, nails, hair, mouth, digestive tract.

Connective—anchors and holds other tissues together—ligaments, tendons, cartilage, bones.

All charts in this chapter Copyright 1947 by General Biological Supply House, Inc., 8200 South Hoyne Avenue, Chicago 20, Ill.

Organic—muscles, passageways, glands, nervous system.

Blood—bears food and oxygen to the cells, carries wastes away; fights yet distributes infections and poisons; contains cells.

BODY SYSTEMS AND THEIR COMMON DISTURBANCES

When these cells or tissues form a working unit, they are called "organs." The heart, for instance, is a combination of muscle, nerve, blood, and epithelial cells working as a unit. Every organ has a function; in fact, it may have several or it may work with other organs in performing a single function.

These group associations are known as "systems," because they do specialized work in the body. Your understanding of their structure and functions is the foundation for improving your own health and your care of others. The systems show how organs are grouped together for specific purposes:

1. **Skeletal**—the bones, the body framework.

2. **Muscular**—the muscles; attached to bones, make body movements possible.

3. **Circulatory**—the heart, blood, and blood vessels, lymph and lymph vessels; carry food, water, oxygen, and wastes.

4. **Digestive**—the mouth, salivary glands, pharynx, esophagus, stomach, intestines, liver, pancreas; liquefy, separate, "process," and absorb food.

5. **Respiratory**—the nose, pharynx, larynx, trachea, bronchi, and lungs; they conduct air in and out.

6. **Urinary**—the kidneys, ureters, bladder, and urethra; eliminate certain liquid wastes from the body.

7. **Reproductive**—the ovaries, Fallopian tubes, uterus, vagina, and mammary glands in woman; the testes and accessory glands and penis in man; to produce and nourish new life.

8. **Endocrine**—the ductless glands; they secrete hormones that regulate various body organs.

9. **Nervous**—the brain, spinal cord, and nerves; control and coordinate the activities of the body.

10. **Special senses**—the eyes, the ears, the tongue, and feeling nerves; communicate influences from "outside."

The Skeletal System . . .

The 206 bones of the skeleton are hard, firm, and form a strong, rigid framework for the body; the framework determines the shape, protects delicate organs, and serves as anchor points for the muscles.

1. Mandible
2. Maxilla
3. Zygomatic or Malar
4. Ethmoid
5. Lacrimal
6. Nasal
7. Frontal
8. Parietal
9. Sphenoid
10. Temporal
11. Occipital
12. Mastoid portion
13. Tympanic part of temporal
14. Occipital condyle
15. Styloid process
16. Condyle
17. Angle
18. Coronoid process
19. Mental protuberance
20. Basioccipital
21. Sphenoid
22. Sphenoidal sinus
23. Medial pterygoid plate
24. Pterygoid process

Human Bones

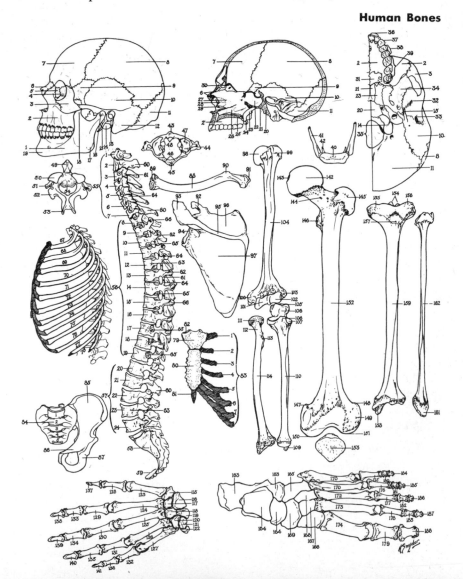

25. Palatine crest
26. Vomer
27. Ethmoid plate
28. Superior concha
29. Inferior concha
30. Crista galli
31. Palatine
32. Articular tubercle

33. Mandibular fossa
34. Great wing of sphenoidal bone
35. Foramen magnum
36. Incisors
37. Canine
38. Premolars
39. Molars

40. Body or Basihyal } Hyoid Bone { 41. Greater cornu
42. Lesser cornu

43. Anterior tubercle
44. Transverse process
45. Posterior tubercle
46. Posterior arch
} atlas or 1st cervical vertebra {
47. Superior articular surface
48. Anterior arch

49. Odontoid process
50. Superior articular surface
51. Transverse process
} Epistropheus or axis 2nd cervical vertebra {
52. Inferior articular process
53. Spinous process
54. Body

55. Cervical vertebrae 7
56. Thoracic vertebrae 12 (8-19)
57. Lumbar vertebrae 5 (20-24)
} vertebral column vertebrae 33 {
58. Sacral vertebrae 5. Auricular Surface
59. Coccygeale vertebrae

60. Spinous process
61. Inferior articular process
62. Transverse process
63. Body
64. Superior articular process

65. Costal fovea or demi facet for head of rib
66. Facet for articular part of tubercle of rib
67-78. Ribs 12 pairs

79. Manubrium or presternum
80. Mesosternum or body of sternum
81. Xiphoid process
} Sternum {
82. Articular surface for clavicle
83. Costal cartilages 7. attached to sternal facets

84. Sacrum

85. Ilium
86. Pubis
} Pelvic or Innominate bone { 87. Ischium
88. Clavicle

89. Articular surface with sternum
90. Tuberosity for conoid ligament } Clavicle { 91. Articulates with acromion of scapula

92. Coracoid process
93. Acromion
94. Glenoid cavity
95. Spine } Scapula { 96. Prescapular fossa
97. postscapular fossa

98. Head, articulates with glenoid cavity of scapula
99. Greater tubercle
100. Medial epicondyle } Humerus { 101. Trochlea
102. Capitulum
103. Lateral epicondyle
104. Humerus

105. Olecranon
106. Semilunar notch
107. Radial notch } Ulna { 108. Coronoid process
109. Styloid process
110. Ulna

111. Head of radius
112. Neck } Radius { 113. Radiol tuberosity
114. Radius

115. Greater multangular
116. Navicular
117. Lesser multangular } Carpal bones of the left wrist { 118. Capitate
119. Lunate
120. Hamate
121. Triangular
122. Pisiform

123-127. Metacarpus   133-136. Phalanges 2nd row
128-132. Phalanges 1st row   137-141. " 3rd row or digits

142. Head
143. Fovea capitis femoris
144. Neck
145. Greater trochanter
146. Lesser trochanter } Femur { 147. Adductor tubercle
149. Lateral epicondyle
150. Medial condyle
151. Lateral condyle
152. Femur

153. Patella
154. Intercondyloid eminence
155. Medial condyle } Tibia { 156. Lateral condyle
157. Tuberosity
158. Medial malleolus
159. Tibia

160. Styloid process	} Fibula	{ 162. Fibula	
161. Lateral malleolus			

163. Calcaneus	Tarsal	166. 1st cuneiform	
164. Talus or astragalus	bones of	167. 2nd "	
	the left	168. 3rd "	
165. Cuboid	ankle	169. Navicular	

170-174. Metatarsus   180-183. Phalanges 2nd row

175-179. Phalanges 1st row   184-188.   "   3rd row or digits

Bones are a collection of cells hardened by calcium and phosphorus from the food we eat. The "periosteum," the membrane that covers every bone, is filled with blood vessels that carry the bone-building materials and minerals to the bone cells. This keeps them alive and fills in the spaces between the cells, thereby maintaining their strength. Bones are not completely hardened until they are full grown, which usually takes about twenty years. Bone cells multiply rapidly in the growing years, but, thereafter, new cells simply replace dead or injured ones and repair breaks. Because of increased connective tissue and less cellular replacement, bones may get harder, more brittle, and break more easily as one gets older. However, *loss of interest in good nutrition* has much to do with this. The three main parts of the skeleton are the skull, the trunk, and the extremities.

The Joints . . .

Because bone ends are articulated, you are able to move your jaws, limbs, and spine in different ways. Strong, fibrous bands, or ligaments, hold jaw, hip, leg, shoulder, arm, hand, and foot joints together; the moving joints are lined with a membrane which supplies a fluid to keep them lubricated. Cartilage plates make a slick, smooth surface.

Your elbow joints move like a door on its hinge and so are called hinge joints; in your shoulders and hips, ball-and-socket joints allow rotating motions, or movement whereby you can swing the limbs in all directions. In these joints, the rounded end of one bone fits into the hollowed end of another. Some joints, as those in the vertebrae, move less freely, and still others, like those in the skull, do not move at all but are fitted closely together with interlocking hinges or notches.

The Bony Framework of the Body

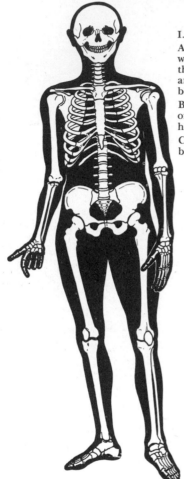

I. The Skeleton:

A. Serves as a bony framework or scaffold on which the muscles are attached and work, enabling the body movements.

B. Protects the delicate organs, especially in the head and chest.

C. Gives shape to the body.

II. Bones are living organs, containing Haversian Canals through which the blood circulates, and bone cells arranged around the canals.

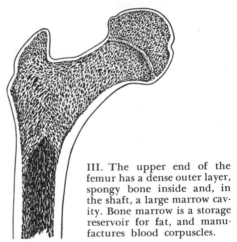

III. The upper end of the femur has a dense outer layer, spongy bone inside and, in the shaft, a large marrow cavity. Bone marrow is a storage reservoir for fat, and manufactures blood corpuscles.

SOME BONE DISTURBANCES

Certain diseases soften, crystallize, or infect bone structure. Injuries occur through accident. Bone disabilities may be classified as follows:

1. **Rickets**—a disease caused by lack of Vitamin D, characterized by swollen joints and deformity.

2. **Fractures**—broken bones. The breaks may be complete or partial, simple or compound (extending through the flesh).

3. **Sprain**—one of the ligaments that supports a joint is

stretched or torn.

4. **Dislocation**—ligaments are pulled so that a bone is displaced.

5. **Infection**—a disease-producing organism damages or destroys bone tissue. Infection of the bone marrow may occur.

6. **Arthritis**—A disease of the joints.

The Muscular System . . .

The muscle cells are arranged in fine elastic threads, wrapped together in bundles; several bundles make one muscle. Every muscle is covered by a sheath whose ends lengthen into tough cords, called "tendons," and are attached to bones.

Muscles are attached so as to give the best leverage, one end to a movable bone, the other to a more stable one. Muscles

The Muscles and Their Structure

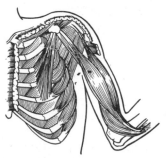

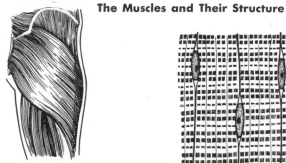

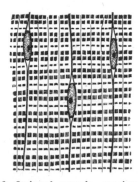

1. Striated muscles are attached to bones by tendons, the fixed end (the shoulder) being known as the origin and the movable end (the arm) as the insertion.

2. The large muscles of the hip move the leg in reference to the body.

3. Striated muscle consists of fibers which are cross striped. Contraction consists in a shortening and thickening of the entire fiber.

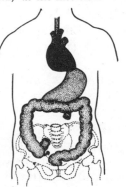

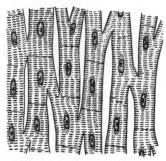

5. Heart muscle consists of short, branching, cross striped fibers with central nuclei. They freely unite with each other.

. Heart muscle is confined ⊃ the heart. Smooth muscle ; found in the stomach, intestine and blood vessels.

6. Smooth muscle is made up of long, thin, spindle-shaped fibers with central nuclei.

usually work *in pairs;* also, for some movements, you use *groups* of paired muscles. Nerves in the muscles communicate the movements; blood vessels supply nutrients and energy, and remove waste.

When muscles are very active, they call upon the reserve amount of sugar stored within the cells. Waste products are produced in the burning process. One of these, carbon dioxide, is removed in the blood to be expelled by the lungs; the other, lactic acid, is removed through the kidneys and the sweat glands. When vigorous or prolonged muscle action produces waste products faster than they they can be eliminated, the waste accumulates in the muscle cells; the muscle feels tired. It may cause soreness later. Continued exercise enlarges the muscle so it can dispose of waste better and produce more power.

There are two types of muscles in the body—*voluntary* and *involuntary.* Voluntary muscles, which you direct consciously, change body positions. Involuntary muscles, those that work automatically, control motion inside body organs, circulate the blood, wink your eyelids, control breathing, move food along the digestive tract, and cause reflex actions.

The Circulatory System . . .

The circulatory system has two main duties—conducts supplies to your cells and takes away waste materials. Arteries, veins, and capillaries carry the blood. The heart provides the force to move the blood through the body.

Blood is made of liquid and certain formed elements. Each part has a special duty. Blood plasma is the carrying agent for blood cells and for carbon dioxide and other absorbed wastes. It also brings hormones and antibodies to the tissues. The liquid is made up of water, dissolved food materials, and a substance called *fibrogen,* which helps blood clotting.

The *red blood cells* get their color from a substance, containing iron, which is called *hemoglobin.* As the blood passes through the lungs, the hemoglobin picks up oxygen which it carries to the body cells through the arteries and capillaries. When the hemoglobin has been cleansed with oxygen, it is bright red; body wastes then make it darker red as it returns through the veins. It takes millions of cells to carry out this routine; they are worn out in less than a month. The liver and the spleen remove them; they are replaced with new red blood cells made in the red marrow of the bones.

White blood cells are colorless cells that protect the body

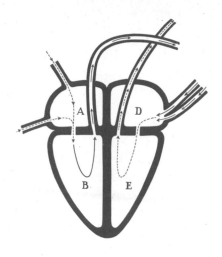

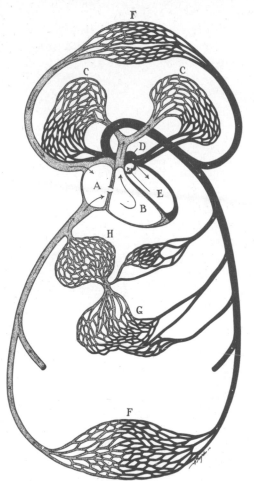

Venous blood comes to the right auricle (A) through the anterior and posterior venae cavae. Then it passes to the right ventricle (B), which pumps it through the pulmonary arteries to the lungs (C). Here it receives oxygen, gives off carbon dioxide, and returns to the left auricle (D). Then it passes to the left ventricle (E) which pumps it through the arteries to all parts of the body. In the general system (F) it gives off oxygen and food and receives waste. Blood going to the intestine (G) absorbs digested food, is collected by the portal vein which carries it to the liver (H), in which carbohydrates are stored and certain impurities are absorbed.

against disease organisms or poisons. At the first sign of disturbance, they multiply, rush to the spot where the invading organisms are at work, and dissolve the damaged tissues after they have destroyed the harmful organisms and isolated the poisons by absorbing them.

A count of the number of red cells in a specific amount of blood will indicate the approximate number in a person's entire blood supply at that time. *Anemia* is shortage of red blood cells.

The white cell count shows the number of white cells. The count is high if infection is present, because the white cells multiply to fight it. A below-average white cell count is one of the symptoms of certain diseases; a count that is too high may indicate blood disease, such as cancer (leukemia).

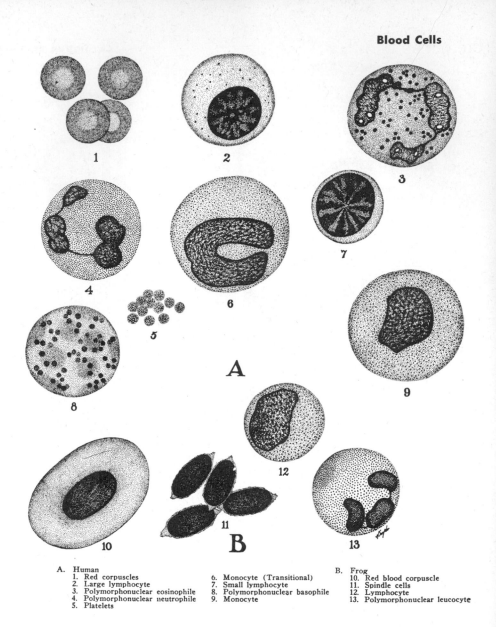

A. Human
1. Red corpuscles
2. Large lymphocyte
3. Polymorphonuclear eosinophile
4. Polymorphonuclear neutrophile
5. Platelets

6. Monocyte (Transitional)
7. Small lymphocyte
8. Polymorphonuclear basophile
9. Monocyte

B. Frog
10. Red blood corpuscle
11. Spindle cells
12. Lymphocyte
13. Polymorphonuclear leucocyte

THE HEART

Your heart acts as a pump; every contraction is accompanied by valve activity that causes "heart beat." Your heart is about the size of your doubled fist; it lies in the left lower part of your chest cavity. It is hollow and is made up of thick, strong muscles that contract, because of a chemical ingredient in heart tissue alone, to force the blood into the arteries. It is divided into four chambers: The upper two, *atria* or *auricles*, receive blood; the lower two, the *ventricles,* pour it out. Therefore, the walls of the ventricles are very strong.

Blood that has delivered its food materials and oxygen and has picked up waste products flows into the right atrium, proceeds into the right ventricle, and is pumped to the lungs to pick up a fresh supply of oxygen. When it has its oxygen, it returns to the heart and enters the left atrium, goes into the left ventricle and is pumped out again, this time on its route to supply oxygen to the body cells.

The atria fill between beats when the heart is resting. When the heart contracts, the atria squeeze down to force the blood into the ventricles below. The contraction extends to the ventricles; this forces the oxidized blood from the left ventricle into the aorta leading to the branches throughout the body, and the unoxidized blood from the right ventricle into the pul-

Heart and Lungs

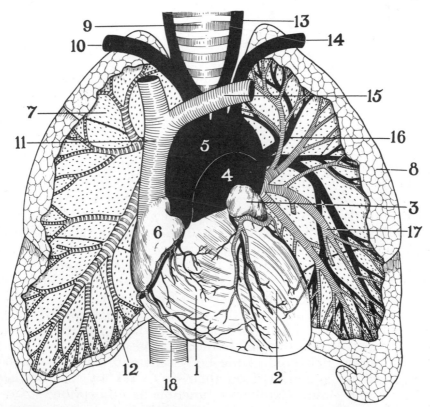

1. Right ventricle	7. Right lung	13. Left common carotid artery
2. Left ventricle	8. Left lung	14. Left subclavian artery
3. Left auricle	9. Trachea	15. Left innominate vein
4. Pulmonary artery	10. Right subclavian artery	16. Pulmonary arteries
5. Arch of aorta	11. Superior vena cava	17. Pulmonary veins
6. Right auricle and atrium	12. Bronchus	18. Inferior vena cava

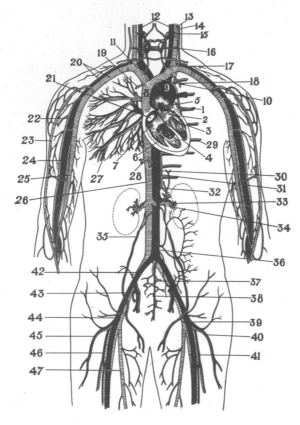

1. Left auricle
2. Bicuspid valve
3. Wall of left ventricle
4. Ventricular septum
5. Aortic valve
6. Wall of right ventricle
7. Tricuspid valve
8. Superior vena cava
9. Arch of aorta
10. Left innominate vein
11. Right innominate vein
12. Common carotid arteries
13. Internal jugular vein
14. External jugular vein
15. Superior thyroid veins
16. Middle thyroid vein
17. Inferior thyroid vein
18. Left internal mammary vein
19. Right internal mammary vein
20. Subclavian artery and vein
21. Opening of inferior vena cava
22. Brachial vein
23. Cephalic vein
24. Brachial artery
25. Basilic vein
26. Inferior vena cava
27. Pulmonary arteries and veins
28. Hepatic veins
29. Intercostal vessels
30. Hemi-azygos vein
31. Descending aorta
32. Coeliac artery
33. Renal artery and vein
34. Superior mesenteric artery
35. Spermatic artery and vein
36. Inferior mesenteric artery
37. Sacral vein
38. Superior hemorrhoidal artery
39. Femoral vein
40. Lateral femoral circumflex vein
41. Deep femoral vein
42. Common iliac artery and vein
43. Hypogastric artery and vein
44. Femoral artery
45. Lateral femoral circumflex artery
46. Deep femoral artery
47. Saphenous vein

monary artery leading to the lungs; this is the only artery in the circulatory system which carries unoxidized blood.

The openings between the atria and the ventricles are fitted with flaps or *valves*. The openings leading to the aorta and pulmonary artery are fitted with the similar valves. They prevent the back flow of the blood.

The heart is covered by a thin sac, the *pericardium*. The membrane lining the heart is called the *endocardium;* the muscular part of the heart is the *myocardium*. The heart muscle gets its own nutrients from the *coronary* arteries that branch off from the aorta. The *capillaries* are the last tiny branches of the arteries. Within the tiny branches, food materials and oxygen are finally delivered to the body cells and waste products are picked up and started on their way back by way of the *venuoles* and *veins*. Capillaries function by absorption, somewhat like sap flow in a tree.

SOME CIRCULATORY DISTURBANCES

Heart disease is the leading cause of death in this country. Overweight puts a great stress and strain on the heart. Attention to diet helps to prevent heart disease.

Some of the more common heart conditions are:

1. **Coronary heart disease:** Either the coronary arteries lose their elasticity and thicken, restricting or stopping the blood flow; or a blood clot forms in one of the coronary arteries and occludes or "plugs" a passage in the heart.

2. **Angina pectoris:** Muscle spasm and temporary interference with the blood supply to the heart.

3. **Heart infections:** Disease, such as rheumatic fever, may attack any muscle group of the heart, causing permanent damage.

The Digestive System . . .

The system in your body which accepts food and by a chemical process makes it into a form that can be used by your body cells is called the digestive system. The process, called digestion, takes place in the digestive tube or alimentary canal, which is from 30 to 40 feet long. The tube is lined with a protective tissue called *mucous membrane*. This membrane which is activated by a nerve system, is smooth and moist, which helps the food to slide along.

After the food is processed, nutrient chemicals pass through the walls of the digestive tube, into circulation, and on to the cells or storage places in the body.

Digestion actually begins in the mouth. Food is cut up by the teeth and rolled around by the tongue; saliva from the salivary glands moistens it so that it forms a ball. The tongue moves the food into a muscular tube behind the mouth, the *pharynx*. Swallowing is the contraction of this tube. From the pharynx, the food enters the *esophagus*, which connects with the stomach. The *stomach* is a pear-shaped bag. Here gastric juices mix with the food. Also it is moved around and mixed by contractions of the stomach wall. When the stomach relaxes, it releases the material into the small intestine. The food is in liquid state, accompanied by bulk, as it passes on from the stomach, a little at a time, into the *intestine*. It takes about four to six hours normally for food to move out of the stomach. In the first part of the intestine, more digestive juices are mixed with the food.

The *gall bladder* and *pancreas* both contribute juices that break up fats, proteins, sugars, and starches into materials that the body can use. These materials begin to ooze out through the walls into circulation as the intestinal contents move along. The process is practically completed by the time the material still in the small intestine enters the large intestine, or *colon*. As the contents move along the large colon, most of the water passes through its walls to maintain the water content of the body. The pulpy fibers, and excess nutrients, mass together and finally reach the *rectum*. This solid waste, the *feces,* contains bacteria and a small amount of water. If it remains in the rectum for some time, it continues to lose water. The mass presses against the

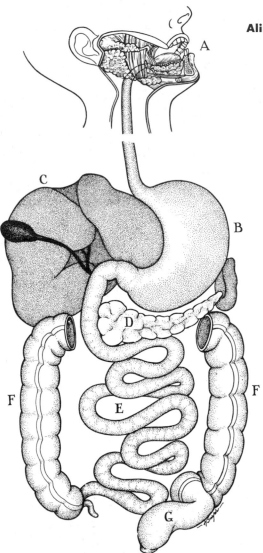

Alimentary Canal and Digestion

A. The mouth. Here the food is broken up into small particles (mastication) and mixed with saliva, which moistens the food for swallowing and begins the digestion of starch.

B. The stomach serves as a storehouse for food immediately after it is eaten. It produces an enzyme, pepsin, which, in the presence of hydrochloric acid, digests proteins. Mechanically it breaks up food into small particles and mixes it with gastric juice.

C. The liver produces bile, which neutralizes the acid food coming from the stomach, helps emulsify fats, and stimulates the action of the intestine.

D. The pancreas produces important enzymes for the digestion of proteins, carbohydrates and fats. Its secretion enters the intestine with the bile.

E. The small intestine (about 7½ ft. long). Here the food is pushed slowly along and is kept thoroughly mixed with digestive juices by peristalsis. Digestion is completed here and most of the absorption takes place.

F. In the large intestine absorption of water takes place and bacteria act on the food mass further digesting carbohydrates.

G. In the rectum the waste mass is concentrated for excretion.

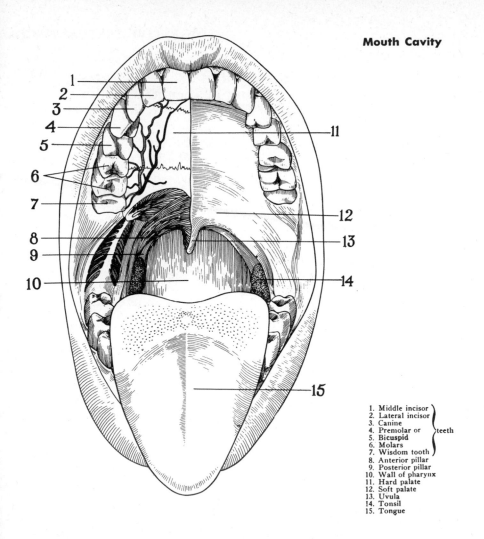

1. Middle incisor ⎫
2. Lateral incisor ⎪
3. Canine ⎪
4. Premolar or ⎬teeth
5. Bicuspid ⎪
6. Molars ⎪
7. Wisdom tooth ⎭
8. Anterior pillar
9. Posterior pillar
10. Wall of pharynx
11. Hard palate
12. Soft palate
13. Uvula
14. Tonsil
15. Tongue

tight *sphincter muscles* that ring the opening of the rectum, the *anus*. This is the signal for emptying the rectum.

Metabolism . . .

What do the cells do with the nutrients? They sustain and re-create themselves, a process known as *metabolism*. It works like this: the cells burn some foods to supply the body with heat and energy; they build and repair tissues with others; certain materials are "stockpiled" to make it easier for the cells to do their work. This happens constantly. The amount of food that is oxidized and the amount of heat produced can be measured. This tests a patient's *metabolism rate*, which must be normal to maintain effective life.

Some of the common digestive disturbances are:

1. **Food poisoning**—organisms or chemicals that cause digestive disturbance and may be carried on into the cells. Symptoms are pain, cramps, vomiting.

2. **Appendicitis**—inflammation of the small tube behind the junction of the small and large bowel. Disturbs digestion, causing pain, vomiting, and cramps.

3. **Gastric ulcer**—a raw spot in the lining of the stomach or intestine, causing pain, some spitting of blood, vomiting.

4. **Acidity, spasms, obstruction**—cause pain and poor digestive action.

5. **Worms**—tapeworm eggs get into the body with unclean meat and fish. They hatch in the intestine and grow to great lengths.

6. **Diarrhea**—a symptom of intestinal disturbances, including most of the above; characterized by frequent and watery discharge of the bowels.

The Respiratory System . . .

Respiration, or breathing, involves two processes—*inspiration,* breathing in, and *expiration,* breathing out. Your body cells must have oxygen to burn food; fresh air contains about 20 per cent oxygen.

Air enters your body through the nostrils, which have two chambers, separated by the *septum,* part cartilage and part bone. (The nerve endings in the septum and in the nasal passages are responsible for your sense of smell.)

When required by outside conditions, air is warmed and cleansed in the air passages, which are lined with mucous membrane. The secretions from the membrane, with its tiny hairlike projections, collect dust from the air.

Air passes from the nose to the tube-shaped *pharynx,* which is both an air and food passageway. It lies behind the nose and mouth; the part behind the mouth is in the throat. The tonsils are at the back of the throat. A leaf-like cartilage, the *epiglottis,* covers the glottis or air opening of the pharynx whenever you swallow, to keep food from entering the air passage.

From the pharynx, the air passes through the *larynx,* which is a sort of box made of cartilages held together by ligaments and situated in front of the neck. Two triangular folds of mucous membrane, *the vocal cords,* extend from front to back. These cords vibrate, as air is forced out past them, to make sounds.

The entering air passes from the larynx into the *trachea*, a tube made of membranes and horseshoe-shaped bars of cartilage. It divides at the lower end into two smaller tubes, one to each lung. These tubes, the *bronchi*, enter the lungs and divide into many smaller branches. The lungs then absorb the air and expel wastes. They are spongy and filled with air sacs, nerves, and blood vessels. Adult lungs, which fill most of the chest cavity, hold about 3½ quarts of air. We take in and let out less than a pint with every breath in ordinary desk work.

The chest cavity is lined with a membrane, the *pleura*, that folds back over the lungs. The surface is moist so that the lungs flex smoothly against the chest cavity as we breathe.

Muscles contract to lift our ribs when we inhale, and relax when we exhale. The diaphragm, a dome-shaped muscle between our breathing and digestive apparatus, flattens when we

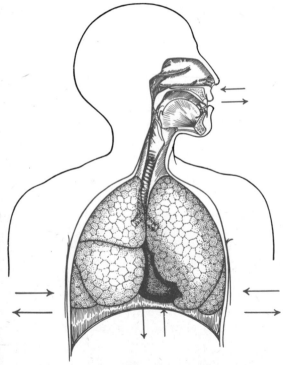

Respiration

External respiration consists of the passage of oxygen (O_2) from the lung alveoli into the blood and of carbon dioxide (CO_2) from the blood to the air of the lung alveoli.

Respiration is the gaseous exchange between blood and air in the lungs (external) and between blood and body tissues (internal). The breathing movements are secondary, to accomplish aeration of the blood in the lungs.

Inspiration is accomplished by contraction of the muscles of the ribs and the diaphragm. This stretches the lungs and allows air to enter from the outside. Inspired air contains about 20% oxygen and .04% carbon dioxide.

Expiration is accomplished by the elastic recoil of the chest on relaxation of the muscles. Expired air contains about 16% oxygen and 4% carbon dioxide.

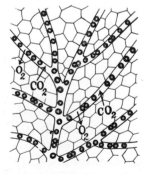

Internal respiration consists of the passage of oxygen (O_2) from the blood to the body tissues and of carbon dioxide (CO_2) from the tissues into the blood.

breathe in and relaxes when we breathe out. The respiratory center in the brain controls breathing without conscious effort by sending messages to the rib muscles and the diaphragm; an increased amount of carbon dioxide in the blood makes the brain send these messages faster.

An injury or disturbance of this brain center interferes with breathing.

SOME RESPIRATORY DISTURBANCES

The Common Cold . . .

The common cold is one of our most notorious menaces. The organism that causes it is a tiny virus. It attacks the mucous membranes of the nose and throat, which try to fight back by pouring out large quantities of mucous fluid. A cold usually begins with a scratchy throat, followed by sneezes and a runny nose. The cold organisms are scattered by sneezes and coughs of those who have colds. Other people breathe them in with the air and may become infected. If your body is weakened already by fatigue, chilling, or irritated mucous membrane, the organisms are more likely to give trouble.

Your best protection against colds is a good general health, which means a balanced diet, a good mental outlook, and the right proportion of rest and recreation. Keep away from people with colds. Do not handle anything they touch. Avoid sudden, prolonged changes in temperature, such as standing outside in the cold air soon after a bath.

If you do catch a cold, stay away from other people. Go to bed and rest. Eat balanced meals, take fruit juices, and plenty of other fluids. Use disposable tissues instead of handkerchiefs, and put them into a paper bag to be burned. Wash your hands often, especially after blowing your nose and coughing. Cover your mouth when you cough or sneeze; once you have a cold you are responsible for protecting other people. Call the doctor if cold symptoms hang on, or if sinus or chest conditions appear. He will possibly prescribe an antibiotic to prevent any further infection.

Some other respiratory disturbances are:

1. **Influenza**—infection more lasting than a cold; attacks the body (especially intestinal tract) when already weakened.

2. **Bronchitis**—cold infection spread to the bronchi.

3. **Pneumonia**—a serious infection of the lungs in which the air sacs fill with fluid.

4. **Pleurisy**—inflammation of the membranes covering the lungs and lining the chest cavity. It causes friction which, in turn, causes severe sharp pain with each breath.

5. **Hay fever**—sensitivity, usually to protein substances in the air.

6. **Asthma**—allergic condition, when the bronchi are also affected.

7. **Sinusitis**—infection in the small cavities in the head bones.

8. **Laryngitis**—an involvement of the vocal cords that causes temporary loss of speech.

9. **Sore throat or tonsillitis**—sore throat is an inflammation of the pharynx and tonsils that sometimes comes on before or during a cold; tonsillitis is a definite inflammation of the tonsils, which lie in the back of the throat. A collection of pus behind the tonsils, an abcess, is sometimes called *quinsy.*

10. **Tuberculosis**—see Chapter 9.

The Urinary System . . .

The urinary system is commonly referred to as the body's "filtration and removal plant" because it is in the kidneys that wastes are filtered from the blood and continued along another path.

Your kidneys are two bean-shaped organs in the small of the back, at the lower edge of the ribs, on either side of the backbone. They are supported and kept in place by cushions of fat. They contain many tiny tubes that filter out the waste products from the blood. Normal urine contains water, salt, and proteins. It is a yellowish, clear fluid with an ammonia-like odor. Its odor, composition, and amount are influenced by your diet, amount of fluids taken into the body, perspiration, emotional disturbances, or any abnormal condition.

Two small tubes, the *ureters,* carry the urine from the kidneys to the *bladder,* a muscular sac that lies in front in the lowest part of the abdominal cavity. The urine enters the bladder a drop at a time from the kidney. The bladder serves as a reservoir. The urine leaves the bladder by another small tube leading to the outside of the body. This is called the *urethra.* Small rings of muscle keep the opening to the urethra closed. When enough urine has collected in the bladder, it stretches the walls, puts pressure on the nerve endings, and gives the signal for the small muscle rings to open. One of them does; the other you control consciously.

There are two common urinary disturbances:

1. **Kidney stones**—salts in the urine harden into tiny granules which may eventually form into stones. These may also form in the bladder, but are called bladder stones.

2. **Cystitis**—inflammation of the bladder which may come from irritation, from infectious material, actions of drugs or poisons, pressure that has not been relieved frequently enough, bladder stones, or high concentration of waste materials in the urine. It is very painful and irritating.

The Skin . . .

Sometimes the urinary system and the skin are classed

Excretion of Waste

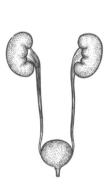

A. The skin excretes water and salts and a small amount of carbon dioxide. It is important in temperature regulation.

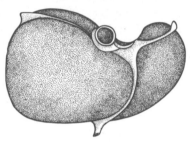

B. The liver removes various impurities absorbed with the food, excretes decomposition products of hemoglobin in the form of bile salts and is important as a storehouse of carbohydrates.

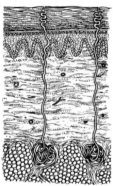

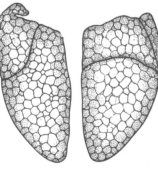

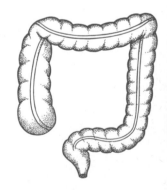

C. The lungs excrete carbon dioxide resulting from oxidation of food in the body, and some water.

D. The kidneys excrete nitrogenous waste resulting from protein metabolism, as well as water and various inorganic salts.

E. Undigested food waste is excreted through the rectum.

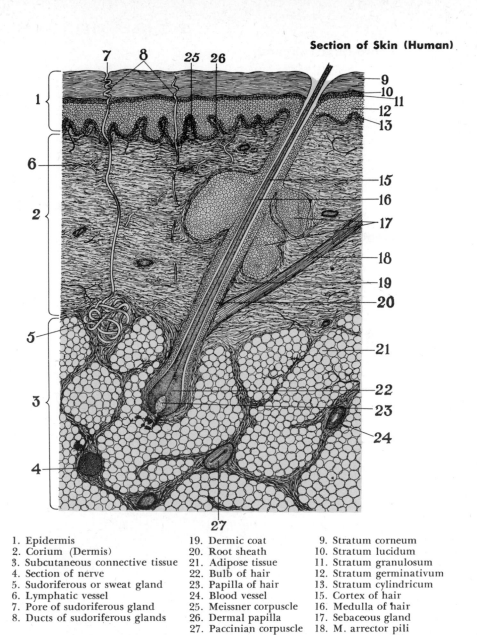

1. Epidermis	19. Dermic coat	9. Stratum corneum
2. Corium (Dermis)	20. Root sheath	10. Stratum lucidum
3. Subcutaneous connective tissue	21. Adipose tissue	11. Stratum granulosum
4. Section of nerve	22. Bulb of hair	12. Stratum germinativum
5. Sudoriferous or sweat gland	23. Papilla of hair	13. Stratum cylindricum
6. Lymphatic vessel	24. Blood vessel	15. Cortex of hair
7. Pore of sudoriferous gland	25. Meissner corpuscle	16. Medulla of hair
8. Ducts of sudoriferous glands	26. Dermal papilla	17. Sebaceous gland
	27. Paccinian corpuscle	18. M. arrector pili

together in the excretory system, since they both have to do with elimination. The skin removes waste products from the body by perspiration. The sweat glands extract water and salt wastes from the blood and discharge them through the pores. These outlets occur all over the body but are more noticeable in the underarms, hands, feet, and forehead. *Skin disturbances* are extremely numerous, and require special diagnosis and care.

The Reproductive System . . .

Our human race goes on because human bodies have systems which enable two cells, one from man and the other from woman, to unite, form a new life, and bring it into the world—the male and female reproductive systems.

The male reproductive system consists of the testes, the prostate, the urethra, and the penis. The female reproductive system consists of the ovaries, the Fallopian tubes, the uterus, the vagina, and the breasts.

An ovum leaves the ovary about midway between two menstrual periods, enters the Fallopian tubes, and makes its way down to the uterus. When the sperm are deposited within the vagina, they enter the uterus and move into the Fallopian

The Reproductive System

A. The male organs. Spermatozoa developed in the testis (1) are collected in the epididymis (2) and travel through the vas deferens (3) to the seminal vesicle (4). The testis also produces important internal secretions.

The bladder (5) discharges through the urethra (6). The prostate gland (7) produces a nutritive secretion for the spermatozoa. Ducts from the seminal vesicles unite with the prostatic tubules, and these with the urethra in the body of the prostate.

B. The female organs. The ovary (1) produces internal secretions and ova. The ova are produced in follicles which rupture through the surface of the ovary. Ova are picked up by the mouth of the oviduct (2), and travel down this tube. Fertilization, if it occurs, takes place in the oviduct. The fertile ovum becomes implanted in the uterus (3) where it develops into a foetus. The vagina (4) is the passage from the uterus to the outside.

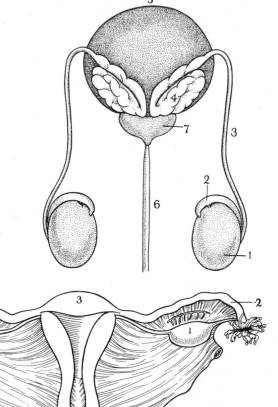

tubes.. If one of the sperm meets an ovum, the two join. A new cell is formed, attaches itself to the wall of the uterus, and a new life begins.

SOME DISTURBANCES OF THE REPRODUCTIVE SYSTEMS

The more common male disorders are:

1. **Enlarged prostate**—The gland enlarges and hardens with age, causes pain, presses on the bladder, and blocks urinary elimination.

2. **Infections**—disease organisms enter through the urethra and cause inflammatory infections. A common male infection is gonorrhea, the organism being introduced by sexual intercourse with an infected person.

The common female disorders are as follows:

1. **Menstrual difficulties**—may be irregular menstruation, bleeding between periods, cramps or abdominal pain throughout the monthly period. A doctor should be consulted for any of these disorders.

2. **Cysts**—small membranous, fluid-filled sacs in the uterus or tubes.

3. **Tumors**—growths which may or may not be cancerous. They sometimes bleed, which may be the only sign that something is wrong. Women should always consult a doctor at any signs of vaginal bleeding between periods.

The Endocrine System . . .

The endocrine glands, located in different parts of the body, pour their secretions directly into the blood stream. These are certain chemical substances or hormones that may speed up or slow down body processes. They depend upon each other; thus too much or too little of one hormone interferes with the work of others.

THE THYROID GLAND

The thyroid looks something like the letter "H," with one arm across the neck in front of the larynx and the upward parts lying on either side. The gland secretes the hormone "thyroxin," which is more than half iodine. This hormone regulates the rate at which the cells burn food. If there is too little thyroxin, the body process and development slow down; if there is too much, the body pace is so stepped up that it burns all food available and uses up stored reserves.

THE PARATHYROIDS

Four small glands, the parathyroids, are attached to the back of the thyroid gland. They secrete a a hormone that regulates the amount of calcium in the blood. Too little calcium causes muscle spasms and convulsions. If the parathyroids secrete too much of the hormone and the body cannot supply enough calcium, the calcium is drawn from the bones, making them soft.

THE ADRENALS

The two adrenal glands are at the upper end of the kidneys. Each has two definite parts and each part secretes a different hormone.

The central part produces a hormone which quickens body action; the heart beats faster, circulation and muscle power increase. In an emergency, the adrenal glands come to our aid. Emotions of fear, anger, love, or grief give them the signals.

The outer part of the adrenals secretes the hormone "cortin," which regulates the action of the salts in the body. Too much cortin hastens sex development in boys and causes male characteristics to appear in girls, such as hair on the face or absence of menstruation. Too little causes extreme muscle weakness, pigmented skin and kidney disturbances.

THE PANCREAS

Small clusters of tissue in the pancreas, poetically called the "islands of Langerhans," secrete the hormone insulin, which regulates the amount of sugar in the blood. If they secrete too little insulin, sugar accumulates; a large amount of sugar poisons the body cells, although the kidneys try to get rid of it in the urine. This condition is called *diabetes mellitus*, which can be controlled by the injection of insulin.

THE PITUITARY

The pituitary gland, about the size of a pea, is attached to the base of the brain in the region behind the eyes. One part, or lobe, secretes a hormone that affects the smooth muscles and raises blood pressure. The other part secretes hormones that affect the other glands: the adrenals, the thyroid, and the sex glands. Too much of this secretion causes gigantism in youngsters, or, in adults, overgrowth of hands and feet. Too little causes undergrowth, or dwarfism.

THE GONADS

The gonads are the glands of reproduction—the ovaries and the testes. The ovaries secrete several hormones: One gives the uterus the sign to get ready for the fertilized cell; another causes thickening of the lining of the uterus and increases its blood supply. The testes secrete the male sex hormone called "testosterone," which controls the development of the male sex characteristics.

OTHER GLANDS

The *pineal* gland is attached to the brain. The *thymus* gland lies behind the breast bone and gradually disappears as the body grows. The function of both of these is not quite clear to physiologists, although they seem to have some effect on growth. If the thymus does not shrivel and disappear by adolescence, it causes pressure on the breathing apparatus and must be removed.

There are certain other glands, such as those in the stomach and intestines, that stimulate organs in the process of digestion. They all are very closely allied; anything that affects one group will shake up the balance. It is generally thought that the leader of the group is the pituitary. Usually good health habits will do more than anything to keep the endocrine glands in good working order.

The Nervous System . . .

Every system in your body works in harmony with all others. You can see why there has to be a "control tower" over all, in a manner of speaking. This system of control and over-all direction is the nervous system.

Your nervous system is organized to bring messages to a main center, which relays them out to the parts of the body which are concerned. The brain and the spinal cord act as the switchboard, and the nerves are the wires that carry the incoming and outgoing messages.

As previously noted, your nervous system is divided into two functional or working types: automatic, or *involuntary,* which means it carries out operative functions, such as digestion or breathing and needs no conscious help from you; and *voluntary,* the one that you direct. Both are vitally concerned with understanding yourself and your family patients. By their actions, your personality is expressed and directed. Many patients cannot help the effects their pain and confinement have upon their nervous systems. Knowing the limits of your "control tower" will give you better understanding of the patient's problems.

Thought on the subject will help you realize how much of your nervous system you control, and how much you depend upon it to operate itself.

SOME NERVOUS DISTURBANCES

Some disturbances of the nervous system are as follows:

1. **Concussions and skull fractures**—concussion usually is caused by a blow to the head that temporarily interferes with the working of the brain centers. The symptoms are dizziness, confusion, headache, and sometimes unconsciousness. Keep the

The Spinal Cord and Nerves

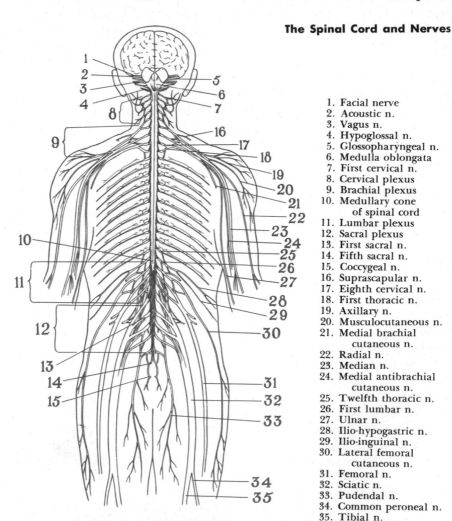

1. Facial nerve
2. Acoustic n.
3. Vagus n.
4. Hypoglossal n.
5. Glossopharyngeal n.
6. Medulla oblongata
7. First cervical n.
8. Cervical plexus
9. Brachial plexus
10. Medullary cone
    of spinal cord
11. Lumbar plexus
12. Sacral plexus
13. First sacral n.
14. Fifth sacral n.
15. Coccygeal n.
16. Suprascapular n.
17. Eighth cervical n.
18. First thoracic n.
19. Axillary n.
20. Musculocutaneous n.
21. Medial brachial
    cutaneous n.
22. Radial n.
23. Median n.
24. Medial antibrachial
    cutaneous n.
25. Twelfth thoracic n.
26. First lumbar n.
27. Ulnar n.
28. Ilio-hypogastric n.
29. Ilio-inguinal n.
30. Lateral femoral
    cutaneous n.
31. Femoral n.
32. Sciatic n.
33. Pudendal n.
34. Common peroneal n.
35. Tibial n.

patient lying at rest for at least twenty-four hours after a severe blow on the head or a fall, because the symptoms sometimes do not appear right away.

Skull fracture comes from a blow that is hard enough to break the skull bones. The break itself or a blood clot may cause pressure on the brain. It may affect brain areas and cause paralysis or lack of speech. X-rays will show how badly the patient is injured.

2. **Meningitis**—inflammation of part or all of the membranes covering the brain and spinal cord, which may leave lasting effects of optic neuritis and muscle contractures.

3. **Infantile paralysis** or **poliomyelitis**—caused by a tiny virus attacking nerve cells. Severe attacks kill or damage these cells and weaken or paralyze single muscles or groups of muscles.

4. **Epilepsy**—a temporary loss of consciousness, along with rigidity or twitchings of the muscles; may be severe to the point of convulsions.

5. **Shock**—caused by wounds or blows. When injured in any way, everyone suffers shock to the nervous system. Time and care are needed for recovery.

6. **Cerebral palsy**—caused by injuries at birth or imperfect development of the brain center that controls action. Some muscles are stiff and unrelaxed, and the victim is unable to co-ordinate certain movements.

THE SPECIAL SENSES

The Ear . . .

The ear is a special sense organ for hearing. It also has a special part in keeping your body upright or in a balanced equilibrium. It has three parts: external, middle, and inner or internal.

The external, or outer ear, is the only visible part. It is made of cartilage and skin, with a small opening into a tube, the auditory canal. This canal runs into the eardrum, a thin membrane between the external ear and the middle ear. The lining of the auditory canal is covered with tiny hairs that secrete the wax which assists hearing by buffering sounds.

The middle ear is a small, irregular cavity in what is called the temporal bone. This cavity is so small that 5 drops of water would fill it. It is separated from the outer ear by the eardrum and the cavity side wall; it contains the *hammer* (malleus), the *anvil* (incus), and the *stirrup* (stapes). Sound waves start vibrations of the eardrum that set these small bones in motion, and they carry the waves across the middle ear. There are openings from the middle ear also to the throat and mastoid cells. That is why infection gets from the nose and throat to the ears.

The inner ear has two parts: the *cochlea* and the *semicircular canals*. The cochlea is shaped like a snail shell. Its coils are filled with fluid that carries the sound waves that enter from the middle ear; the base of the stirrup bone fits into the opening between the middle and inner ear. When the stirrup sets the fluid in the cochlea in motion, the tiny receptive nerve endings pass the vibration to the auditory, or hearing, nerve, which carries them to the brain. The brain interprets these vibrations as sound.

Three canals, shaped like horseshoes, lie behind the cochlea. They are partly filled with fluid that is set in motion by head or body movements. Because this fluid also has communication with the brain, we are able to keep our body balance.

The Human Ear

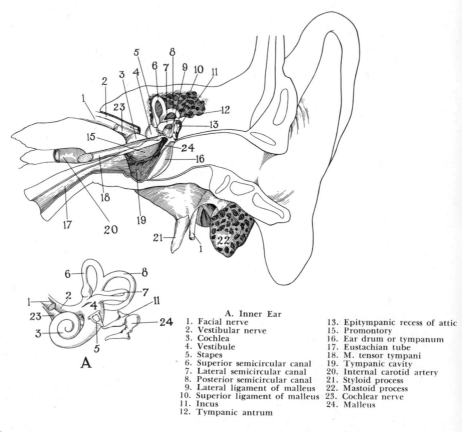

A. Inner Ear

1. Facial nerve
2. Vestibular nerve
3. Cochlea
4. Vestibule
5. Stapes
6. Superior semicircular canal
7. Lateral semicircular canal
8. Posterior semicircular canal
9. Lateral ligament of malleus
10. Superior ligament of malleus
11. Incus
12. Tympanic antrum
13. Epitympanic recess of attic
15. Promontory
16. Ear drum or tympanum
17. Eustachian tube
18. M. tensor tympani
19. Tympanic cavity
20. Internal carotid artery
21. Styloid process
22. Mastoid process
23. Cochlear nerve
24. Malleus

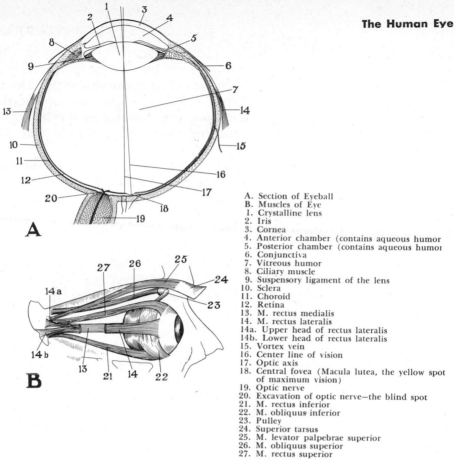

A. Section of Eyeball
B. Muscles of Eye
1. Crystalline lens
2. Iris
3. Cornea
4. Anterior chamber (contains aqueous humor)
5. Posterior chamber (contains aqueous humor)
6. Conjunctiva
7. Vitreous humor
8. Ciliary muscle
9. Suspensory ligament of the lens
10. Sclera
11. Choroid
12. Retina
13. M. rectus medialis
14. M. rectus lateralis
14a. Upper head of rectus lateralis
14b. Lower head of rectus lateralis
15. Vortex vein
16. Center line of vision
17. Optic axis
18. Central fovea (Macula lutea, the yellow spot of maximum vision)
19. Optic nerve
20. Excavation of optic nerve—the blind spot
21. M. rectus inferior
22. M. obliquus inferior
23. Pulley
24. Superior tarsus
25. M. levator palpebrae superior
26. M. obliquus superior
27. M. rectus superior

Ear Disturbances: Sometimes wax collects in the auditory canal and interferes with hearing. Poking with a toothpick may cause serious injury if it should puncture the drum. Gentle syringing with clear water will remove it. If hearing becomes affected, a doctor should be consulted.

Defective hearing is, of course, the major ear disturbance. It is a common affliction. Injuries to the hearing center in the brain, to the auditory nerve, or to the eardrum cause hearing loss. As people grow older, hearing difficulties are likely to appear.

The Eye . . .

The seeing apparatus of the eye consists of the bulb (eyeball), the optic nerve, and the visual center in the brain. The eyeball is round, hollow, and has three layers. The outer, tough layer is called the *sclera.* This layer is transparent only at the center-front of the eyeball. This transparent section is the *cornea*. It is covered by a thin membrane, the *conjunctiva,* which also lines the eyelid. The next layer contains many blood vessels and the *iris*. The iris gives color to the eye. In the middle of the iris is an opening, the *pupil;* the muscles in the iris control the size of the pupil, regulating the amount of light coming into the eye.

The inner layer of the eyeball is the *retina,* which contains the nerve fibers of the optic nerve and the nerve cells sensitive to light. Just behind the pupil, the *lens* brings the light rays into focus to make an image; the image is reflected on the retina and is carried by the optic nerve to the visual, or seeing, center in the brain.

The tear glands are above the eyeballs. They keep the eyeballs moist. Small tubes, or ducts, carry off the excess tears, but, when you cry and these little ducts cannot carry the excess, they overflow as tears.

Defective Vision: If the eyeball is too short, the light rays are focused behind the retina instead of on it. This causes *farsightedness*. In *nearsightedness,* the eyeball is too long or the lens too strong. The light rays are focused in front of the retina.

Defective shape of the eye prevents focus of the rays on one point in the retina; this causes blurred vision or *astigmatism*. Glasses are lenses that help the eye lens in bringing the light rays into focus on the retina for correcting various defects.

SOME EYE DISTURBANCES

1. **Conjunctivitis**—this condition is commonly referred to as "pink eye," or inflammation of the conjunctiva. It can be caused by an organism, by exposure to wind, plus heat exhaustion or fatigue.

2. **Trachoma**—a communicable type of conjunctivitis caused by a virus. The eyes are red, swollen, and blisters form.

3. **Glaucoma**—hardening of the eyeball, in middle-aged or elderly people, which leads to blindness. An operation can check it.

4. **Cataract**—caused by a thickening of the lens in the eye, which interferes with the focusing power and shuts out light. This comes on gradually. If and when it gets to the point where no light is allowed in, the lens may be removed by surgery and glasses used to substitute for lenses.

• Name the systems of the body and discuss each.

Understanding your family.

Home is the center.

Satisfaction in being able to help.

Work hand in hand.

The expense of illness.

5: YOUR PLACE IN THE FAMILY

Understanding Your Family . . .

In these days when pulling-apart demands are made on each member of the family, it is not always easy to live, work, and play together. Dad has his job, which may demand more than eight hours a day from him. There are community activities for both him and the mother of your family. You, too, are likely to be busy in school, club, and church activities. Yet, the give and take of planning, the sharing in decisions and in activities, provide the framework in which qualities of co-operation, consideration for others, thoughtful choosing, and other essentials for successful living are formed.

Understand your family; then you will understand more effectively how to look after a sick member.

Home is the Center . . .

Living centers around your home and family. You look forward to a job, marriage, a home, and children. Your home life should prepare you for these responsibilities.

There are many things that affect home life. Income is undoubtedly high on the list. Income helps determine quality of food, housing, clothes, opportunities for travel, social advantages, and recreation that you will have. It affects health,

71

too, because having good health habits is especially important in making your activities count.

Nationality may affect your family customs and eating habits.

Religion may have a great influence.

Climates, and whether you live in a town or country area, make a difference in the way you live.

Whether the family is large or small affects your home. In the larger family there may be more of sharing and tolerance for each other's rights. Members of a smaller family may be closer. The number of small children or the presence of very old members may affect your family life; they both need special care and attention.

If you have older brothers or sisters who grow up and leave the home center, your family undergoes adjustments. Perhaps one parent dies, or separation occurs; this has a profound affect on the home. Sometimes such changes mean a distinct difference in the manner of living—moving to a smaller home or apartment, having less money for food and other basic expenses.

Exactly how do you "rate" your home? Compare advantages you have with those of other homes in your group. You will find many good qualities in all, because girls interested in nursing—really interested—come from the best kind of family, whose members do not fear misfortune, where love and faith in each other help make up for illness or any lack of physical goods.

Satisfaction in Being Able to Help . . .

Knowing how to help gives you much satisfaction when your family needs you under stress. You think you know every member well, but do you? Start now to think more about the likes and dislikes of others. This interest in them will be worth a lot more than if you think only of yourself. A sick member cannot be separated like a freak from the rest of the family, if your ties are strong—just because he happens to be sick. Try to remember that younger members are persons, with their own special traits. You are in a position to learn and know these things firsthand. What a wonderful opportunity to use your talents for real personal care, when needed the most.

Work Hand in Hand . . .

When there is a sick member in the home, he needs special attention, causing some changes. But regular home life does not come to a stop, nor does it revolve completely around the sick member. Too much attention can be sometimes more harmful than too little. Your duty is, of course, first to the patient. You want to make him comfortable and to do what the doctor prescribes; at the same time, you consider family needs by planning your patient's program to fit in with others' meals, use of bathroom, and freedom to bring in friends and enjoy music or other recreation together. See that the patient gets plenty of rest while younger children are at school, or playing outside. Nagging them into silence at all times is worse than caring for the ill. We are apt to overdo "quiet" and begin whispering, but gradually the family learns what noises are bothersome to the patient. All members have rights, and will co-operate if you treat them as human beings. Of course, quarreling and nagging are not good for anyone concerned.

Knowing that such a plan is being worked out, the patient will get well faster, especially if it is your mother. Mother knows that her role is a big one, but, when she sees you are helping the family to maintain their regular lives, she will be more content to remain in bed. Even Dad won't want his illness to upset the household!

The first step in any co-operative venture is important: Explain how everyone has something to offer in making the patient well. Make younger members feel that this is *a job to*

After doctor's approval, younger members of the family may visit Mother.

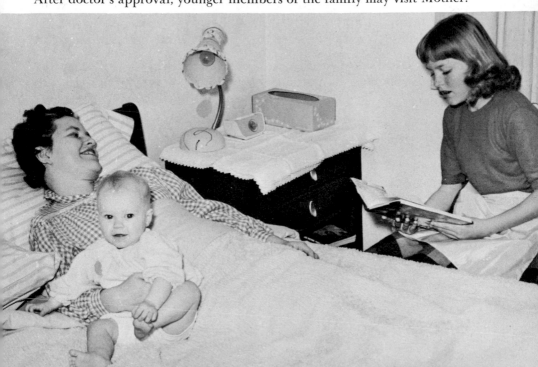

do together. The doctor may ask you to limit visitors in to see the patient; this sometimes is hard to enforce, especially when there are young children in the home. Explain why this is necessary and why the visits must be short. There may be an elderly member in your household; she may resent being told when she may or may not enter the sickroom. Seek out her help in any possible way; let her carry on other tasks within the home that will leave you free to care for the patient; ask her for advice when you know her experience can be valuable.

The Expense of Illness . . .

Perhaps you have had illnesses that required only home remedies and brief nursing care—and you were well in a day or two. There have probably been other times when a doctor should have been called at once, but it was delayed in the hope that the illness would pass. Usually behind such delays is a financial reason—the doctor's fee. There are many kinds of worries when an illness comes unexpectedly. Perhaps it strikes the wage earner who has little or no savings to fall back upon. Your parents must decide how the illness is to be treated and when to call the doctor, but you can help keep expenses down in other ways.

You can make some equipment for the sick room, using what you have on hand in the home. Other special equipment may be required for a short time only. Possibly it can be rented; many hospitals and supply houses have this service. Is a high bed needed? It may be easier for you if you have your patient in

Low bed raised on wooden blocks; holes for bed legs are drilled in tops of blocks • Shoulder support made by cutting a heavy carton diagonally and taping one side over the opening.

Curved basin and paper cups
for medical and nutritive
servings.

a hospital bed, which is higher than the usual home bed, but if height is all that is lacking, solicit Dad's aid in making blocks for under the legs of the home bed. A wooden box will serve the same purpose as a chrome footstool. In short, let the kind of illness, the length of it, and the family budget be your guide as to whether you improvise, rent or buy specific equipment; for instance, mixing bowl or basin, plastic bedpan or chrome; plastic mouth basin or chrome—or a coffee can. Can you offer some suggestions?

"IN OTHER WORDS . . ."

You can become so interested in your patient's welfare and helping to keep the family running smoothly that you will have little time for thinking about yourself. Although this is good to a certain extent, it is important to plan so that you have

Bed tray cut from a heavy
carton.

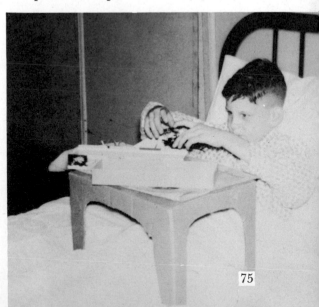

some time alone for rest and for your homework and other personal activities. It is important to keep your body in good working order since it wouldn't be good for the home nurse to work herself ill. Try to plan your patient care so that you may rest or enjoy your own activities when he needs you the least; let another member of the family take over in the sick room during this period. It may be that your patient has developed a habit of napping after meals; place the call bell within reach in case he awakens and needs you; then go on to other tasks or rest with a clear mind. When you relax, concentrate upon it; when you are within the confines of the sick room, give it your full attention. Only with planning, family co-operation, and care of your own needs, can you successfully manage during a long illness.

• Has there been an illness in your home lately? How did you meet the situation?

• Do you have difficulty getting people to co-operate with you under normal conditions? If so, find the reason why.

• Suppose Mother is taken ill tomorrow with bronchitis. How do you explain to your small brother and sister about not visiting her while she is in the contagious stage?

• Suppose you noticed an aching in your back after caring for Mother in her bed. What could be done?

NURSE'S RECORD

Your responsibilities.

Safeguards in the home.

Patient environment.

Care of the sickroom.

General cleaning tips.

Flowers and plants.

6: CONVERTING THE HOME FOR ILLNESS

When a person is sick in the home, family members must be willing to make sacrifices and accept changes in their routine. Noise should be kept at a minimum. It may seem hard, but remember how much harder life is for the sick person, restricted to bed and unable to care for himself.

YOUR RESPONSIBILITIES

You are responsible for the care of your patient's room and the bathroom. It will also sometimes be necessary to give attention to the other parts of the house to reassure or relieve your patient of needless worry—especially if Mother is ill. Cooperation with the other members of the family is a big item at this time, especially if they include brothers and sisters old enough to share housekeeping duties. Someone has to take charge and work out a plan that will fit in with adequate care to the patient, patient's room, and household duties. Try to organize your day—or, even better, a weekly schedule—listing those duties that must be done at a specific time, such as preparation of meals, and those that may be slipped in, such as laundry, once or twice a week. Leave yourself a margin for emergencies that may come up. You can always adjust the schedule to the needs of the sick room and your other activities. School will naturally be one of those items not on the adjustable list, so thought must be given to planning adequate time for homework and your other obligations. Study the plan offered. What adjustments are necessary to make the plan fit into your home pattern if Mother is ill?

Daily Time Plan if Patient is Mother . . .

7:00 A.M. Morning care of patient.
(Temperature, pulse, respiration, washing of face and hands, brushing teeth, hair combing.)

7:20: Into kitchen to prepare breakfast.

7:40: Prepare patient for tray. Bring tray to bed, place in position for patient to feed self. Help where needed. (Cut bacon, butter toast).

7:50: Awaken younger children of family. Start preparing family breakfast.

8:05: Call family to breakfast; eat with them.

8:35: Clear table; rinse and stack dishes in sink; remove tray from patient's room. Supervise children dressing; attend to personal toilet.

8:50: Send younger school children to school.
Leave instruction for person attending patient while you are at school. (This could all be written out the night before with special instructions as to bathing, lunch, and medications or special treatments). *If you are to continue day's care,* then:

9:00: Give patient medication if so ordered. Give bedpan or assist to bathroom. Prepare patient for bath, assemble all necessary equipment, and bring to bedside. Bathe patient.

10:15: Tidy room; arrange flowers. Attend to any special needs, treatment. Leave patient comfortable.

10:30: Attend to other household duties.

11:30: Start lunch preparation; wash breakfast dishes.

12:00 N: Prepare patient for lunch. Bring tray to bedside; arrange in comfortable position for patient.

12:15: Your own lunch.

12:40: Remove patient's tray to kitchen; give attention to medications, if any. Prepare patient for rest period.

1:00: Stack dishes in sink. Use next two hours for shopping, recreation, any chores or rest.

3:00: Attend to patient's needs.
Prepare for younger childrens' return from school.

3:30:   Family and patient visiting.

4:00:   (If you are now returning from school):
Start dinner preparations. Supervise children in preassigned chores or assign chores now—setting dinner table, washing lunch dishes, grocery errands, feeding family pets, etc.).

5:00:   Afternoon care of patient; prepare for tray.

5:20.   Serve patient meal, helping where necessary.

5:30:   Family meal.

6:15:   Remove tray from patient's room to kitchen; supervise younger family member in answering any patient needs, tidying up room.

6:30:   Wash dinner dishes, tidy kitchen.
Plan for next day's routine and menu.

7:15:   Relax.
Do homework.
Start younger children on preparing for bed.

9:00:   Prepare patient for night.

9:30:   Personal care for night.

9:50:   Lights out.

Plan to save yourself steps. It is always better if the patient can be on the main floor, but if he must be upstairs, use a basket or box to carry as much as possible at one time. You can work faster and more efficiently if you have everything nearby before you begin each kind of work.

SAFEGUARDS IN THE HOME

The home should be the happiest, safest place in the world; instead, one-third of all accidents occur there. People slip on loose rugs, fall over toys or down stairs, or are careless when using various pieces of equipment. You are familiar with your own home; you should know where "weak" spots are. Be on the lookout constantly to insure a safe home.

Remove small rugs from places on slippery floors that you and your family must use. These may be in the hallway, your patient's room, or in the room of an elderly person. If they are absolutely necessary, see that rubber cups are attached to the corners to keep them from sliding. Be careful about dark hallways or stairways; replace all burned-out light bulbs at once. Encourage the younger children to remove toys from places where people might stumble over them.

Falls are not limited to those who are on their feet. It is not uncommon for children and sick people to tumble out of their beds. Stand nearby when your patient turns himself; most beds with innerspring mattresses give with the weight of the body and this adds to the danger of falling when the patient reaches out for something.

When using *electrical equipment,* remember that water is a conductor of electricity; always be sure your hands are dry before you insert a plug into the outlet; never turn a light switch on or off, touch a radio or fan while in the bathtub or standing on a wet floor. See that worn-out or frayed cords are replaced on appliances, particularly the iron. Disconnect equipment and turn off motors as soon as you have finished using electrical appliances; excess heat or smoke from a motor indicates that something is wrong and in need of repair.

PATIENT ENVIRONMENT

All of us feel better when we are in pleasant surroundings with everything in order. To the patient who must spend all his time in bed, this is a great factor in his comfort. For example, a person of a naturally nervous disposition may suffer acute agitation at the sight of a picture hanging off balance; he can be disturbed by having to look at a crack or a cobweb on the ceiling.

Of course, good housekeeping does more than benefit the mental state of the patient. It gives less chance for harmful organisms. It makes serving the patient easier. It supports our own prestige as a nurse.

Environment includes all of the home conditions that affect a person—and one of the most important of these is the *ventilation.* Keep the ventilation of the room adjusted so the patient will feel comfortable and safe. A small intake of air in a room is adequate if the air keeps moving.

The important thing to remember is that every person has his own idea about the air in his room; the fear of drafts or a desire for wide open windows is easy to understand. Ideas about ventilation have changed; people at one time thought the night air was poisonous and outside air dangerous for sick people; research has shown us that this is not true. We also know that forceful, cold air is not necessary. Good ventilation means providing a clean supply of air, with the proper amount of moisture, at a comfortable temperature.

The problems of ventilation vary with the climate, the season, the living quarters, and personal preferences.

DON'T MONKEY
with anything you <u>don't understand</u> !

NATIONAL SAFETY COUNCIL ⊕ CHICAGO • PRINTED IN U. S. A.

How to Ventilate a Room . . .

Warm air is lighter than cold air, so it tends to rise; the outside air usually is cooler than inside air. If you open a window from the top and the bottom, the cooler fresh air comes in the bottom and the warm air escapes through the top. Some windows are not made so that they can be opened by this method, but they may be adjusted and the air kept circulating by the use of an electric fan; if you cannot open the windows in the patient's room, open them in another room, leaving the door to the patient's room open.

Water in a basin placed on the radiator or a small jar placed behind the radiator (or room heater) will increase the amount of humidity or moisture in the air. Comfort is balance between the temperature, the amount of moisture in the air, and the pure air in circulation. A comfortable room temperature for a bed patient is between 65 and 70° F. If moisture can be regulated, as with a dehumidifier, the body feels most comfortable when humidity is kept at 70 per cent; and the circulating air is comfortable when free from drafts and extreme changes.

In warmer weather, when an electric fan is used to keep the air currents circulating, place it so the air will not blow directly on the patient. Window ventilators or air coolers are available to keep room temperatures down, but again care must be taken that the patient is out of direct air current contact (draft). *Air conditioning* equipment cleanses and cools or heats air, brings it to the proper degree of humidity, and circulates it. If economically possible, a single room unit is very desirable for the bedfast patient in humid localities.

CARE OF THE SICK ROOM

Everyday cleaning in the patient's room includes dusting floors, furniture, window sills, mirrors, rugs, and other objects. It means picking up and removing discarded items and papers. Once a week the room should be vacuumed, with attention to the draperies and upholstered furniture.

The best time to tidy up and carry out your housekeeping duties is right after the patient has had his bath and the bed is made. *Lint* tends to circulate when you change the bedding. *Settle the patient* comfortably before you begin; he may be able to walk into the living room, or may wish to sit in a chair. If he cannot, offer a magazine, a book, a TV program, or supply him with whatever he desires. Since a bath in itself is tiring, he may wish to nap. *When he is settled,* you will be able to work more rapidly without having to stop in the middle of a task. *Be orderly* as you work; pick up newspapers and other litter before you begin. *Clean* higher pieces of furniture before the lower. *Begin at the top* and work down. *Remove rugs* to be dusted well away from the room. *Dust the floors last,* using even, smooth strokes so as not to stir up the dust; add the final touches.

After using the dust mop, shake the dust from it into a paper bag or newspaper. Keep an oil-treated mop in a metal receptacle, if possible, since dust adheres to it readily. Untreated mops should be washed occasionally in warm, soapy water, rinsed in clear water, and dried. If the mop part is removable, it may be washed in the washer. An oil-treated mop may be cleaned in warm water to which ammonia has been added. Hang mops by their handles to keep them from becoming matted and to give them a chance to dry.

Soft cloths, such as cheesecloth, dampened with oil or furniture polish, pick up the dust without scattering it. *Apply polish* to the cloth sparingly since dust clings to oily surfaces and an excess of polish leaves a greasy coat. *Wet dust cloths* can be used to clean painted surfaces. A dry or slightly dampened dust cloth is best for varnished or shellacked finishes. *Wash used dust cloths* in plenty of hot water and dry them. *Store oily dust cloths* in metal container to prevent fire hazard.

Liquid spray cleaners are effective and easy to use in cleaning *mirrors* and *windows.* Clear, warm water with a small amount of vinegar might be used. Use a *lint-free cloth* and be careful not to get the cleaner on mirror frames, since some cleaners will remove the finish.

The Bathroom . . .

When you use the family bathroom for your patient, see that it is left clean. Clean the tub with scouring powder; clean the toilet bowl with a long handled brush and a special cleanser; clean the metal fittings, the mirror, and the floor; empty the wastebasket. Keep necessary articles for the care of the patient out of reach of the children. Encourage other members of the family to keep the bathroom clean after use so that it will always be tidy.

GENERAL CLEANING TIPS

Your nursing equipment should require essentially the same cleansing as household articles. *Rinsing:* Loose material should be rinsed from all utensils before they are washed. Hot water hardens or coagulates protein material, such as eggs and meat juices. Body wastes and blood also contain protein matter. On the other hand, cold water will not wash away grease, but hot soap and water will dissolve it. For this reason, after the initial rinsing, you use hot soapy water on most household and nursing equipment.

Rinse all equipment well to remove all soap or cleaning agent; dry it well to prevent rust and store it in its rightful place so that you know exactly where it is when it is next needed. Clean equipment every time you use it.

The *bed linens* should always be fresh, smooth, and immaculate. Not only is this essential for health and comfort of the patient, they certainly are more attractive than soiled, mussy ones. Remembering that hot water coagulates, be sure to remove all body discharge and blood stains immediately with cold water, then wash in hot soapy water; use warm water and soap for grease and oil stains. For all unknown stains, use water, since it is the safest thing. There are other cleaning solvents (solutions that dissolve stains or bleach them.) They include gasoline and naphtha, which are dangerous because of their explosive vapors. *Carbon tetrachloride* is non-explosive but *gives off poisonous fumes.* Never use it. Very good special solvents are available today for every use. Read the labels for their specific applications.

Sometimes it is difficult to remove certain food stains, but if they are attended to immediately, most of them can be removed. *Fruit juice stains* will come out if the stained area is stretched over a basin and boiling water is poured directly through the stain. *Coffee and tea stains* come out in warm water and soap; so does *hot chocolate.*

Give gentle care to the delicate bed jackets or gowns of your patient, by washing in warm water and soap; or, better still, follow the manufacturer's advice. Most manufacturers include laundry suggestions with such articles. Some general rules for laundering are as follows:

1. Wash colored and white things separately.

2. Remember that very hot water, bright sunlight, bleaches, and strong soaps and detergents fade colors.

3. Use plenty of water and enough soap to make a good suds.

4. Use warm water for silk, rayon, nylon, and woolen materials.

5. Rinse well to remove every trace of soap and bleaching agent.

FLOWERS AND PLANTS

Flowers tend to brighten and freshen any room, so you can see why people send flowers to the patient. Try to arrange the flowers attractively. Expensive vases are not essential. By making the most of what is on hand, you will be pleased with the results. You can cover an empty coffee can or jar with aluminum foil or have one of the younger family members paint it. Colorful ribbons dress it up. Here are some simple rules to follow when arranging flowers.

1. Choose a container of appropriate size; a few flowers will look better in a small vase.

2. Use a tall container for long-stemmed flowers; put short ones in lower holders.

3. Cut the stems in varying lengths. Balance clusters high and low on opposite sides.

4. Put together flowers that blend in color.

5. Strip off any foliage that comes beneath the water line.

Discard wilted or faded flowers. In order to keep them fresh as long as possible, the stems should be cut on a slant under water; this allows the water more surface to enter. Stems cut straight across also tend to fill with air so that the water cannot get through. Change the water in the flower container every day; keep the container clean; dry the outside after filling with water.

Place the flowers where your patient can see them. Sometimes *strong* floral scents are distasteful; if this is the case, put the flowers as far from the bed as possible. Don't be afraid to experiment with arrangements; this may be pleasing to the patient and encourage him to try it as he improves.

All potted plants need a basin or pan under them that will not leak. Many plants may be watered from the bottom—by filling the container under the pot. Ask the florist's advice if special care is needed for certain plants.

• Suppose a member of your family were ill with measles and the window blinds had to be kept drawn. What would you do about ventilation?

• What problems come up when your home has only one bathroom? What can be done about this situation when you are caring for a sick member of the family?

• What precautions should be taken when using an electric heater in the bathroom?

• How could you raise the bed in order to give more effective nursing care?

• Make a study of your home, as if you were planning for patient care. Where will the sick room be? How can it be improved? How will you manage your day, with the help of the family? Bring notes on special problems to class for discussion.

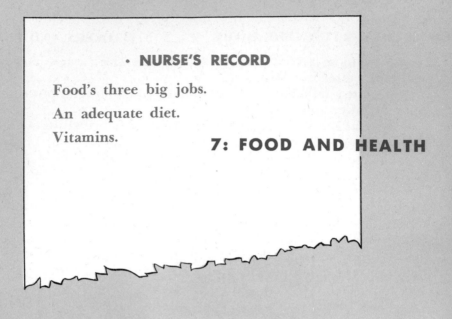

Food's three big jobs.

An adequate diet.

Vitamins.

7: FOOD AND HEALTH

We learn in our foods courses that nutrition is the science that deals with food at work—food on the job. When you and your family eat the right food, it does far more than keep you alive and going. The right food helps you to be at your best in health and vitality. It can help you stay young longer. An individual well fed from babyhood has a more likely chance to enjoy a long prime of life. But, at any age, you are better off when you are better fed.

We have scientific information to help us estimate how much of each food material any given individual needs every day, in relation to his way of living and what is going on inside his body. He can plan his meals according to the kind of work he does, the amount of income he has, his age, and unusual conditions of his system.

Dietetics is the use of this information to plan certain meals or a daily diet for any individual when he is well or when he is ill. A *dietitian* is an expert in this field.

FOOD'S THREE BIG JOBS

You think of food as including cereals, vegetables, meat, fish, eggs, milk, cheese, desserts, from which you choose three meals a day and the snacks in between. The body cells, however, are only interested in extracting from food, as you understand it, the materials they can use. These materials are called *nutrients,* meaning to nourish or to feed. They are listed with their uses in the body:

Carbohydrates (starches and sugars): provide energy.

Fats: provide energy; build fatty tissue.

Proteins: build and repair tissue; provide energy.

Minerals: build and repair tissues; regulate body processes.

Vitamins: regulate body processes.

Water: provides avoirdupois; carries nutrients, lubricants, regulating cells, and wastes.

Food's Three Big jobs are:

1. To provide materials for the body's building, maintenance and repair. Protein and minerals (plus water) are the chief ingredients of tissue and bone. Children must have these food materials for growth; all life long the body continues to require supplies for upkeep.

2. To provide regulators that enable the body to use other materials and to run smoothly. Vitamins do important work in this line, and minerals and protein, too.

3. To provide fuel for the body's energy and warmth. There is some fuel in every food.

AN ADEQUATE DIET

The amounts of nutrients present in individual foods vary considerably. Some foods contain large amounts of one nutrient and small amounts of another; other foods contain small amounts of several nutrients. The combinations are many. The trick, then, is to provide the essential nutrients in the amounts necessary to keep the body healthy. Such food combinations make up an adequate diet.

Carbohydrates . . .

Carbohydrates are the sugars and the starches that are burned up in the body as fuel for energy. We can measure energy in calories. Tables are available that tell us exactly how many calories a given amount of food will produce. If your food provides your body with more than it needs for energy, your body stores the excess as *glycogen* in the liver and fatty tissues.

Carbohydrate material comes mostly from the plant foods. Foods high in starches include flours, cereals, cornstarch, tapioca; macaroni and spaghetti; bread and crackers; potatoes. The

Kind of food	Size of serving	Protein	Calcium	Iron	Vitamin A value	Thiamine	Riboflavin	Niacin	Vitamin C (ascorbic acid)	Food energy (in calories)
						B-vitamins				
Leafy, green, yellow vegetables.	½ cup			*	****				**	30
Tomatoes, tomato products.	½ cup			*	***			*	***	35
Potatoes	1 medium			*		*		*	*	105
Sweetpotatoes	1 medium			*	*****	*		*	***	165
Other vegetables	½ cup								*	40
Citrus fruits	½ cup								*****	55
Other fruits	½ cup				*				*	70
Milk, cheese, ice cream.	1 cup milk	*	***		*	*	**			170
Meat, poultry, fish	4 ounces	**		**	*	**	*	***		225
Eggs	1 egg	*		*	*		*			80
Dry beans and peas, nuts.	¾ cup beans cooked	**	*	***		**	*	**		215
Baked goods, flour, cereals.	2 slices bread	*		*		*	*	*		130
Butter, fortified margarine.	1 pat				*					50
Other fats (includes bacon, salt pork).	2 tablespoons									230
Sugar, all kinds	2 teaspoons									35
Molasses, syrups, preserves.	2 tablespoons			*						115

***** More than 50 percent of daily need.
**** About 40 percent of daily need.
*** About 30 percent of daily need.
** About 20 percent of daily need.
* About 10 percent of daily need.

Food Fare, U. S. Department of Agriculture

body changes the starches into sugars and puts them to use in that form.

Foods high in sugars include cane, beet, and corn products; foods that are rich in sugar, such as syrups, frostings, candies, and cakes; preserves, jams and jellies; honey; sweet fruits.

Large amounts of sugar in any form dull the appetite for other essential foods. Sugar may ferment in the digestive tract and irritate it.

Fats . . .

Fats are found in foods that come from both animals and plants. They are concentrated forms of energy and act as insulation against cold, as well as a lubricant. A gram of fat will produce 2½ times as much energy as an equal amount of carbohydrate. Food sources of fats from animals are cream, butter, whole milk and whole milk cheese; fat meats such as bacon and salt pork, poultry fat or beef suet; fish, such as sardines, mackerel, and salmon; egg yolk.

Plant foods high in fats are oleomargarine and other fat spreads; shortenings; olive oil; chocolate; avocados; coconuts and other nuts.

Foods fried in fats take longer to digest because the fatty coating over the food must be digested first.

Overweight and underweight: Why are some people very thin and others the opposite? Remember—the body uses up carbohydrates and fats for energy. Any carbohydrates and fats that are not used will be stored away in the body as fat. The more sugars unused, the more fats are stored.

It is not *what* you eat, generally speaking, but *how much*. Second helpings of fat-making foods are an invitation to more pounds. On the other hand, the reducing diet that cuts down on the fat-making foods must still be balanced by including some energy-making foods because the body needs some of the carbohydrates to burn the fat it has stored.

It works like this: Suppose the body has a small amount of stored fat. If the diet is low in energy providers and the person is active, the body will be forced to fall back upon its basic store of fat; as the fatty tissues are used up, the person may become underweight.

A very few people are fat because their bodies get along on less fuel than usual. This is because certain of their glands do not function properly. This condition is rare, but, if you think you are such a person, go to your doctor for help. If he says that your fat is caused by overeating, take his word and follow the diet he recommends. Remember that the doctor can tell you what to do but it's up to you to do it. It takes will power—or maybe it's "won't power."

A home nurse is happier if she has a nice figure and strong arms rather than a load of ugly fat that makes life a burden for her. Your patient will benefit from a strict, non-fattening diet, too.

Proteins . . .

The best food sources of proteins are lean meat, poultry, shell fish, eggs, milk, and cheese. The next best sources are soybeans, nuts, cereals, bread, dry beans, and peas. Fruits and vegetables supply some protein. The proteins are not stored in the body; any excess is eliminated.

Many popular family dishes, such as meat and vegetable stew, egg sandwiches, macaroni and cheese, cereal and milk are highly nourishing combinations. For in the body's remarkable chemistry, the high-grade proteins team with the less complete proteins in many companion foods and make the latter more useful than if eaten alone.

A nurse and her patient benefit from a balanced protein diet. Protein gives strength and rebuilding values.

Minerals . . .

Minerals are important for healthy bones, nails, and teeth. They also maintain *muscle tone* and keep the body fluids in balance. Some minerals are used in the body more readily than others; some are lost in waste. Foods vary a great deal in the amounts of minerals they contain, so we will discuss some of them singly, although briefly, since you will probably cover these in other classes.

Calcium . . .

Calcium is one of the chief minerals in bones, nails, and teeth. About 99 per cent of all the calcium in the body is used for framework. Small, but important, the other 1 per cent remains in the body fluids, such as the blood. Without this calcium, muscles can't contract and relax and nerves can't carry their messages.

For calcium to be used properly, vitamin D and phosphorus are needed, too, in right quantities. Many people go through life with bones that are calcium-poor. If a child gets too little calcium in his food or if his bones fail to deposit the calcium properly, then the bones will be smaller than they should be, or malformed, as when the legs are bent in rickets. Older people who are calcium-poor may have brittle bones that break easily and mend slowly.

The outstanding calcium food is milk. Next best are some of the leafy vegetables, especially turnip tops, mustard greens, and kale. Other sources are clams, oysters, maple syrup, molasses, and almonds.

Iron . . .

Without its iron supply, the red blood cells could not carry oxygen from the lungs to each body cell.

You get iron from many foods; liver is the best source.

Leafy vegetables are next. Some of the other foods that contain iron are egg yolks, meats, peas and beans of all kinds, dried fruits, molasses, bread, and other cereal foods.

Other Minerals . . .

Although the amount of *iodine* in the body is small, the thyroid gland's action depends upon it. The most familiar bad effect of getting too little iodine is the swelling of the gland, called goiter.

Along the sea coast, and in some other parts of the United States, iodine is contained in the drinking water, vegetables, and fruits grown in the local soil. But too little iodine in water and soil is the cause of a wide "goiter belt" across the country, particularly around the Great Lakes and in the northwestern states. If you live inland, improve your weekly diet with salt-water fish or shellfish. A more common method of acquiring iodine into the diet is by using iodized salt.

Salt, or sodium chloride, is usually in good supply, as we take it with our food. The body loses salt in perspiration so the amount of salt taken in should be increased if the perspiration is excessive, because salt is important in regulating the body fluids.

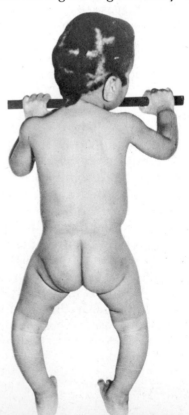

Child with legs bowed as a result of rickets, vitamin D deficiency.

ROSE LEE NEMIR, M.D., N.Y.U.-BELLEVUE MED. CENTER

Copper, potassium, magnesium, sulphur, zinc, and *cobalt* are all found in the body in small amounts. An ordinary adequate diet supplies the body needs, it is thought.

Water . . .

Approximately three-quarters of the body weight is due to its water content so you can see the importance of water in the diet. Cells cannot do their work without water; it forms a large part of the blood and urine; it is necessary as a solvent for the minerals to carry on their functions; by its moistening process, it enables the lungs to take in oxygen and give off carbon dioxide; it regulates body temperature.

The amount of water taken into the body must equal the amount lost, in order to maintain the normal body water balance. Water is lost from the body in several ways—by evaporation through the lungs, from the body surface, in the urine, and in the bowel movements. Water in food and beverages replaces some of this but we must make up the needed amount by drinking water. Most authorities say that the average adult needs from 6 to 8 glasses of water every day.

In some *body disturbances,* it is necessary to alter the fluid intake: it is lessened to ease the burden upon certain organs and increased to flush certain parts and aid in elimination of wastes. This explains why we force or cut down on fluids, measure the fluid intake and the urine output, and note the amount of perspiration in certain cases.

VITAMINS

Nearly twenty vitamins that are known or believed to be important to human well-being have been discovered to date. Vitamins have been known since 1911; they were named with letters of the alphabet for lack of exact information on their make-up. Vitamins, we have found, are chemical compounds so now we call some of them by their chemical names. Chemists have learned to prepare these in the laboratory. This has made it possible to learn more about the ways vitamins work by using them in pure form. Doctors can now give large amounts of certain vitamins when necessary.

Vitamins are widely distributed in foods, no two of which contain exactly the same combinations. Because most vitamins are not stored in the body, and the body cannot make its own in all cases, it is very important to assure a daily supply; an all-around vitamin deficiency may not cause a specific disease but does impair the general health. Most vitamins are associated with deficiency diseases rather than what they do for us. We know that the following vitamins are important:

Vitamin A . . .

Children must have vitamin A because it promotes growth; we all need it because it maintains normal vision, supports normal reproduction, keeps the skin and mucous linings in good condition, thereby strengthening our resistance to infection.

You can get vitamin A from some animal foods; good sources are liver, egg yolks, butter, whole milk and cream, and cheese made with cream content. Fish-liver oils which children take for vitamin D content are rich in vitamin A, too. Other sources include all forms of greens, broccoli, and especially carrots. A bright yellow color usually suggests the vitamin A foods. Surplus amounts are stored in the body fats; it is not destroyed by cooking.

Vitamin B . . .

There was once supposed to be only one vitamin B. Then the vitamin was found to be complex and has been separated into about a dozen vitamins, each with particular duties and importance. Thiamine, riboflavin, and niacin are the most generally known and best understood. Getting enough of these in food helps the nerves, the appetite, the digestion, the morale, and skin. Signs of a deficiency of thiamine are poor appetite, irritability, listlessness, loss of weight and strength, and poor intestinal tone. A very great deficiency causes changes in the reproductive system and beriberi. Beriberi is a disease of the nervous system that leads to paralysis and, finally, to death.

Recently identified B's are folic acid and vitamin B-12, both important for healthy state of the blood. They are being used medically with success in treating two hard-to-cure diseases—pernicious anemia and sprue, an ulcerative disease affecting the digestive tract.

The best sources of vitamin B are the germ portions of cereals; peas, beans, and soybeans; the lean meat of pork; liver, beef heart; meats from the glandular organs; dried yeast. Thiamine is found in most vegetables and egg yolk. Getting ample milk in the diet is important for B's, too, and for riboflavin in particular.

Night blindness is a sign of vitamin A deficiency. These pictures show the loss of vision in dim light after exposure to bright light. The person with normal vision and the one lacking vitamin A both see the headlights of an approaching car as in the first picture. After the car passes, normal vision sees much of the road as in the second illustration. Only a few feet of road are visible to the deficient person, as in the third picture. Note that he cannot see the warning sign.

PHOTOS BY VITAMIN MANUAL, UPJOHN CO.

Since this vitamin group is easily destroyed by heat and air, food that supplies it should not be overcooked or kept warm for a long time. Also much B-1 can be lost in cooking water when it is discarded. Some nutrition experts advise keeping the water in which B-1 rich foods are cooked, and using it again to prepare soups or other foods in which the water will eventually be consumed.

Foot drop (peripheral neuritis) caused by poor nutrition. Rigid ankles shown in the first picture could be flexed moderately, as in the second picture, after 2½ weeks of thiamine therapy

PHOTOS BY HENRY FIELD JR., M.D., MED. SERV., VETERANS ADMIN.

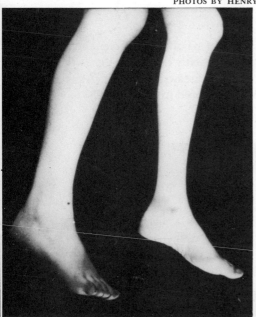
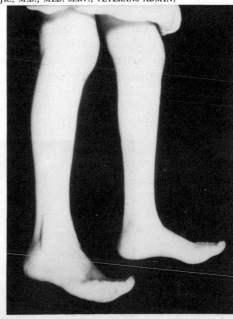

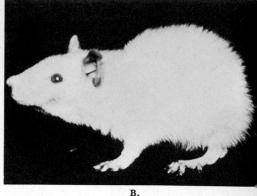

A.   B.

Thiamine deficiency gave this rat neuritis, causing the back to arch and
the legs to extend. The rat had trouble walking and keeping balance.
Picture B shows the same rat nearly normal 8 hours after receiving
thiamine hydrochloride.

PHOTOS, VITAMIN MANUAL, UPJOHN COMPANY

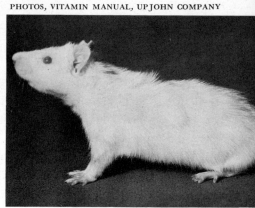

A.   B.

Generalized dermatitis and growth failure in riboflavin-deficient rat (A).
Improvement after one month of treatment with riboflavin—growth has
resumed and fur is growing on the formerly diseased skin (B). After two
months of treatment, the rat has recovered his health (C).

C.

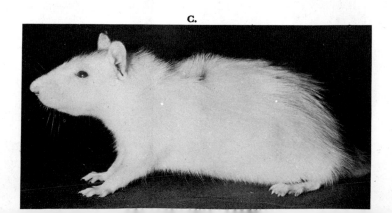

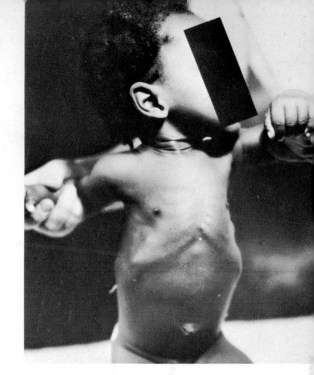

RUSTIN MCINTOSH, M.D., COLUMBIA UNIV.,
COLLEGE OF PHYSICIANS AND SURGEONS

This child's poor rib formation and enlarged joints were caused by deficiency of vitamin C.

Vitamin C . . .

Tissues throughout the body are kept in good condition by vitamin C, also called ascorbic acid. A marked deficiency of vitamin C in the body causes scurvy, a disease marked by tender, bleeding gums, swollen, painful joints and weakened muscles. A lesser deficiency causes listlessness, irritability, and lowered resistance to disease.

Because the body cannot store this vitamin, you need some food rich in vitamin C every day. All of the citrus fruits are excellent sources. Half a glass (4 ounces) of orange or grapefruit juice, fresh or canned, goes far toward meeting the day's needs. The same is true of half a grapefruit, a whole orange, or a couple of tangerines.

Abnormally large red blood cells indicate pernicious anemia (A). From 48 to 72 hours after treatment with vitamin B-12, normal cells have replaced enlarged ones (B).

A.   VITAMIN MANUAL, UPJOHN COMPANY   **B.**

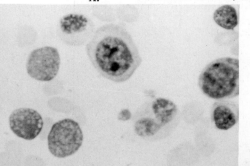
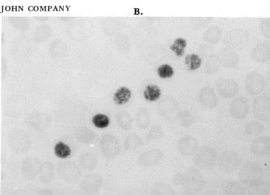

Flabby tissues and loss of strength result from rickets. Growth is retarded and joints enlarged. Note leg crumpled weakly under rat's body.

Other sources of vitamin C include tomatoes and tomato juice, canned or fresh; fresh strawberries and cantaloupe; also green food, such as cabbage, green pepper, and green lettuce. The potato's many values include some vitamin C; it is present in milk but pasteurization destroys it.

Vitamin C is destroyed by exposure to the air and loses its strength in storage. Cooking at a high temperature destroys it. Fruits and vegetables canned commercially *retain this vitamin* because air is excluded from them during the canning process.

Vitamin D . . .

Vitamin D, the sunshine vitamin, works with minerals to form straight, strong bones and sound teeth. It is created in the body with the aid of an agency such as sunlight. Babies with bow-legs may have had too little vitamin D. This is called rickets, a deficiency disease whereby the bones do not calcify, causing them to bend into deformity. A mother, before and after her baby is born, must provide herself with enough vitamin D to prevent rickets from developing in her baby and to preserve her own bones and teeth. This vitamin is not stored in the body and must be created every day. Natural foods are not good

These are leg bones (tibia) taken from rats in various stages of rickets. (A) shows normal growth; (B) is affected with rickets—note calcified areas at ends; (C) is in healing process, after treatment with cod liver oil; (D) is healed. Bones remain permanently widened at the ends.

A.   B.   C.   D.

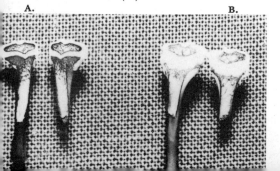
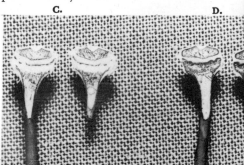

agencies for vitamin D. The best are the fish-liver oils; cod liver oil is the most dependable and gives vitamin A, too. Cow's milk is low in vitamin D but the amount of this vitamin in milk may be increased by irradiating the milk, by adding concentrated vitamin D, and by adding vitamin D to the diet of the cows. Water does not dissolve vitamin D, and ordinary cooking temperatures do not affect it.

Other Vitamins . . .

We know that vitamin K is necessary for the clotting of the blood. Bile must be present in the digestive tract to absorb vitamin K from foods; if there is a deficiency of this vitamin or a lack of bile in the digestive tract, the blood clots slowly and hemorrhages result.

Food sources of vitamin K are leafy, green vegetables, cauliflower, soy bean, tomatoes, and orange peel.

Vitamin E is called the reproductive or antisterility vitamin. So far, it has not been proved whether this vitamin is essential to humans but some animals definitely require this vitamin to reproduce. It is found in many foods, especially wheat germ oils, seeds, green leaves, milk fat, and meats.

This chick was fed a diet deficient in vitamin K, resulting in spontaneous bleeding under the skin.

"IN OTHER WORDS . . ."

Taking food apart chemically, scientists are learning more exactly, nutrient by nutrient, what each familiar food can provide for the body's needs.

To get all the nutrients needed, it's wise to eat a variety of foods. Sometimes we fall into the habit of letting our choice foods "get in a rut." Too often we build our meals out of what's in the cupboard rather than building our cupboard supplies out of what should be in our meals! This is where you can be of considerable help to the homemaker in your family. Perhaps she, too, works part of her day outside of the home, and does not always have the time to plan a well-organized meal. Why not suggest that you plan the meals together in advance? The rush at the last minute often makes us skip parts of a meal—for instance, we may skip that interesting salad or hot vegetable. You can make eating an adventure. Look around at the foods that are available. Talk them over; try a new one now and then. Before long you and the members of your family will like many more foods. The cooking experience you receive under your homemaker's guidance—whether it be father, mother, older sister, grandmother, or housekeeper—will certainly come in handy when you are the sole planner of your own family meals or must take care of a patient. The following suggestions will help you when that time comes; perhaps you already do family cooking, all or in part, and this should be a great experience and challenge for you.

1. Plan your meals so that the daily food includes needed quantities of protein, minerals, and other nutrients.

2. Cook with up-to-date methods that keep delicate vitamins and minerals from being wasted.

3. Make a collection of nutritious recipes that the whole family enjoys, and use them all reasonably often.

4. When using one of these favorites, vary the meal with different food combinations.

5. If an inexpensive dish seems dull, vary flavor with seasonings, or combine with other foods in different ways.

6. Use contrast in food colors, flavors, and textures. A bright-colored food, something crisp, for example, can heighten the eye and appetite appeal of a meal.

7. Give children small servings, remembering that big amounts may be discouraging. It's better for a child to form the habit of cleaning his plate and asking for second helpings, if wanted.

8. Introduce a new food to a young child in sample tastes, and at the start of a meal when he is hungry; if he doesn't like it at first, try again another day.

• Do you remember all the foods you ate yesterday? How did they measure up in nutrients?

• Why is it necessary for young children to have more milk daily than adults? What do you understand by "irradiated"?

• If you wanted a quick supply of energy, which would you eat, a slice of bread or a piece of candy? Why?

• What are some of the new pieces of equipment on the market today for health-guarding food nutrients in cooking?

• Prepare a sample menu for a day, giving special attention to getting in all the essential nutrients.

NURSE'S RECORD

Daily food guide.

Wise buying.

When you cook for a patient.

Kitchen housekeeping and safety.

Your patient's tray.

Feeding the patient.

8: NUTRITION IS UP TO YOU

You need up-to-date infomation about nutrition and preparing food, first, for your own health and, secondly, for the health of your patient. Diet is an important part of nursing. It's true, you do not always prepare the patient's food yourself, but you will be responsible for carrying out the doctor's orders if you are to aid in the patient's recovery. You cannot guide someone else in planning and preparing your patient's meals unless you know how yourself. It is not easy to change family methods of cooking food; however, if you stress that you are all interested in the welfare of the patient and his recovery depends upon all members of the family working together toward this end, it can be managed with tact.

DAILY FOOD GUIDE

You have explored nutrient values here and probably studied the subject in other courses. You know of the importance of having enough of nutrient foods in the diet. You should be ready to choose the foods for daily food plans of well people, to understand the needs of those who are ill. The plan

Milk and milk products food group.

Meat and protein food group.

here discussed is the "Basic 4," or Daily Food Guide. The "Basic 7" may be used also.

Food Groups . . .

The planning of meals will mean study of the broad food groups listed:

1. *Milk group*—milk, cheese, ice cream.
2. *Protein group*—meat, poultry, fish, eggs, dry beans and peas, nuts.
3. *Vegetable-fruit group*.
4. *Bread-cereals group*.

Fruit and vegetable food group.

PHOTOS BY NATIONAL DAIRY COUNCIL
Bread and cereal food group.

Foods within each group are similar so one may replace another and give many choices in each group. You can get all the right kinds of food needed for health by using this simple guide. Be sure to include in your meals each day at least the minimum number of servings from each group listed and illustrated. Since you are still in the growing stage, provide nice large servings of each.

In order to help you choose your foods that the body needs every day, the Daily Food Guide (sometimes called the Basic 4) is charted as follows:

GROUP	FOODS	WAYS OF USING THESE FOODS

Milk	milk
	cheeses
	butter or other spread
	ice cream and other
	  milk by-products
		As a drink; in cocoa; over
		  cereals; in vegetable soup;
		  in vegetable or fish chow-
		  der; cream sauces; custards;
		  puddings; over baked fruits.

Vegetable-Fruit	*Green leafy:*
	  beet greens
	  Brussels sprouts
	  cabbage
	  chard
	  dandelion greens
	  spinach
	  lettuce
	
	Yellow:
	  carrots
	  parsnips
	  squash
	  sweet potato
	  turnip
	  yellow beans
	  yellow corn
	
	Others:
	  asparagus
	  beans
	    string
	    lima
	  beets
	  cauliflower
	  celery
		As salad of raw vegetables.
		Cooked and seasoned with salt
		  and butter.
		Cooked and served with
		  cream sauce; on toast or
		  over cooked rice; baked po-
		  tato and cole slaw; scal-
		  loped cabbage or onion; po-
		  tato with cream and cheese
		  sauce.
		In soups:
		  Potato, tomato, carrot,
		  onion, spinach, pea, bean,
		  asparagus, etc.
		In chowders and in stews.

corn
egg plant
green peas
kohlrabi
okra
onion
radish
potato

Fresh or canned fruit: Fresh
orange   Stewed
grapefruit   Baked
tomato   Canned
apple   Preserved
banana   With cereals
blackberries   In puddings
blueberries   In salads
peach
pear
rhubarb
strawberries

Dried:
apricots
dates
prunes
raisins
peaches
apples

Proteins	*Animal:*	*Serve meat:*
	cheese	In vegetable stew.
	egg	Cooked with macaroni, spaghetti, rice, potato, vegetables.
	fish	
	fowl	
	meat	In meat loaf.
	milk	
	Vegetable:	*Serve fish:*
	dried beans	In chowder.
	kidney	Baked with cream or cheese sauce.
	lima	Stewed with tomato.
	navy	Broiled.
	dried peas	In fish loaf.

GROUP	FOODS	WAYS OF USING THESE FOODS
	lentils	In salad.
	nuts	*Serve eggs:* In custard, in cream sauce over vegetables, scrambled, poached, etc.
		Serve beans: Baked with tomato, in soups with corn and milk.
Cereals	*Whole grain:* brown rice cracked wheat rolled oats whole corn meal	*As cereal:* In soup, pudding Macaroni served with tomato or cream sauce. Rice served with tomato sauce or with dried fruit or meat dish.
	Refined: polished rice spaghetti macaroni noodles farina crackers	In milk toast. For sandwiches of cheese, vegetables, meat. Spread with cheese and tomato.
	Whole grain breads: graham oatmeal rye whole wheat crackers PLUS EXTRAS:	In puddings—bread and apple. Toast and serve with tomato and cheese sauce. Serve with fruit sauce or molasses.
Fats and Oils	butter bacon lard peanut butter salt pork vegetable fats vegetable oils other animal fats	*Serve butter:* in cooked vegetables in puddings on bread *Serve oil:* with salads with vegetables Use other fats in cooking

The following sample menu is offered to help you plan your meals. With the use of the above lists, no difficulty should be encountered.

BREAKFAST

Fruit
Cereal
Bread and butter
Milk for children
Coffee or tea for adults

LUNCH

One of these "meat substitutes"
    milk
    eggs
    cheese
    dried beans or peas
Vegetable
Bread and butter
Simple dessert or fruit
Milk

DINNER

Meat, fish, or "meat substitute"
Potato
Another vegetable
Bread and butter
Fruit or simple dessert
Milk for children
Coffee or tea for adults

Energy Needs . . .

Energy needs must be considered when planning family meals, depending upon whether members do light, moderate, or heavy work. Plan for giving more energy by adding extra amounts of carbohydrates and fats. You may either increase the servings of these foods or add other foods in the food groups.

You will want to plan your patient's menu to fit in with the family menu as much as possible, except perhaps for special handling, when necessary; this saves time and work for you or whoever prepares the meal. Be guided by the doctor's orders, your patient's preference, and the food budget.

WISE BUYING

The same need exists for a food buying plan as for a house-keeping plan; there are several general factors always to be considered. In meeting the nutritional needs for the patient and the family, you must think of (1) the cost of meals, (2) the types of meals, (3) making meals attractive, (4) choosing foods that go together in flavor, (5) individual preferences and special requirements—for activity, age, illness, or injury.

It is possible to have a balanced diet whether the food budget is small, medium, or large. First, you must know how to judge the quality of meats, fruits, and vegetables and how to interpret the labels on canned or packaged goods. Secondly, proper storage and use of left-overs are required.

Here are some *helpful guides* to help you plan your meals and select food with an eye toward health and the budget:

1. Choose ripe, firm *fruits* except for bananas and pears—they ripen after they have been picked.
2. Select crisp, firm *vegetables* of good color.
3. Buy *fresh foods* that are in season. They are less expensive.
4. Read the *labels* on canned and packaged goods. Labels tell the amount, the grade (quality), and the ingredients used.
5. Buy *staples* in quantity if you have storage space and if there is no danger of their spoiling before they can be used.
6. Buy from markets and stores where the handling and care of food is *hygienic*.
7. Take advantage of lower food prices during *sales*.
8. Be sure that bargains are really of good quality. You won't save anything if you have to throw away part of what you buy.
9. Substitute dried or evaporated milk for fresh milk in cooking.
10. Use fortified margarine for part of butter requirements, especially in cooking.
11. Substitute dried, canned, or frozen fruits for fresh ones when just as satisfactory for the use.
12. Plan a week's menu in advance to save time and money.

Storage . . .

Points to remember in food storage are how to keep them safe from spoiling, wilting, or absorbing odors from other foods. Food should be covered or placed in plastic bags; left-overs

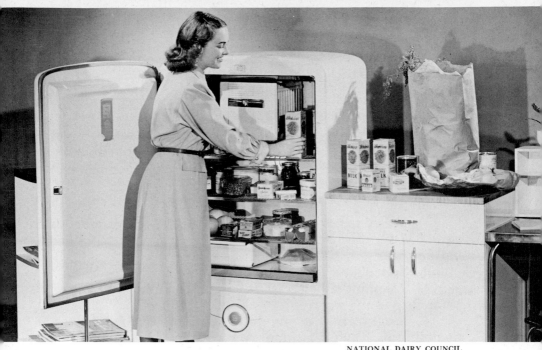

Proper storage makes cooking easier and saves money.

should be used as soon as possible. Perishables should always be stored in the refrigerator; if space is limited, it is best to buy smaller quantities.

Left-overs . . .

Good left-over food should not be thrown away. Small left-overs, or big ones, fit into many dishes. A switch in recipes here or a novel dessert there—and your left-overs are put to work in many interesting ways. Egg yolks can substitute for whole eggs, for example. If bread is a bit dry, then it's just right for French toast. Other left-overs have a way of adding food value or a fresh touch—such as fruit in muffins or vegetables in omelet.

Frozen Foods . . .

Frozen foods have the same food values as fresh foods. They seem more expensive, but there is no waste in preparing them, and they are convenient to use. The choice of frozen foods is increasing all the time, ranging from fruits and vegetables to complete dinners and specialties. They require very little time in preparation, if time is an element to consider in your needs.

109

WHEN YOU COOK FOR A PATIENT

Cooking is the science and art of preparing food for the human body by the application of heat. It has three main purposes: (1) to kill bacteria, (2) to make food easier to digest, and (3) to improve the flavor and appearance. Although we cannot go into the methods of cookery, there are some general rules for working, especially from the health and efficiency standpoint.

1.   Wash hands with soap and water. Have fingernails clean. Wash the hands whenever necessary. Use hand towels only for hands; dish towels for dishes only.

2.   Hair should be neatly combed or a hair net worn.

3.   Assemble all necessary equipment and food materials before beginning work.

4.   Save work by saving dishes; measure dry materials first, then liquids, then fats, and you will need to use only one cup.

5.   Clean as you work; put dishes to soak as soon as they are emptied.

6.   Never taste from a mixing or stirring spoon. Use a clean tablespoon.

7.   Think out a plan of work; then work quickly, quietly, and carefully.

8.   Use tested recipes; time everything to come out right for top nutrition and flavor.

9.   Follow diet specifications, making necessary adjustments of family menu.

10.   *Use* the Daily Food Guide.

KITCHEN HOUSEKEEPING AND SAFETY

Housekeeping rules for health protection apply to the care of the kitchen. Cleanliness comes first—old food remnants, soiled dishes, or other kitchen dirt may contaminate the entire home. Eliminate flies and other insects. People with colds or other infections should not be in the kitchen or working in the preparation of food; they are more of a menace than a help. The care of the refrigerator, the disposal of garbage, and good kitchen ventilation all have an effect on health.

Washing Dishes . . .

When washing dishes:

1. Scrape or rinse off all waste foods. Wipe greasy pans with a paper towel.
2. Sort dishes as to size and kind.
3. Use plenty of very hot soapy water. Exception: Coffee and tea pots should be washed in clear hot water.
4. Rinse with clear hot water.
5. Wipe with clean, dry towels.
6. Wash glasses first, then silver, then china, and, lastly, cooking utensils.
7. Scour pans with the proper cleanser.
8. Handle the patient's dishes separately, if his illness is contagious.
9. Use automatic dishwasher according to manufacturer's directions.

Care of the Refrigerator . . .

Some general rules to remember:
1. Warm foods or foods of strong flavor should not be placed in the refrigerator.
2. Keep foods of a kind together. Place liquids where they may be easily seen.
3. Keep milk and butter covered.
4. Keep refrigerator door closed and work quickly when putting in or taking out food.
5. Examine refrigerator daily, that no food may be left to spoil and cause bad odors.

To clean:
1. Remove all food and ice; take out shelves and ice racks.
2. Scrub shelves and racks with scrubbing brush and hot soapy water; scald and place in sun or outside to dry, if possible (except shelves with plastic trim.)
3. Scrub walls and floor of refrigerator in the same manner. (For last rinse, use solution of 1 teaspoon baking soda in one gallon of water.) Leave refrigerator door open until it is dry. Replace racks, ice, shelves, and food, wiping all food dishes on the outside.
4. Close door and wipe exterior with a damp cloth.
5. Set control for proper temperature regulation.

Safety . . .

Many accidents may be charged to carelessness or thoughtlessness in the kitchen. The first test of good housekeeping is to keep the stairways clear; brooms, pails, mops, and empty bottles belong elsewhere. Use safety matches and keep them out of reach of the children. Turn the handles of cooking utensils on the stove inward, to prevent them from upsetting and to keep children from reaching for them. Use potholders for handling hot things. Wipe up spilled grease, water, or parings immediately to prevent slips and falls.

If grease catches fire in a frying pan, cover the pan tightly with the lid or throw salt or soda on the grease. *Never use water* in the pan. Keep sharp knives in separate drawers from other utensils, or in a wall holder. Never cut toward your hand with a sharp knife. Turn off gas burners tightly. Keep sharp utensils, electrical equipment, ammonia, cleaning fluids, and scouring pads out of reach of children.

If pilot light goes out, call the gas company. Keep all electric outlets in good condition. Do not use frayed electric cords. Stay away from water when using small electrical equipment.

YOUR PATIENT'S TRAY

Eye appeal is the first appeal to anyone's appetite. Modern equipment is so varied and colorful you can make any table or tray look tempting without expensive linen, china, or silver. Of course, if you have these things on hand, it helps cheer the patient to have a dressed-up tray, but there are so many attractive substitutes in cotton, paper, plastic, and stainless steel that can add much to your patient's tray or table.

The photographs included here show arrangements at the family table and on the bed tray. If you have no bed tray for your patient, you may make one by placing two chairs, one on either side of the bed, and stretching a table leaf across the tops, or perhaps there is a handyman about the house who could make one from an empty crate. Bed trays are fairly inexpensive; most variety stores carry them in stock. The type with folding legs is the best for use for the person who must have all his meals in bed. It is more comfortable. Oblong, straight-sided trays are more practical for serving a full meal than round trays.

You may want to serve the complete meal at once, or in courses, as is your family custom or your patient's preferences. You can be more certain of keeping hot food hot, and cold food cold, if you serve a meal in courses, and the tray will be less crowded.

Always use a tray to carry a glass of water or any kind of

Make the tray neat and easy to use.

nourishment; choose one of an appropriate size—a plate is a good substitute for a tray. Most bed patients need a drinking tube; glass tubes are hard to keep clean and break easily, while paper straws serve just as well and may be discarded after use. Choose the kind that may be bent to serve your patient better.

Time the preparation of a meal so that the food can be served when it is ready; some dishes lose quality when they must stand. Keep servings small, for the sight of large quantities may take away the appetite. Serve hot dishes hot and cold dishes cold; cover hot dishes. A cake tin inverted over a plate will keep the food hot. Avoid dribbles of food on the edges of the dishes. Fill cups and glasses about three-quarters full to avoid spilling the contents. Remember to add a little extra touch whenever possible; a flower or a bit of green.

FEEDING THE PATIENT

A tired, uncomfortable patient will neither take nor digest food well. Plan to carry out any lengthy treatment well ahead of meal time. Your patient will have better effects from his food if he is comfortable, happy, and relaxed. As far as possible, have him ready for a meal before you bring in the tray. See that all personal needs are satisfied, and that he is washed and ready. If he is able, help him to the bathroom and assist him to wash. Ad-

If the patient can come to the table, a simple but attractive place setting will usually be best. ONEIDA, LTD.

just his pillows, or, using your improvised backrest (see Chapter 16), raise him to a sitting position.

A patient with a poor appetite sometimes eats more if you can plan to give him a meal during the time he is allowed to sit up in bed or in a chair. *Do not let him become overtired* before the tray arrives.

For the patient who can feed himself, you may still do little courtesies such as spreading the bread, pouring the tea, and cutting the meat. Always warn your patient about extremely hot foods to prevent his burning his mouth, especially if he is using a drinking tube. Encourage him to help himself—it develops his self-confidence and his sense of progress toward getting well. Occasionally, you will find a bed patient, especially a younger member of the family who is having his first experience, who will resist all attempts to suggest that he feed himself. Change this attitude by gradually leaving him with more responsibility for handling his food, taking it for granted that he prefers to feed himself.

You will have to feed the very young, the very ill, the handicapped, and the irrational patient to make sure they get the necessary food and help them avoid possible injuries or spillings. Use your own judgment about how much the patient can help—even if it is just letting him hold his bread. To the blind person, explain each forkful; describe his tray and the food arrangements; place the glass in his hand carefully and steady his head if he wishes to help himself.

Have the bed tray in place and the patient in position before you bring the food to the bedside. Let him know you have the time to give him his food and that you enjoy doing it.

Steps in Procedure	Remember
1. Bring food to bedside. Place on bed tray or lap pillow.	Have all patient needs attended to beforehand.

Steps in Procedure	Remember
2. Open the napkin and place it under the patient's chin.	To protect the bedclothes.
3. Cut the food into small pieces, if necessary.	To help in chewing and digestion.
4. Pour tea or coffee and butter bread.	Patient's preference, or diet requirement, in cream and sweetening.
5. Take up small portions at a time.	Alternate different foods with each other and with liquids.
6. Feed the patient slowly.	At his own rate of eating.
7. Wipe the patient's lips with the napkin when necessary.	
8. Remove and fold the napkin.	
9. Wash the patient's face and hands, if necessary.	
10. Remove the tray, dispose of left-over food and wash the dishes.	
11. If keeping a chart, note any comments.	Note the appetite, the amount eaten, any signs of discomfort, such as nausea.

- Compare what you ate today with the foods listed on the Basic 4 chart.
- Suppose you had 2 pounds of good pot roast beef left over from dinner last evening. List the ways it could be made to serve at another meal.
- Plan a week's menu for a family if there are some differences in energy requirements and one person that dislikes some necessary food.
- Suppose your patient refused his supper and yet had very little food intake all day. What would you do?
- Set up a tray for a 160 pound, 50-year-old man's breakfast; for lunch; for dinner. Be sure the food is not wasted!
- What are several safety factors at work in the kitchen?
- Inspect the family refrigerator. If it needs defrosting, clean it out and wash it at the same time.
- In what order do you wash the food ware?
- Why is it important to check the labels on foods?

Arthritis and rheumatism.

Cancer.

Diabetes.

Heart and circulatory illness.

Tuberculosis.

Poliomyelitis.

Allergies.

9: TREATING SPECIFIC ILLNESSES

How much are you expected to know about the diseases that cause illness? Enough to make you a safe and understanding person. This means that you should know enough about specific diseases so that you will recognize causes and symptoms; enough of treatment so the doctor, the visiting nurse, or the therapist may guide you in your home care of your patient. This part of the book will give you the information about some of the diseases you meet face to face; most of them create big health problems.

The Long Illness . . .

A long illness is also called a chronic illness. When he is recovering, the patient is *convalescing*. The length of a person's illness, as well as the ailment itself, has definite effects on his mind and body. You need to know something about both the specific affliction and its effects on him before you can take care of him intelligently and sympathetically.

ARTHRITIS AND RHEUMATISM

Next to heart trouble, arthritis disables more people than any other disease—ten times more than tuberculosis or diabetes, and seven times more than cancer. It is more common than tuberculosis, diabetes, and cancer combined. It leads to more pain and crippling than any other disorder. It affects the rich and poor alike. However, many people in the lower income bracket go untreated because they cannot afford medical care; others, who are better off, waste huge sums on unproved treatments.

Causes of Arthritis . . .

Arthritis is an inflammation of the joints of the body. Its exact cause has not yet been determined. It is known that fatigue, overwork, exposure to cold and damp, poor diet, emotional and physical shock often come beforehand. There are also certain other diseases which may precede it, such as rheumatic fever, gout, or a group of so-called collagen diseases. This last group of uncommon diseases often mimics the symptoms of rheumatoid arthritis and involves many of the same structures.

In addition, arthritis frequently appears when there is an infection in another part of the body. Arthritis itself is not infectious, yet it may follow an injury to a joint. It may attack suddenly in one or more joints, or it may begin gradually, with an infection in one joint, then move to another until many joints are involved. It may quiet down, with stiffness, pain, and swelling disappearing for periods as long as several months or years, then return again.

There are many forms of arthritis, but the two most common are rheumatoid and hypertrophic or osteo-arthritis.

Rheumatoid Arthritis . . .

The rheumatoid type is a generalized disease that produces an inflammation of many joints. In its most common form, it may begin slowly with pain in one or several joints. Some of the first signs are stiffness, loss of weight, poor appetite, and great fatigue. Later, the joints swell and become painful. In some cases, the inflammation may quiet down and disappear entirely after a month or so, but in others it may quiet down partially or completely, then reappear from time to time. Some types cause deformities. The muscles may contract spastically, thus adding to the deformed effect.

Hypertrophic Arthritis . . .

Hypertrophic or osteo-arthritis is a degenerative, chronic joint disease which usually occurs in older people. It sometimes follows injury or a continued strain to a joint; it occurs most frequently in stout persons, whose weight-bearing joints suffer more strain. Increased deposits of bone begin to surround the joints and cause stiffness; gradually they become painful and fixed. The disease affects the joints by causing changes in both the bone and cartilage. It does not disable people as quickly as rheumatoid arthritis since it comes on gradually.

Treatment . .

Although, to date, there is no specific cure for arthritis, there is much that can be done to prevent deformities and to reduce the pain. Special exercises supervised and prescribed by the physician are very important in maintaining joint motion and muscle tone. He will prescribe the amount and the kind of exercise in order to keep a proper balance between exercise and rest. Although rest is always the best remedy, bed rest over a long period will weaken and waste muscles. You see why exercise and activity must be within the limits of pain and fatigue, and why the doctor's supervision is necessary.

Heat is usually applied; this brings more blood to the joint and favors healing. Hot baths, heat lamps, hot wax, or hot compresses may be used.

When deformities develop or if the patient comes to the doctor too late for preventive treatment, splints and casts are sometimes used to correct the existing deformities; traction may be applied to certain joints. If there is a marked deformity, surgery may be performed.

Diet is very important in arthritis; the underweight arthritic should gain weight and the overweight individual should reduce. The patient's resistance is built up by hygienic surroundings and a diet high in calories to suit the individual's needs; concentrated mineral-vitamins are usually given with orange juice and wheat germ.

Nearly all arthritic patients are helped by a warm, dry climate such as found in the southwestern states. Sunbathing is usually prescribed at a regular time, with the length of time definitely set. Sunbathing is omitted when fever is present or when the victim suffers from certain other ailments or extreme old age. Other forms of heat are then used.

Aspirin and salicylates are usually prescribed. They will not cure the infection but they do relieve the pain. Strangely, these are the only medicants that have proved effective. There have been many drugs used hopefully in the treatment of arthritis: Cinchophen, arsenicals, gold compounds, sulphur, snake venom, and others. There is no evidence of their value, but there is evidence that some severe toxic or side reactions result from the use of some—especially gold and cinchophen. In recent years, a hormone substance, cortisone or ACTH, has been proving of value. ACTH is a pituitary gland substance; cortisone is made chemically from ox or sheep bile. The action of both of these drugs is more rapid than gold treatment, but, for the most part, action (relieving of pain and more freedom of motion of the affected joints) goes on only for as long as the drug is given or for short intervals after the drug is discontinued. As yet, there are still dangers involved with the use of such drugs.

Nursing Care . . .

Arthritis can be a frightening thing to a person who has always been well; pain makes him irritable, and he may be oversensitive about being useless and a burden to everybody. If he is the wage earner, he worries about not being able to work and what the treatment is going to cost him. He has probably tried many drugstore remedies, yet when he finally goes to the doctor, he finds he is not making progress as quickly as he hoped he would.

Treatment and recovery from arthritis are sometimes very slow. It pays to be frank with the patient: Explain or have the doctor explain that improvement is a slow process that depends upon his willingness to work with everyone concerned with his welfare. Encourage him to do the little things for himself that the doctor allows; show him that activity is an important part of the treatment. When he gets moody and depressed—and he will—help to guide his interests elsewhere.

You will be in a position to note the progress of your patient. His daily temperature, pulse and respiration, and general appearance are to be determined carefully. Note, when bathing him or helping him to move, whether the pain seems to be greater or less from day to day. Be careful not to jar the bed; get help in moving him if necessary.

Since he feels more comfortable when warm—circulation to the skin may be impaired—give attention to his bedding and pajamas. Outing flannel will be soothing and warm to the skin.

If any limb is in traction, wrap a light blanket about the part. Be sure the room and bath water are comfortably warm when you give his bath. Warm the back-rub solution and your hands before you touch him. Give special attention to pressure areas where the skin may become irritated—over elbows, shoulders, heels, and other points of pressure. Remember, the circulation is poor, skin is thin, and any prolonged pressure is an invitation for the skin to break down and become infected. (Watch for these signs around any brace or cast.)

One of the primary aims in the treatment of arthritis is to prevent body deformities. This means the patient should be encouraged to stay in a position that allows the most normal joint action and still prevents contraction or drawing up of the muscles. If the bed mattress sags, call this to the attention of the doctor; he may want a board put under the mattress to offer firm support. A foot board or box over the feet makes a good cradle to keep the weight of the covers from pressing the toes; a pillow against the soles of the feet will add support. Give special attention to his head position; most arthritics have a tendency to hunch their heads forward, and draw up their knees. This encourages muscle contracture. Use only one pillow under the head and very little support under the knees; keep the body in normal position with arms and legs extended. You will want to add a pillow here or a small sandbag there to make your patient comfortable. When you are caring for a member of the family, your sympathetic nature may want to overrule your good judgment, even though giving in to a patient's desire for sedatives or other relief may do great harm. The best advice is to consult the family physician before doing anything of which you have doubts.

In all forms of severe illnesses, rest is important. Naturally, you will not move a severely inflamed joint any more than necessary, but a certain amount of exercise is necessary. The doctor prescribes the exercises that the patient will do under your supervision. The kind and amount will depend upon the patient's condition. It will be limited to what he can do with minimum pain. Some clinics have a physical therapist who gives these instructions in the clinic, or, in some cases, comes to the home to check the patient in his home surroundings. It is important to have him or her supervise the use of the overhead traction, leg traction, or heat applications. In other instances, your family doctor may wish to ask the neighborhood visiting nurse to offer needed help and assistance. If the patient has been hospitalized during a severe attack, the hospital may provide this supervision from the outpatient department. Patients who cannot afford a private doctor should have someone to act as go-between to the local health and welfare department, if available.

Since diet is an important part of your patient's treatment and you wish to encourage it, make his tray as attractive as possible. Keep variety in the diet, yet use foods to promote general well-being and health habits. Encourage him to feed himself, if his condition permits it. Help him with the difficult parts and stand by to assist when needed.

One final important note: Most people think that an arthritic gets enough exercise just doing odds and ends of house work. This is not true. He needs special exercises. Even if an arthritic is well enough to lead a fairly normal life, regular examinations are necessary and a schedule of supervised care must be maintained. Otherwise, he may fail again.

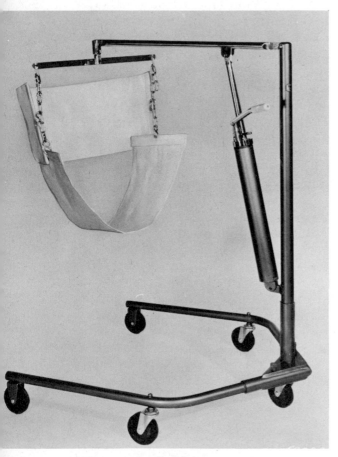

The hydraulic lift is used to help people who are allowed out of bed but who cannot move easily by themselves. Pictures on the next page show an arthritic patient being lifted from the bed to a wheelchair.

PORTO-LIFT MFG. CO.

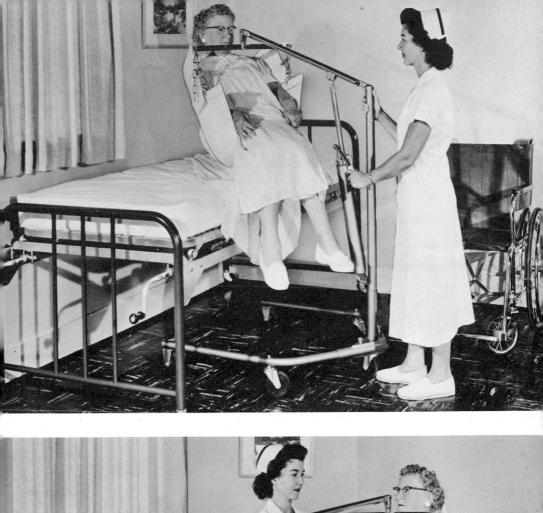
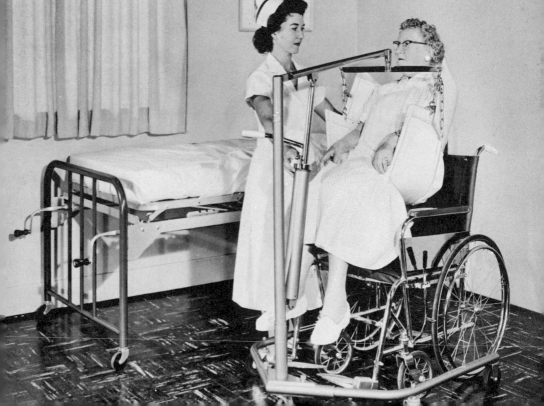

ARTHRITIC

GENERAL DIET—NO. 1

Harry E. Thompson, M. D., Tucson, Arizona

List of amounts of foods in 100-calorie portions. Pick out any you want to make the required calories a day to have a balanced diet containing protein, vitamins, minerals and roughage, but moderately low in starches. The amount of *calories* is prescribed by the doctor.

½ lemon in glass orange juice or water on arising.

1. **Soup:** Clear soup, no caloric value / Cream soup, 1 cup

2. **Meats:** Bacon, three strips, crisp

Daily
red
meat.

Those
underlined
are desirable.

Beef (corned without fat) slice 4 × 1½ inches

Beef, roast, lean, 1 ordinary slice, rare

Chicken, slice 6 × 2½ × ¼ inches

Chicken salad, ½ cup

Fish, cod, cabrilla, sea bass or trout, steamed or broiled, 3¾ × 2½ inches

Fish, crab meat, ¾ cup

Fish, halibut, 3 × 1½ × 1 inch

Fish, oysters, six large to twelve small

Fish, sardines, four, 3 inches long

Fish, shrimp, 20 or ⅔ cup

Ham, boiled or baked, 4¾ × 4 × ⅛ inches

Lamb chops, lean meat of one chop 2 × 1½ × ¾ inches

Liver, 6 × 4 × ¼ inches

Steak, hamburger, 2½ inches diameter × 7/8 inch thick

Steak, sirloin, etc., 1/10th of a pound

Sweetbreads, ⅛ of a pound—Kidney, ⅛ of a pound

Turkey, 4 × 2½ × ¼ inches

3. **Vegetables:**
vitamins,
minerals
and
roughage.

Two
fresh
green,

Artichoke, 1

Asparagus, fresh, 9 stalks

Beans, string, ⅔ cup of 1 inch pieces

Beets, fresh, four beets, 2 inches diameter (⅓ cup sliced)

Broccoli, 4 stalks

Brussels sprouts, 1 quart box

Cabbage, shredded, 3¼ cups; chopped, 4-5 cups

Carrots, fresh, 1⅔ cups of ½ inch cubes

two cooked daily.	Cauliflower, one small head, 4½ inches diameter Celery, four cups of ¼ inch pieces Corn, fresh, on cob, two ears, 6 inches long Cucumbers, two 9 inches long Eggplant, six slices 4 inches diameter, ½ inch thick Mushrooms, fresh, 20-25, 1 inch diameter Onions, two small, seasoning only Parsnips, one 7 inches long, 2 inches diameter top Peas, canned, drained, ¾ cup Potatoes, sweet, ½ medium ⎫ Potatoes, white, one medium ⎭ *Only twice weekly* Spinach, cooked and chopped, 2½ cups Squash, hubbard, cooked, one cup Tomatoes, fresh, 2-3 medium Turnips, two cups, ½ inch cubes Watercress, 5 bunches, 3 inches long, 3 inches diameter Lettuce, no calories Chard, no calories

4. **Fruits**
     and
     Juices:
 	
Vitamins,
minerals
and roughage.
 	
Citrus
preferred.
	Apple, fresh, 1 large
	Applesauce, ⅜ cup
	Apricots, canned, 3 large halves and 2 tablespoons
	     juice
	Bananas, one medium
	Blackberries, stewed, sweetened, ¼ cup
	Cantaloupe, 1 melon, 4½ inches diameter
	Figs, dried, one ½ inch large
	Grapefruit, ½ large
	Grapes, malaga, 20-25 grapes
	Oranges, 1 large
	Pears, fresh, 2 medium
	Pineapple, canned, 1 slice and 3 tablespoons juice or
	     ¼ cup shredded
	Prunes, dried, four medium
	Rhubarb, fresh, four cups of 1 inch pieces
	Strawberries, fresh, 1⅓ cups
	Tomato, 1 cup
	Watermelon, ¾ slice 6 inches diameter

5. **Bread:**	Graham, 100 per cent, slice 3¾ × 3 × ½ inches Rye, 1⅓ slices, 3½ × 4 × ½ inches White, 1 slice 3¾ × 3½ × ½ inches Whole-wheat, 1 slice 3½ × 3½ × ½ inches
6. **Butter:**	One piece 1¼ × 1¼ × ¼ inches

7. **Eggs:** 1⅓ eggs

8. **Milk:** Skim, 1⅛ cups / Buttermilk, 1⅛ cups
Whole, 5/8 cup

9. **Cereals:** Cornflakes, ¾ cup / Rice, puffed, 1⅓ cups
Farina, cooked, ¾ cup / Wheat, puffed, 2 cups
Grape-nuts, ¼ cup / Wheat, shredded, 1 biscuit
Oats, rolled, cooked, ½ to ¾ cup

10. **Cheese:** American, 1⅛ inch cube / soft cream, 2 tablespoons
Cottage, 5 tablespoons / Swiss, slice 4½ × 3½ × ⅛ inch
Full Cream, piece 2 × 1 × ⅜ inch

11. **Sugar:** 1 oz.

12. **Cream:** 2 full tablespoons (heavy)

13. **Desserts:** Gelatin, no calories / Sponge cake, one serving
No pies or   Fruit as above / Ice cream, one serving
pastries.   Custard and blanc mange / Sherbet, one serving

14. **Beverages:** Coffee or tea at breakfast, no calories
Milk as above
Cafein-free coffee substitute, hot chocolate

15. **Dressings:** Mayonnaise, 2 teaspoonfuls
French, 3 teaspoonfuls
Olive oil, 1½ teaspoonfuls

Vinegar
Lemon juice } no calories
Mineral oil

CANCER

Although cancer is not one of the common things about which people consult their doctors early, it is a very common cause of death—ranking second only to heart disease. It can be cured if discovered in time. Although no age group is free from cancer, it does appear more frequently with age.

Some indications are that a virus may be the cause, but cancer apparently is not contagious, nor is there any direct evidence that it is hereditary. It may be possible that people inherit a tendency toward cancer. This means that if the parents have had cancer, their children should be on the lookout for signs in themselves. There have been several facts discovered about the distribution of cancer, according to the American Cancer Society: For example, cancer of the liver is common in the Malay Peninsula and along the eastern Mediterranean, but rare in other regions. Jewish women show a low number of cases of cancer of the cervix, and Japanese women do not often develop cancer of the breast. Cancer of certain specific parts of the body tends to show up in definite age groups: In persons under 20 years of age, the most common forms are leukemia, cancer of the brain, kidney, eye, and bone; in men over 70, the more common types are cancer of the prostate, stomach, colon, lungs, and rectum.

Just what is the nature of these destructive cells that afflict the human race so much? You have already learned that every living thing, from birth to death, is in a constant state of change—growing, degenerating, suffering injury and repairing the damage, reproducing, taking in a variety of foods and changing them into usable energy, fitting in with environment, or—failing to find an adjustment. All these activities within the body normally involve the death and orderly replacement of millions of cells every day.

Cancer is an abnormal condition of cells. They often form and operate in a disorderly kind of growth. When irritations or injuries have caused repeated replacement of cells, at times something seems to go wrong in the repair process, overpowering the growth control center and resulting in a wild structure of cells. Whether the cellular change is caused by an invading virus or by an erring of the cell mechanism, we know that the cells multiply, separate into specialized groups, and invade the surrounding tissues. If this process is allowed to go unchecked, it will bring disability, pain, and death. Cancer cells that can be identified as malignant under the microscope, may have their origin in some other part of the body. Some types of cancer spread more rapidly than others. From the original site, cells may spread by several methods:

1. By moving directly into nearby tissues.
2. By spreading along the lymphatic vessels.
3. By traveling through the lymphatic vessels to nearby lymph nodes (small bodies that filter out harmful substances in the system).
4. By traveling through blood vessels to other parts of the body, especially the lungs, bones, and liver.

5. By invading a body cavity, especially the abdomen and chest, and spreading through it.

Common Points of Infection . . .

Experience has shown that certain conditions give rise to or result in cancer. These are:

1. Long-continued irritation, such as strong daily exposure to sunlight or friction on a mole.

2. Constant exposure to certain irritants, especially in industry, such as coal soot, flour dust, or paint.

3. Benign lesions or tumors that have a tendency to change to malignant, such as growths in the mouth or rectum.

These conditions do not always lead to cancer; also, some people develop cancer even *within the body*, at protected points, though they have none of the above symptoms. It seems likely that several factors working together cause cancer.

Symptoms . . .

No one can tell if he has cancer without seeing a doctor. This is why repeated emphasis is placed on the annual physical health examination. One danger signal is enough to send the person to the doctor immediately. There are seven danger signals as listed by the American Society:

1. Any sore that does not heal.
2. A lump, or thickening, in the breast or elsewhere.
3. Unusual bleeding or discharge.
4. Any change in a wart or mole.
5. Persistent indigestion or difficulty in swallowing.
6. Persistent hoarseness or cough.
7. Any change in normal bowel habits.

Pain, which may be an early indication in other diseases, unfortunately may be the last to appear in the cancer patient. Weakness and loss of weight are symptoms of other disease conditions—but they may also mean cancer.

Treatment . . .

At the present time, there are three methods for the treatment of cancer: (1) surgery, (2) X-ray, and (3) radium. Doctors may use one or a combination of the three, depending on the type and the stage of cancer being treated.

A high caloric diet supplemented by vitamins is usually

prescribed. Transfusions of whole blood are given to poorly nourished patients. Antibiotics may be prescribed to reduce the incidental infection in ulcerating cancer.

Sedatives must be strong enough to keep the patient comfortable; when mild drugs no longer give relief from pain, narcotics are prescribed.

Nursing Care . .

Cancer patients who have gone to the doctor early have an excellent chance of being cured. Treat these patients as you would any other person recovering from an illness. But some still go to the doctor too late; these people are referred to as *terminal* patients. Terminal used in this sense means the patient has a fixed period of time left. This means an added responsibility to the nurse. It is important to make the patient's last days as comfortable as possible and at the same time be careful that no spoken word will hurt him. A patient may not always be told how serious his case is. His hope is a prop as you try to help him. It is your understanding and sympathy that will set the pace for the entire family under trying circumstances. This may seem like an enormous responsibility, but your training will be just what is needed by the loved one who suffers and by others in the home. Concentrate upon doing each day as much as possible for the patient, with the cooperation of your family.

Some cancer patients are in bed for months. They may become very thin. The skin over bony surfaces should be kept dry and clean. Rub it with alcohol frequently; use rubber rings and pads to relieve pressure. Change the bed frequently or as necessary when control over bladder and bowels fades; use absorbent pads under the hips to save yourself time. Turn your patient frequently to relieve pressures and avoid lung congestion. If there is a broken-down skin area—a sore—change the dressing frequently.

The diet should be high in body-building foods and vitamins. Encourage the appetite by serving small portions of food on an attractive tray. Encourage him to feed himself, and point out how nearly normal is the diet he is allowed to have. The hopeful patient will try to eat, with your encouragement. Sometimes, after radium treatment, the patient may be nauseated and unable to take solid foods; when this happens give him liquids high in calories.

Follow the doctor's orders about giving medications for

pain. If the patient finds no relief in drugs given by mouth, it will be necessary to inject them. The doctor will not always be available when these are required; but a call will bring a visiting nurse to give the injection and to teach you how to do it yourself, with the approval of the doctor. She will stand by for emergencies, and be available to talk over your problems.

DIABETES

Diabetes mellitus is a disease in which the ability of the cells to make use of simple sugars is lost or reduced. You will remember that sugar and starches in the diet are changed into simple sugars; a certain portion of protein and fat foods are also converted into sugar form for supplying energy and other needs. Doctors Banting and Best found that the pancreas secretes a substance which is necessary to make these changes; they named the substance "insulin." If insulin is lacking or not produced in enough quantity, sugar accumulates in the blood and causes problems of many kinds.

Insulin is a hormone normally manufactured in the body by the pancreas. Damage to the groups of cells that manufacture insulin—the "islands of Langerhans"—is one cause of the disease.

This disease occurs in all climates and races. Although the disease itself is not passed on directly, the tendency may be inherited. Race seems to be a factor, too, since it occurs more commonly in Jews and Italians than in other peoples. Children and young people do have it, but most diabetics are middle aged or over. Most of the older diabetics are overweight when the condition is discovered.

Symptoms . . .

Many people have diabetes without knowing it. The symptoms come on so gradually that they go unnoticed. As the sugar builds up in the blood, the kidneys work overtime trying to eliminate it. Since the patient is unable to utilize the sugars in his body, he is constantly thirsty and hungry. Other symptoms are fatigue, sudden loss of weight, and a tendency toward infections, especially of the skin. Diabetes can harm the organs and the eyes, and throw its victim into a coma.

Some people learn that they have diabetes for the first time when they have a routine urine test as a part of a checkup or if they are in the hospital for some other condition. Sugar in the urine may be a symptom of various ailments, however, so that other tests are made to determine the amount of sugar in the blood and to find out how well the body actually handles the sugars.

Treatment . . .

The treatment of diabetes, in general, consists of the regulation of the diet and the administration of insulin. Some diabetes is so mild that dietary treatment alone will control it.

Diabetes is under control when the patient is at his proper weight, has very little or no sugar in his urine, has a safe level of sugar in his blood, and has no symptoms. The object of treatment is to help him lead as normal a life as possible and to keep him at his normal weight.

Weight is important since *the diabetic's diet is calculated in relation to his weight and activities;* usually it is based on the tables of average weights that have been worked out in relation to age, sex, and height. Then the total number of calories is estimated, enough to supply energy for the patient's activities. A man doing light work would not need as many calories as the man of the same build doing heavy work. Women need fewer calories. The doctor will make special diets for the patient who is on a bed-rest schedule or who has a more severe diabetic condition.

Nursing Care . . .

To care for a mild, diet-controlled form of the disease, one person in the home should be responsible for preparing and serving; in most cases, the diabetic may have the same diet as other members of the family, but there are some things you should know, in addition. Your greatest challenge is to plan a diet that the patient will follow in spite of restrictions. Diabetic manuals are published by companies that distribute insulin. These manuals are available upon request to the company or through your doctor or pharmacist.

It is difficult to be clever about food when you have no guide, so the Combined Committee on Calculation of Diabetic Diet of the American Diabetic Association and the American Diabetes Association has prepared a simplified method for calculating diabetic diets. This method is based on the idea of *food exchanges.* The foods allowed are divided into seven groups, according to their composition of carbohydrate, protein, and fat. The foods in each of these groups, in the amount listed, all have approximately the same value of carbohydrate, protein, and fat. For example, when one serving of *bread exchange* is planned in a meal, any of the foods listed in that exchange may be used in the specified amount for one serving, whether it is bread, potatoes, crackers, or cereal. This gives you the opportunity to add variety to the diet.

Insulin . . .

Severe diabetics cannot be controlled by diet alone; the body must have extra insulin to regulate its use of sugars. The doctor determines the dosage according to the excess amount of sugar found in the blood and urine.

Insulin is usually manufactured from the pancreas of a hog or cow. There are three kinds: *Regular,* given before each meal, takes effect immediately and continues to work from 4 to 12 hours; *protamine-zinc,* given once a day, goes into action more slowly, and its effects last through 24 hours; *globin* has an action about halfway between that of the other two kinds, lasts from 12 to 24 hours. You can see where the use of the latter two cuts down the number of injections required, although the patient may need a dose of regular insulin to take care of his breakfast.

Each diabetic needs a diet planned especially for him. Divide the food for the day into the prescribed meals and feedings. If the patient is taking *regular insulin,* you probably will serve him three meals 5 or 6 hours apart, 20 minutes after he has had his insulin. If the patient is having *protamine-zinc insulin,* he will need an extra meal before bedtime. With *globin insulin* he will need a mid-afternoon and late-evening feeding. If a diabetic refuses or leaves a large part of his meal, report to the doctor, since his diet is planned in direct proportion to the amount of insulin he is receiving.

When caring for the diabetic, other members of the family must help prevent the smuggling of extra food to the patient. You can teach them why the patient must not break his diet routine. The following information will help you to understand these reasons more clearly.

The purpose of the insulin is to keep the sugar level in the blood at normal; too much insulin will bring this level below normal. Too little food will do the same thing. This kind of reaction is called *insulin shock.* The signs of regular insulin shock are easily recognized: The patient feels hungry, perspires heavily, trembles, and is very jittery, a short while after he has had his regular insulin. With *protamine-zinc* insulin, the symptoms may appear several hours after the injection—attended by headache, drowsiness and nausea.

Every member of your family should become familiar with shock symptoms. Emergency treatment will prevent further reaction. The patient must have orange juice or sugar every 15 minutes until he feels normal again. This gives him a quick supply of sugar to bring the sugar level of his blood up to normal again.

A diabetic who takes insulin should be taught always to carry a few lumps of sugar with him; he should also carry an identification card (1) saying that he is a diabetic, (2) giving the name, address, and telephone number of himself and of his doctor, and (3) instructing to give sugar or candy immediately. Most insulin comes with one of these cards; if not, the pharmacist will supply one.

There is one more danger to the diabetic, *acidosis*. Acidosis may develop if the patient forgets to take his insulin or eats more food than his prescribed diet allows. He may go into diabetic coma (unconsciousness) if he does not have treatment. The symptoms of acidosis are drowsiness, irritability, nausea and vomiting, pains in the abdomen, arms, or legs, breathing difficulty, and a *sweetish odor from the breath*. The patient's face will be flushed, but his skin dry and cold; he feels and looks very ill.

The most important treatment is insulin, given in carefully regulated doses under medical supervision. The sooner the doctor is called and can begin treatment, the better the chances for preventing diabetic coma.

General Care . . .

If you give the severely afflicted diabetic his daily bath or assist him in any way, you will have the opportunity to check his skin for any areas of irritation. Diabetics are especially susceptible to infections. Give particular care to the feet—drying well between the toes, cutting the nails straight across to prevent ingrown toenails. Do not attempt to treat ingrown nails, bunions, or corns. If you notice any change from normal, tell the doctor and he will prescribe the treatment.

The skin of a diabetic burns easily, yet he is likely not to be aware of extremes of heat and cold sensations. Never use an ice bag or heating pad or bottle without orders from the doctor; if they are necessary, be very careful of the temperatures and check your patient frequently. If his feet are cold, use bed socks, plus a flannel gown and an extra blanket.

A child diabetic presents a more serious problem. A child is normally active. His diet is calculated in relation to his activity. Exercise and other activities help him to burn up sugar, but, when he is more active, he burns more sugar than his diet allows. He will need more sugar as he takes on extra activity. It is very important to the child to be like his friends; it seems second nature for the crowd to drop in at the ice-cream bar for a snack. The doctor has no wish for youngsters to be set apart;

Different sized syringes are necessary for giving various kinds of insulin. Note the different gauges for measuring the units of insulin.

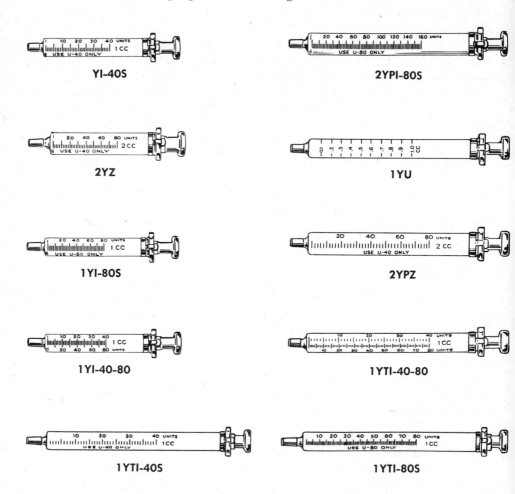

After proper instruction diabetics, even children, can administer their own insulin.

when asked about this situation, he will work with you and offer suitable suggestions to cope with it.

It is important that the diabetic condition be discovered early so that treatment may be started before the condition reaches the severe stage. The American Diabetes Association is

PHOTOS BY BECTON, DICKINSON AND CO.

Insulin must be injected into the subcutaneous tissue under the skin. Notice the slant and placement of the needle.

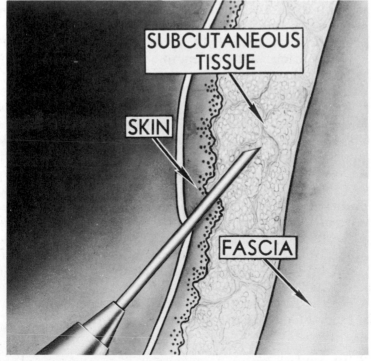

very active in diabetic education, working with local and state authorities, and publishing a magazine called the *A.D.A. Forecast*. Clinics provide treatment and teach families and patients how to look after themselves. You can help by encouraging every member of the family—especially if one is diabetic—to have periodic health examinations and by explaining how the treatment for the disease helps a victim to lead a normal life.

HEART AND CIRCULATORY ILLNESS

It has been mentioned before that heart conditions are today's leading cause of death. They also injure the health of millions, young people as well as the middle-aged and elderly. Rheumatic heart disease may follow the childhood disease, rheumatic fever. The heart is also involved in some diseases that affect the thyroid gland, the lungs, the kidneys, and other organs.

Many organizations have worked and planned together for progress in the understanding and treatment of heart diseases, so the future for the heart patient holds a brighter picture than formerly. Studies are constantly going on to find out the causes of heart disease and high blood pressure. The American Heart Association holds yearly community drives to encourage research and to give financial aid to those who need it. They publish pamphlets for distribution to the public. Television has done much to support the program.

Everyone may help fight heart disease on two difficult fronts: Prevention and treatment. Certain heart conditions cannot be cured, yet, like most other diseases, they may usually be treated successfully if discovered early. Victims can lead useful, happy lives and live a long time. They may have to change their way of living but do not need to become invalids.

Good health habits and a periodic check-up by the doctor are important preventives. The more common types of heart diseases result from infections; a healthy body builds up resistance to infections. Periodic health examination may discover the condition before it becomes serious. Most people do not know or suspect they are in trouble until the heart begins to fail, yet certain signs and symptoms are suspicious. The doctor finds these from the patient's history, through listening to the heart, and by use of X-ray and the electrocardiograph—an instrument which records the way a heart acts.

A healthy heart may be damaged by a thickening of artery walls. High blood pressure occurs frequently in persons over thirty-five, who may seem perfectly normal otherwise. Continuous pressure eventually brings about heart or kidney failure, or cerebral hemorrhage. Such patients often complain of headaches and of seeing "spots" before the eyes. No cure has been found, although certain drugs help, along with the slowing down of more strenuous activities.

Thrombosis is caused by a blood clot brought in from some other part of the body. Heart and blood vessels may be in excellent condition till this happens.

Defects may be formed within the heart of the fetus before birth (*congenital* heart defects). Authorities say physical strains and emotional stress may make heart trouble worse but do not cause it.

Symptoms . . .

The all-important job of the heart is to keep the blood circulating. When the heart cannot take care of this task properly, look for these symptoms:
1. Shortness of breath.
2. A rapid or unusually slow pulse.
3. Swelling of the feet and ankles.
4. Any discomfort in the chest after slight exertion.
5. Mild or severe pain in the breastbone, pit of the stomach, or radiating into the neck and either or both arms. This usually occurs with exercise, after meals, or in cold weather.

Not all of the evident symptoms may appear at first; also they may be mild or severe, depending upon how advanced the case is.

There are common symptoms which usually are associated with heart disease but which may stem from other sources. Only the doctor can determine the true cause. These are:
1. Pain in the heart region, occurring when exercise is not involved.
2. Rapid pulse.
3. Irregular pulse rate.
4. Consciousness of heartbeat.
5. Skipped beat.

The heart is so remarkably sturdy that it often makes its own adjustments to difficulties, "covering up" symptoms of failure. The doctor will discover this during a health examination. The treatment is learning to live according to the strength of the heart.

Treatment . . .

1. Complete rest in bed. Patient may have to be kept in a sitting position for better breathing.

2. Sedatives for relaxation and rest.

3. Digitalis, a medication that slows the heart rate. The doctor orders the dosage according to the needs of the heart. Some people are allergic to this drug and must be watched closely for such symptoms as nausea, vomiting, loss of appetite, and a very slow pulse.

4. Medication to help the patient excrete water. In heart disease, the body may hold more water in the tissues due to the impaired circulation.

5. A low salt diet. Salt tends to hold extra water in the tissues.

6. Oxygen, in cases of extreme heart weakness.

Nursing Care . . .

The most important thing concerning heart patients—commonly called *cardiacs*—is *rest*. Minimize exertion of the patient by the way you give him his bath, make his bed, and serve his meals. Mental rest is as important as physical rest, so try to think of all his needs or wants before he asks for them; refrain from discussing subjects which may worry him, and try to keep talkative visitors away. If your patient is the wage-earner in the family, he will naturally worry about the cost of his illness and his financial responsibilities, so perhaps his employer may have an important part in freeing him from worry. Remember that anyone who has always led an active life will have difficulty in sitting back and allowing others to take over; explain that rest now may decide his future.

Good rest physically depends upon a comfortable position for the patient's body. Heart patients who have difficulty breathing will feel more comfortable in an upright position. A back rest made of pillows with something sturdy underneath, and a rolled cotton blanket under the knees, will help him endure this tiring position. Shift his position slightly from time to time and adjust his pillows often. Cool pillows refresh him. Support his arms with small pillows. Don't wait for him to tell you he is uncomfortable; this is one of the times you are permitted to coddle your patient.

The cardiac patient may be in bed for some time. His circulation is damaged, and tissues may be swollen. These fac-

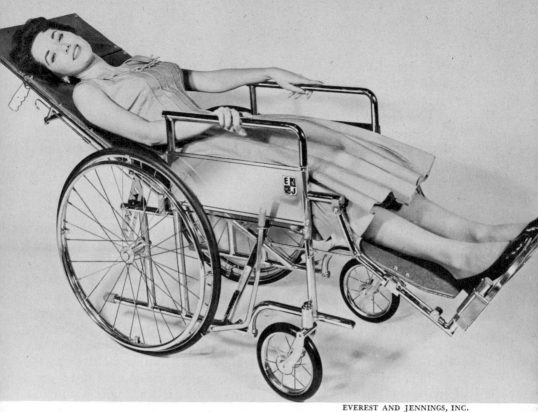

A heart patient can relax in a semi-reclining position when first allowed up after a long period of confinement in bed.

tors—along with a position that puts continued pressure on the buttocks, the end of the spine, the elbows, and heels—invite pressure sores. Massage these or any other pressure points with alcohol frequently. Keep the sheets dry and free from wrinkles; a soft sponge rubber ring under the hips reduces pressure on the end of the spine.

Since heart damage usually causes an upset in the water balance in the body, it is necessary to keep an accurate account of all fluid the patient takes and eliminates over a 24 hour period. If your patient has no control over his bladder, note the number of involuntary urinations.

The doctor may order a light laxative to insure daily bowel elimination, since enemas are likely to tire the patient.

Watch the effects of medications; report to the doctor any signs of distress or any unusual reactions. If medication has been prescribed for emergencies, always keep it handy.

Many cardiac patients are confused at first; protection against falling out of bed may be necessary. The patient should not be left alone. Restraints are harmful because people fight against them, and this exertion increases the tension on the heart.

The diet is planned for the highest nutritional aid, to build up resistance, and, at the same time, to keep the weight down and prevent surplus fluid from collecting in the body tissues. Salt may be restricted or eliminated entirely; tea, coffee, and certain proteins may be restricted, since they tend to speed up the heart action.

The mouth becomes dry when fluids are restricted; the patient may breathe through his mouth. Use a swab and a mouthwash and freshen his mouth before meals and at other times, as often as necessary.

Give only small amounts of food at one time; be sure to record every drop of fluid served during and between meals. Never tempt the patient by leaving fluids on his bedside table.

Diversional or other activities within the limits of his heart are good for the heart patient. The doctor will prescribe the activities; always talk a new idea over with him before starting. It is hard for a cardiac to make up his mind to a new way of living. Help him to make the most of his limitations and to feel that he still counts to the family.

TUBERCULOSIS

Years ago tuberculosis ranked first among the causes of death in this country. Today, it is seventh on the list. Yet it is still serious. Knowing how it is caused and spread has placed heavy emphasis upon prevention and treatment while the disease is in the early stages.

Tuberculosis is an infectious disease due to the *bacillus tuberculosis*. It may involve almost any organ in the body but does most of its damage in the lungs. It may affect persons at all ages but most commonly it makes its appearance during late adolescence and early adult life. The attack may be acute or prolonged; because it may be prolonged, it is very important from an economic viewpoint.

Tuberculosis spreads from one person to another by contact or droplet infection. Once the organism enters the body, it may be slow to develop, so the signs may not appear at once; this is how people may have active tuberculosis in an advanced stage and never know it. In case of minor exposure, a healthy body with strong resistance will counter the attack; weak resistance may result in infection from a slight contact. Of course,

140

keeping away from persons who have tuberculosis lessens the danger.

How does the healthy body defend itself against the bacillus? First, it surrounds the organisms with a hard capsule formed of cells and fibers. This capsule, or "tubercle," walls off the germs from the surrounding tissues. The tissues themselves mass together and build a barrier to prevent the germs from spreading farther. The enclosed germs may die, or they may live inside this capsule for a long time, until the body resistance becomes lowered, when the barrier weakens and they invade the lung tissue.

Most deaths from tuberculosis result from lung damage. But if the organism enters the blood or lymph stream, it may be carried to another organ. Tuberculosis may infect the bones, the joints, the skin, the glands, and the kidneys.

Tuberculosis infection shows up in a *chest X-ray*. A hard capsule shows that the germ has once attacked your lungs but your body controlled it, or shadows may appear, giving evidence of active tuberculosis. Many cases have been found while taking chest X-rays of school children. The service is made available to others through the Red Cross X-ray mobile units. Programs are sponsored by state or local health groups, in co-operation with the schools, industries, hospitals, and social agencies.

A tuberculin *skin test* will show whether or not a person has been attacked by tuberculosis. If the test is negative, it means that the body has never been attacked; if it is positive, it shows that there has been an attack at some time. It will not show whether or not the tuberculosis is active; so the next step is the chest X-ray.

The major control of tuberculosis is directed toward discovering the disease and treating it before it has a chance to spread. Isolating victims is another protective measure. There are many hospitals in this country just for tuberculosis patients. Modern treatment can often make it possible to recover and go back to regular work or do limited work.

Symptoms . . .

Early tuberculosis may not present any outward symptoms but, as the organisms succeed in breaking down the body's resistance and start destroying body tissues, there are definite signs.

• Constant tiredness.
• Loss of weight.

- Coughing and spitting up of blood.
- Pain in the side.
- Fever.
- Night sweats.

Treatment . . .

The treatment of the patient depends upon how far the damage has gone. It is always wise for the patient himself as well as all members of his immediate family to know what he is facing. Even the smallest infection means giving up work and other activities. It may take the victim away from his family. Throughout the convalescent period, the patient must follow a strict routine to give the damaged lung tissue a chance to heal.

Rest *in bed* is the big factor in treating tuberculosis. This does not mean merely lying in bed but *resting* every part of the body as well. Body tissues use added oxygen with every movement; oxygen is delivered to the tissues from the lungs, but now the lungs must be relieved. Hospital care is recommended partly for that reason. When the patient is in a hospital or sanatorium, he is in the "same boat" as everyone else; at home, he may find it difficult to adjust while the others are so active.

When the infection has been brought under control, if the patient understands that rest is an important part of his treatment and will follow orders, he may be allowed to go home. The doctor hesitates to send a patient home if there are small children present, although protective measures against spreading the disease will be taught him as well as his family.

The diet is planned to make the patient gain weight slowly and, up to a certain point, according to age and height; he is usually kept 5 to 10 pounds above his normal weight. Because tuberculosis consumes body proteins, meat is an important part of the diet. Milk supplies the needed calcium and vitamins.

Fresh, uncontaminated air is important, too—one of the reasons why tuberculosis hospitals and sanitoriums are located outside the cities. *Outdoor* air treatment is preferable, in a place where the patient can be exposed to warm, but not hot, sunshine.

Pneumothorax is often used in active tuberculosis. This treatment consists of introducing clean, germ-free air into the *chest cavity* (not the lung itself) on the infected side. This collapses the lung for complete rest. As the lung gradually absorbs the air, the treatment is repeated. It is usually required *over a period of two years.*

Nursing Care . . .

Many patients are released from the hospital or sanatorium before they are completely cured. However, the disease has been brought under control and the patient has learned and adjusted to a *get-well* routine. In being willing to care for him, you accept a wonderful responsibility. His co-operation depends upon your attitude. You guard him from overdoing; your explanations and awareness of his needs give him hope. It is sometimes difficult for him to realize that he is not fully recovered. He looks and feels well, giving him a false impression of his progress. Younger patients miss their normal activities, school, and friends. They worry about the future and how they are going to "catch up."

Encourage your patient to relax; keep talkative or hard-of-hearing persons under control. Carry out the routine that has been established for rest periods *without exceptions*. Keep bad news or family problems away from him; discourage his contact with exciting radio or television programs. If he is on strict bed rest, feed him, keep him from lifting articles from the bedside table. Provide a rack to hold his newspapers and books. Remember that for the person who has always been active, these helpful suggestions may prove annoying; it is your responsibility to explain and then explain again the great benefits that they mean to him.

Keep a careful record of the patient's temperature. It has a tendency to rise slightly in the afternoon, perhaps only 1/10 of a degree but this is important. Months may pass before his temperature is normal in the afternoon. As long as this variation in temperature occurs, it should be taken *and recorded* every four hours while the patient is awake. Pulse and respiration are important, too. Usually a high temperature will show a rapid pulse and respiration. These factors show much concerning the activity of the infection.

Fresh air is important, but be careful that the patient is not chilled. Close the windows to warm the room before giving him his bath or for any other treatment involving exposure. Use extra blankets in colder weather; protect him when he is outside. If he is permitted to sleep in the outdoors on the porch, keep the bed in a protected corner. *Never expose him to hot sunshine* for any length of time. If exposure to sunshine is ordered, start with short periods at first, gradually increasing the time according to the doctor's orders.

The diet usually differs very little from the family menu;

143

use the Daily Food Guide; your aim is to build up his body resistance. If he is underweight, he will need plenty of cream, butter, and eggs. He must have at least a quart of milk a day and extra vitamin C in the form of citrus fruits. A well-balanced diet will be beneficial in building up the resistance of the other members of the family, too. Watch the patient's weight carefully to see that it does not go more than 5 to 10 pounds over normal. No useful purpose is served with extra added weight. He will be bedfast for a long time, so try to give him variety.

Sometimes the patient may still have a cough when he comes home from the hospital. Have him collect his sputum in a covered container, and burn it every day. Small moisture-proof envelope-type containers may be bought at the drugstore for the patient to carry in his pocket when he walks around. This is a very important part of his nursing care, for your own protection and to protect other members of the family; sputum, which is alive with tuberculosis organisms, is one of the *quickest* disease spreaders.

Limit the amount of visitors to the sickroom. If the patient is advised to stay in one room, keep a smock there that you may use when you enter; see that others do the same. Burn all discharges from the mouth and nose, and the dressings from a tuberculous wound. Keep the bed linen and clothing separate from the family linen; it should be *boiled* 30 minutes and then washed. *Boil all dishes* and treatment equipment such as his bath basin and tooth glass. *Burn all food* left on his tray.

Teach the young patient to cover his nose and mouth with three layers of disposable tissue when he coughs or sneezes. Pin a paper bag to the side of the bed, for disposal of the tissues. He must be taught and cautioned repeatedly not to put pencils or other things into his mouth. Teach the other members of the family and visitors not to handle these things, also.

Gradually the patient is allowed activity. It is a great time for him. He may only feed himself at first, but for him it means one step nearer a normal life. He still needs definite rest periods, even when he is allowed up and about. The way back to a normal life is long. When the patient who has had active tuberculosis finally reaches the stage where his infection is arrested or halted, then he is no longer a danger to other people and no longer needs isolation. Many people have recovered and returned to normal, fruitful lives. They may return to an old job or seek a new one which will not be harmful to health. Their chances of staying well and useful are excellent providing

Patient progresses from wheelchair . . .

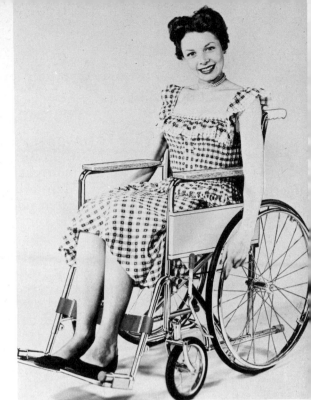

. . . to walker which provides
support and helps build confidence to walk alone.

PHOTOS BY EVEREST AND JENNINGS, INC.

they get enough rest, keep on a proper diet, and avoid chances of re-infection.

POLIOMYELITIS

Poliomyelitis, or *polio* for short, is a virus disease which affects the gray matter of the central nervous system. It is sometimes characterized by paralysis of various muscle groups. It usually attacks children, but adults are occasionally its victims.

Some people believe that polio always cripples. This is not the case; about half the victims recover without paralysis; approximately twenty-five per cent experience a mild form of paralysis, which has very little effect upon their lives. This means there is only the remaining twenty-five per cent with moderate to severe handicaps. Even these individuals have a good chance toward normal living patterns because mechanical supports and rehabilitation help overcome most of the major difficulties or help make adjustment less trying.

The virus of polio presumably enters the body by way of the mucous membranes of the upper respiratory tract, but whether the disease is spread by carriers or by direct contact is not, as yet, known. We only know that it is an infectious disease which often spreads through whole communities, usually during a long, hot season. The virus causes paralysis by traveling along the nerve tracts to the muscle groups. The nerve cells are literally attacked. Some may be hurt temporarily, others permanently. A muscle becomes paralyzed if enough of the nerve cells are destroyed.

Researchers have worked many years trying to control or prevent polio. Immunization is now seen, with the use of vaccine. It is made available to all through most local health agencies or through the family doctor. Treatment consists of a series of three injections, the first two within a month of each other, the third following from 7 to 12 months after the second. Immunization also is achieved orally. Boosters are now stressed. Booster means supplying the body with small amounts of vaccine from time to time to keep the immunization at a high level. We know that in rare cases people who have received immunizations have still fallen to attacks of the disease. Only through continuing research will the reasons and prevention be further clarified. Cautious parents will not take a chance on whether the vaccine offers full prevention; it has been proved that it cuts down on the incidence, proof enough that every child should be given his opportunity. In fact, every adult should make it his personal responsibility to see that he and all members of his family are so protected.

There are other factors that health agencies urge the community to stress. They caution parents about taking their children into crowds, such as shopping centers, public picnic grounds, and beaches, when the disease is prevalent. Parents are cautioned to keep their children from becoming over-tired or chilled. We are asked to keep all garbage covered and to use window screens. Many doctors recommend that tonsil operations be postponed during a polio scare. Read all available information, and give the subject adequate attention so that you will not panic if someone in the family is afflicted.

Symptoms . . .

After exposure to polio, it takes from 7 to 18 days for the infection to develop. The *onset* is sudden, with fever and a sense of laziness; often there is a cough, some vomiting, and diarrhea, which may be misleading at first. A mild attack of polio will go this far and then subside. Or, in a day or so, the victim becomes ill again, complaining of stiffness in the neck and back along the spinal cord. Tenderness and stiffness may appear in the muscles of the arms and legs. This is a forerunner of paralysis, so no time should be lost in contacting the doctor. No matter how mild or severe the symptoms are, this is the highly infectious stage and the patient should be isolated and all safety precautions maintained.

Paralysis may be mild or extensive, depending on the extent of nerve damage. Usually, groups of muscles in the legs are affected. In the upper back, the shoulder girdle is often affected; sometimes the diaphragm is paralyzed. The paralysis usually goes to the maximum degree but does not increase thereafter. Once it appears, it persists for several weeks, and then gradual improvement begins.

Death may occur early in the paralytic stage from paralysis of the muscles of respiration, but in most cases poliomyelitis is not death-dealing.

Treatment . . .

Immediate care is necessary. The patient should be sent to the hospital as soon as the first signs are recognized. There trained personnel will carry on the necessary treatment. You remember that some muscles may be affected only slightly; this means that the nerve cells throughout these areas are only partly damaged, but they will need help and rest to start to repair themselves. Where the nerve fibers have been completely damaged, they will not be able to revive.

Respirator treatment may be necessary if the breathing muscles are affected. The affected muscles must be retrained for use. Braces and supports help; sometimes they must be used permanently. In some cases, an operation may be necessary to transplant tendons from healthy areas of the body to the affected parts. Surgery may make it possible for the patient to walk again.

Hot, moist compresses relieve pain and muscle spasms. Gentle, passive exercise helps restore strength to paralyzed muscles. This is begun as soon as possible, along with massage. Water tanks are used, wherewith muscles are taught to relax in complete immersion, to begin their long comeback period. Underwater exercise, as when swimming, encourages almost every muscle in the body, even though the person is unaware of it.

Nursing Care . . .

Your part in the care of the polio patient begins when he returns home. Through patience and persistence, the patient achieves gradual recovery. The days will drag; he will sometimes be discouraged and irritable, which is understandable.

The doctor and physical therapist will guide you. Hot, moist applications may still be necessary just before exercise time to relax the muscles. Exercises to strengthen certain groups of muscles are a big responsibility, since they may mean the difference between a flaccid, useless limb or a useful one. It is easier for a patient to carry on his exercises in the presence of another, even if the person merely stands by, talks, or reads. You may help with the apparatus or by actual limb manipulation. If he needs braces and supports, you will check their adjustments and stand by while he is learning to walk.

His diet should be normal and well balanced.

ALLERGIES

The body is equipped to manufacture antibodies to protect itself against harmful invasion by alien substances. The antibodies may be in the body tissues or circulating in the blood. When certain substances enter the body, the antibodies attempt immediately to destroy them. The reaction between the antibodies and the foreign substance may harm the tissues, causing unpleasant effects.

Some people are more susceptible than others; we say that these people are sensitive or *allergic* to the foreign substance. They produce another substance called *histamine,* which is responsible for the unpleasant symptoms that appear. These symptoms will be described under each allergy.

Hay Fever . . .

Winds and dust carry many pollens to which people are allergic. Some are sensitive only to certain flowers or plants when their pollens are in circulation; others are sensitive to almost all vegetable or plant pollens—in the spring, trees; in summer, grasses; in the fall, ragweed.

Hay fever begins with the swelling of the mucous membrane of the nose, accompanied by sneezing and itching. Sometimes it is bad enough to interfere with breathing; the eyes become red, itch, and are sensitive to light; the throat may become inflamed and sore. If a cough is present, the reaction may be mistaken for a cold. The patient will be in general good health, but the symptoms make him feel miserable. The symptoms vary from day to day or even from hour to hour; there may be periods in which the person is free from symptoms entirely.

It is possible to isolate the offending pollen or group of seasonal pollens to which the patient is sensitive; science also has found that irritation is caused by substances such as dust, feathers, and cosmetics. In the latter case, filtered air is about the only solution.

For pollen isolating, "scratch" or skin tests are done on the skin; from the nature of the reaction, the severity of the allergy, as well as the specific cause, may be determined. Pollen extracts are made up for the individual, based on his skin tests. Over a period of months, he is given small doses of the mixed pollen extracts until his desensitization point has been reached. Thereafter it is only necessary to have periodic doses to keep him immunized. They do not cure the allergy, but they relieve the symptoms.

Antihistamine drugs are usually given along with the above program, or they may be the only treatment; these drugs tend to tighten the blood vessels and cut down congestion in the nose and throat. The use of ordinary nose drops and throat sprays helps to relieve the symptoms temporarily.

Food Allergies . . .

Food allergies may cause symptoms resembling hay fever,

with these differences: Some persons merely sneeze; another person may be afflicted with swelling of nasal mucous membrane and a discharge. This type of allergy may go on to develop a skin rash and itchiness. It may cause difficulty in breathing, and progress to the stage of nausea, vomiting, and diarrhea. Protein foods, such as milk, eggs, and shellfish usually are responsible.

Bronchial Asthma . . .

Asthma is an allergic disturbance caused by a spasm of the muscles surrounding the bronchi and oversecretion of the bronchial glands. Like hay fever, it may be seasonal or nonseasonal. The breathing is wheezy and distressful. The hay fever patient may develop asthma or may have symptoms of hay fever and asthma at the same time. In many cases of asthma, emotion—anger, excitement, fear, or anxiety—is an important factor in bringing on the attacks. In adults, pollens and dusts may be responsible. In children, egg white, certain cereals, or animals may give trouble. The effects of asthma over long continued periods are much more serious than hay fever. In children, the overlong obstruction of the bronchioles may cause changes in the shape of the chest or an over distention of the air sacs in the lungs. In persons with *heart disease,* the increased effort in trying to breathe may have serious effects.

An asthmatic attack may start suddenly. The patient coughs, his chest feels tight; he begins to wheeze, his breathing is slow and difficult, especially as he forces the air out of his lungs. He becomes blue and perspires heavily; his hands and feet are cold; his pulse is weak. Many patients cough heavily during the attack but rarely raise any sputum. The attack may last from half an hour to several hours. When it is over, the patient seems normal, with no discomfort. It seems to the observer that death is near when the attack is most severe. However, this is an illusion, unless the victim has a heart problem.

In the hands of a specialist, the allergic patient can have some hope of being cured or of having the attacks cut down in number and severity. Many people recover naturally after years of suffering. It is important to find the protein substance which causes the attacks, and begin the desensitization program. During the severe attack, drugs, usually a form of adrenalin, are administered to relax the tightened bronchioles. They may be given by injection, but the chronic asthmatic should always have a spray nearby, containing the medicine prescribed by his doctor.

The antihistamines have been used with some success in symptomatic asthmatic treatment. That is, they relieve the symptoms but not the cause.

Migraine . . .

Migraine used to be called a "sick headache." The attacks come periodically, may be more severe than other headaches, and are difficult to relieve. Before the pain begins, the victim may be aware of flashes before the eyes. The pain may be accompanied by nausea and vomiting. The attack lasts from a few hours to several days. It may leave suddenly, or fade away gradually. It leaves the patient drowsy and exhausted.

Warm, soaking baths, vibrator applications and massaging at the base of the neck, quiet, and a pleasant atmosphere will help.

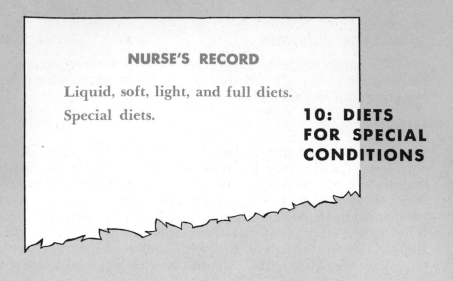

NURSE'S RECORD

Liquid, soft, light, and full diets.

Special diets.

10: DIETS FOR SPECIAL CONDITIONS

When the doctor puts a sick person in the family on a special diet, it means he is using the *diet therapy* method to help treat the illness. You recognize that an adequate diet is important for maintaining health and preventing disease; now we take up diet in the treatment of illness and disorders.

Assume that you are ready to put what you have learned to work: You have the doctor's orders to guide you and know what precautions you must take in seeing that your patient maintains an adequate diet; you also know your patient's food habits. These may be influenced by his racial customs and nationality. This means you will have to build your menu plan about his preferences, his customs, his nutritional needs, and the doctor's special list.

Now you see how handy it is to have the Basic 4 food group lists (Chapter 8) at your fingertips; how it makes finding and choosing substitutes easier. Many patients are on a diet prescribed as a part of the treatment of more than one body disturbance. For example, the patient with a kidney ailment also may be a diabetic. It may be up to you to remind him of why he can't have certain foods and why he should have others. You can and may often have to use camouflage—or mild trickery—to get him to like his meals. For instance, milk may be camouflaged by using it in cream sauces, soups, and omelets.

Attitudes about food must be dealt with, especially if nutritional science is completely new to your patient. A person who believes in food fancies—for instance, that fresh vegetables are meant only for rabbits or that he cannot live without coffee—should not be expected to accept the special diet all at once. It takes patience, understanding, and planning on your part to encourage him to try again and again till he succeeds.

LIQUID, SOFT, LIGHT, AND FULL DIETS

It is still your primary job to satisfy the body's complete nutrition needs but, since the illness may have been the result of some abnormal condition, certain foods may not be used. Try to adhere to the normal family menu as nearly as possible; change only those foods in kind and amount necessary, keeping in mind always that the diet must be such as not to promote any other disease or deficiency.

The typical meals for the chronic invalid or convalescing patient might be:

MORNING

Fruit
Choice of cereal
Egg, if desired
Toast, rolls, or muffins with butter
Coffee with sugar and cream

NOON

Hot dish, salad, or soup
Crackers, roll or bun
Dessert
Glass of milk

NIGHT

Tomato juice, fruit juice or fruit cup
Meat or fish
Green vegetable
Potato
Salad
Dessert
Tea or coffee, as desired

Diets for sick people are classified as liquid, soft, light, and full or general. If there are no special requirements, the patient may have any of the foods listed on his particular type of diet.

Liquid . . .

The liquid diet is prescribed for acute digestive illnesses, after surgery, or in certain types of organic disorders. It may be either limited or full liquid. *Limited* means *strictly liquid*. Feedings may be given every two, three, or four hours, as prescribed. Milk is the major source of protein, since meat has been eliminated. To add calories, the milk may be supplemented with cereals, eggs, and ice creams.

LIMITED LIQUID DIET	FULL LIQUID DIET
Meat broth	Soup—clear, strained, or creamed
Whole milk	Milk, cream
Egg white	Milk sherbet
Cereal gruel	Plain ice cream
Strained fruit juice	Well-beaten eggs in beverages
Tea, coffee	Cereal gruels
	Strained vegetable or fruit juices
	Tea, coffee

Satisfactory caloric and nutrient requirements may be met indefinitely with the full liquid diet if the patient is confined to bed. The limited liquid diet will not do this although it does maintain the nutrient and fluid balance. The patient will lose weight. In padding the milk, remember that high carbohydrates or fat amounts will cause fermentation in the intestines and may result in diarrhea.

Adjustments must be made if the patient cannot have eggs, milk, or salt. Such rare limitations are covered by especially prescribed diets.

Soft Diet . .

The soft diet containing semisolid foods and liquids, should contain only such foods as may be swallowed without chewing, and which contain no roughage. The diet is easily digested.

SOFT DIET

Soups—clear, strained, vegetable, creamed
Eggs—all ways except fried
Milk, cream, butter, cottage cheese, cream cheese
Potato, baked or mashed
Strained fruit juices, sieved cooked fruit
Cooked cereals

Toast, crackers—limited amounts
Scraped beef; white meat of chicken or turkey; fish
Milk puddings, plain ice cream, custards, gelatins, sherbets, sponge and
    angel-food cakes
Sugar—small amount
Tea, coffee

Too much stress cannot be put upon the attractiveness of food and service. At times food becomes a lifesaver. With good nursing care, it is oftimes more effective than medication.

Light Diet . . .

The light diet has more variety than the soft diet and precedes the full diet stage. It is fairly high in calories; features easily digested foods.

LIGHT DIET

Soft diet foods
Broiled lamb, ground beef, liver; bacon
All but strongly flavored vegetables, such as dried beans, cabbage, etc.
All fruits
Salads and salad dressings
All cereals except bran products; macaroni, spaghetti, noodles
All kinds of bread except if containing bran
All desserts except rich pastries
Small amounts of sweets, such as jam and jelly
Butter, margarine, cream
Tea, coffee, milk

Full or General Diet . . .

The full diet is the general or normal human diet; it has to be modified to meet individual needs, but it allows a wide range of foods and includes everything excepting those foods which may cause a body disturbance in your particular patient's case. Remember, if your patient is *confined to bed,* or *is very inactive,* calories should be limited. Consult low-calorie lists.

SPECIAL DIETS

The doctor prescribes the special diet to suit the needs of his individual patient. There are so many types of special diets, it would be impossible to give more than a general idea of them here. The more common ones will be discussed in this chapter; there is more about diets for the ill in Chapter 13.

Infections and Fevers . . .

Fever is caused by an imbalance between heat production and heat elimination. Proteins are used up quickly, depending upon the grade of infection. A fever interferes with the appetite, so you may need to give small feedings more frequently. Unless otherwise prescribed, only a liquid, semiliquid, or soft diet is advised.

Elderly People . . .

The diet of old age, or geriatrics as it is now called, is not unlike the diet of children. It should be easily digested, relatively smooth, and bland. To change the eating habits of those of advanced years is not easy. Yet, to combat the ills that normally accompany advancing age, good nutrition is important. Careful attention needs to be paid to adequate supply of protein, minerals, and vitamins. It is often advisable to add vitamins to make up for the reduction in the amount and variety of foods. Caloric intake should generally not exceed 2200, or be less than 1200, per day.

Well-fitted dentures or teeth kept in good condition, interest in life, a sense of belonging to the family, all help immeasurably to give an older person the appetite he needs.

Constipation . . .

A poorly balanced diet or lack of nutrients may be one cause of constipation. The idea that to be normal there should be a bowel movement every day may lead to unwise use of laxatives that harms the system and inhibits natural movement. Many individuals remain in good health with but one movement every two or even three days. Others have two or three movements a day and yet show no ill effects. To stimulate movement of the intestine, bulk is necessary. The diet should include plenty of vegetables high in cellulose; fruits; whole grain cereals; plenty of water, milk, cream, and butter. Fats in the diet soften the contents of the intestines.

Exercise is very important.

Diarrhea . . .

Diarrhea is the opposite of constipation, a condition characterized by too frequent stools with more fluid being lost than normally. It is a symptom of such intestinal disturbances as typhoid fever, colitis, and poisonings, or it may be the result of improper dietary habits and the use of laxatives. The diet prescribed depends upon the cause of the diarrhea but usually consists of fluids only, at the onset, continued until it is advisable to add solid foods gradually. It is better to give too little food rather than too much until the symptoms disappear. Explain to the family and your patient that the intestine is in a highly irritated state and needs the rest; in this condition, the bowels cannot process much food.

Anemia . . .

There are several types of anemias. The diet prescribed by the physician will depend upon the type the patient has. Generally he requires foods that will supply the body with iron substances—liver, rare beef, eggs, spinach and other green vegetables, and fruits. The diet does not carry the entire responsibility of treatment since science has discovered liver extract and blood-enriching forms of vitamin B-12.

Allergies to Food . . .

A common form of food allergy is reflected in a digestive disturbance—heartburn or sour stomach. Other forms are hives, hay fever, and asthma. Allergy specialists have found chocolate, milk, and eggs to be high on the list of foods most likely to produce an allergic reaction. Others are pork, strawberries, tomatoes, and cabbage. The doctor can seek these foods out by means of skin tests, which consist of scratching the surface of the skin and placing one drop of food extract on the scratched or roughed-up surface. Within a few moments, a raised or reddened area appears if the individual is allergic to the food tested.

Before the days of skin testing, it was up to the doctor to find the offending foods by placing the victim on a basic nonallergic diet which consisted mainly of lamb, rice, and canned pears. Other foods were added one at a time until the allergy-producing food was found.

There is always a problem working out a menu for the person with food allergies. Food substitutes must be rotated often so that allergies to the substitutes do not appear! Sometimes the allergy foods may be used unnoticed in food combinations which must also be watched carefully. For instance, if a person is allergic to milk, it includes milk in cakes, cooking, and desserts.

With mild allergic reactions, the offending food may be served occasionally without causing too great a disturbance. A person allergic mildly to milk could have milk in some form perhaps twice a week and suffer no acute reaction, but he could not have milk every day without symptoms of his allergy appearing.

- Tell about your own experiences with one of the diets discussed in this chapter.
- What do you understand by "special diets"?
- Plan a day's menu for someone who is allergic to wheat and wheat products. What would constitute the biggest problem?
- What are the most common allergic foods?

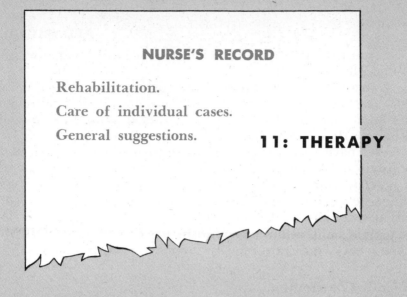

NURSE'S RECORD

Rehabilitation.

Care of individual cases.

General suggestions.

11: THERAPY

One of the more inspiring and interesting parts of nursing is helping those who are handicapped find out life is still to be fulfilled and enjoyed. When you are caring for a member of your family in your own home, you have a great edge over the professional nurse or therapist who sees the patient only a short time each day. You live with him; you are familiar with his personality; he is not just another "case" to you. You know his physical defects and the way to adjust the environment to them. You are not bringing in strange looking apparatus to frighten him. In short, you are in a better position to study your patient *as a whole*.

It is natural to think that you can do less for the handicapped person without some special training or skill. Indeed, there are many trained specialists to help people through the big problems, such as polio, amputation, and cerebral palsy. But you help your patient greatly when you help him to help himself. In most cases, we do not realize this; we stop just when we should carry on more vigorously.

REHABILITATION

Rehabilitation, in simple language, means helping a person become as useful as he can be with what he has to work with. In the military, rehabilitation goes a little further by assuming a person must be useful to the extent that he will be able to earn a living when released.

Rehabilitation encourages him to help himself, gives him hope, teaches him to use his hands and mind. It begins with the simple routine acts of daily care: Encouraging him to brush his own teeth, comb his hair, to feed himself.

You have the greatest opportunity to do this kind of rehabilitation. When the patient comes home from surgery, when he is recovering from an acute illness at home, you are with him as he begins to be active again; you are his closest companion through the days or weeks that follow. You can help the patient hold onto the ground he has gained, keep him from slipping back, and encourage him to move steadily ahead.

Patient's Contribution . . .

Sometimes a patient is willing to be helped only if he realizes the need of knowing something about treating his illness. If he is not aware of this need, you must tactfully make it appear that he is doing the asking. For the first step of rehabilitation is: The patient has to be in a state of mind to help. The prospect of long-drawn-out illness brings mental depression, a feeling of uselessness and self-pity, unless you give him something else to think about. He will respond to treatment more if he feels he can be useful. A simple activity may lead him to think about using muscles that are affected by his condition. It might encourage experiments which could lead to a new vocation. Besides the crafts, a patient can learn bookkeeping, magazine subscription and other mail-order selling, or the background of a small retail business while he is convalescing.

The doctor is your ally in the period of rehabilitation. He will tell you how much the patient can do. Here again, we come back to the individual patient—you must think of his particular illness, his temperament, and his interests.

Attitude . . .

The key to keeping a patient interested or busy lies in his own attitude. The more things a person will *try out,* the more he will want to know. For the person who always has wanted to experiment with or read up on specialties, this is his opportunity. He may have his own ideas of what he wants to do to keep his mind and hands busy, but because you know his interests and his way of thinking, it will be easier to find

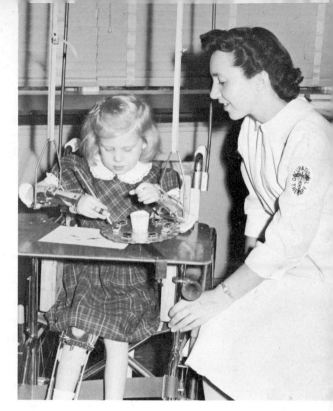

AMERICAN OCCUPATIONAL
THERAPY ASSN.

Six-year-old polio victim paints to strengthen finger and arm muscles while a therapist aids and encourages her. Notice that the child's arms are in an overhead sling.

something to satisfy his need. Of course, you must always consider his physical condition and the things he can do safely.

CARE OF INDIVIDUAL CASES

The Cardiac Patient . .

The kind of activity allowed the heart patient depends upon the kind of heart condition he has. The doctor will advise. Physical activities may be permitted; they may be limited; they may be forbidden. His first activities may simply be to brush his own hair or to turn over by himself. Then he may be permitted to hold up his newspaper. Later he may be allowed a few moments in a chair. He can *read* in fields that may lead to a future vocation. Perhaps he can use his hands for games or to work on a hobby, such as stamp collecting, making toys, or drawing plans for remodeling the home or place of business. This reminds him that he is a part of the family and gives the other members a share in the illness. Of course, when all activity is forbidden, as in severe cases resulting from rheumatic fever, you will concentrate your efforts on making him as contented as possible, setting up devices so he can read, adjusting the TV set, helping him to feed himself.

The Diabetic Patient . . .

Although many diabetics lead a normal life, serious complications such as infections or gangrene may make hospitalization or home bed rest necessary. With such a patient, you must always think of the dangers of new infections. Healing processes are slow, so you will keep sharp tools or rough materials away. His eyesight may be poor, so he must have good light to work in. His muscles are weak, so pay attention to his posture and use soft supporting pillows to prevent fatigue, loss of muscle tone, and bone deformities.

After Surgery . . .

The patient returning home after surgery usually no longer needs complete rest. The nature of the operation will be your guide as to what activities to encourage. Choose non-strenuous movements and exercises for the patient who has had abdominal surgery, to avoid rupture; for the woman who has had a breast removed, encourage the important exercises prescribed by the doctor. Listen very carefully to his instructions so that you understand them perfectly. This is important if a deformity is to be prevented by the exercises. The breast muscles tend to contract thereby limiting the motion of the arm on that particular side. Help her to stretch those muscles by encouraging her to powder her nose and brush her hair. The doctor will tell you how much she can do safely, and when. Remember, her spirits will be low; a cheerful, matter-of-fact, loving atmosphere will lift her morale tremendously.

In almost every case of surgery, there will be a period when it is advisable to follow certain *group exercises* for muscle re-development. The doctor will instruct you on these, or see that a visiting nurse comes to instruct you and your patient.

The Cancer Patient . . .

Patients who have had an operation to remove a cancerous growth are treated as any other person convalescing after a surgical procedure. Many who have had cancer will get well; but fears, superstitions, and gossip make it difficult to believe that cancer is not always fatal. The hope of a satisfactory return to a normal life is the best reassurance that your patient can have; your cheerful, matter-of-fact attitude and your sincerity give him confidence. Your thoughtfulness—with special interest in preparing his favorite foods, watching his favorite television program—will do much to remove old fears and let him know he may carry on normal activities.

Remember, the patient probably can return to his old activities. He should be encouraged to regain his interest in his job and other affairs.

The Tubercular Patient . . .

The way back to normal living for the tubercular patient is a long one. When he returns from the hospital or sanatorium, he has been taught many safety measures. The family usually has been instructed by the doctor, too, and every member examined for possible tuberculosis.

The patient has definite rest periods, and his activity is increased very gradually. He is allowed to do only those things that require the least output of energy. Remember, he has been at rest for a long time. His muscles need to become accustomed anew to normal movement, for any new or prolonged activity will cause muscle stiffness and soreness. He usually can feed himself and look after his own toilet before he is released from the hospital. With careful budgeting of a time schedule, his routine will soon be a habit and every member of the family learns to give a little extra thought to the awareness of the situation and the precautions that all must take as self-protection.

The Polio Patient . . .

Anything that interferes with the nervous system will affect muscles or groups of muscles. If the legs are affected, the mattress may be pulled away from the foot of the bed enough to allow the heels or toes to extend over the end. A board should be attached to the foot of the bed to hold the feet at right angles when they are resting against it. This will allow pressure exercises. The position of a child should be changed frequently.

The diet will be suitable for the severity of the illness. Usually a soft diet is best since swallowing may be difficult. To have a normal amount of fluids is important, but the kidneys are undergoing additional strain now and should not be overworked by additional forced fluids at this time.

If the patient's mind is affected (in certain types) he will be able to do very simple things, but, as muscular response improves, he will be able to try more difficult activities.

In spite of paralysis, usually the polio patient can still think actively and use unaffected muscles. When his condition permits, muscle motion under water may be started. Other exercises must be developed as prescribed. All manipulation, active or passive, must be limited to that which does not cause pain, spasm, or fatigue. As he improves, he may take part in some of his former activities. If he is an athlete, he can still watch competitive games on television or listen over the radio. As he improves, he may be able to watch the game from the sidelines on the field. In every event, he should be encouraged to be as nearly like people of his own age group as possible.

Most afflicted children over six years of age suffer from acute anxiety. They have heard much about polio. They dread the horror of being crippled. Discovering the child's fears is so important in planning his treatment. Talk about them, answer his questions honestly, and if there is doubt rely upon his doctor. Together, you can keep the child informed of his progress and help him regain confidence.

Tell him he is going to be all right. He probably will recover fully, and your belief will encourage him to try. There is no doubt that improvement will follow.

Polio patient is lowered into whirlpool bath. Gentle currents of water stimulate and relax muscles.

PORTO-LIFT CO.

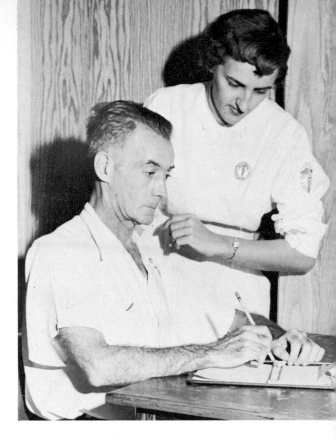

Newly blind patient learns to write as part of the adjustment to his changed way of life.

Failing Eyesight . . .

The patient whose eyesight is failing is harassed by fear and bewilderment. He needs to develop his sense of touch as a substitute for his eyes. Remember that he is as well as ever, but must learn to find and hold a picture in his mind of where the furniture is placed and how to find his way about the house. If the sight is extremely low, you must be careful not to startle him; touch him lightly as you speak to him; speak softly and frequently to let him know in what part of the room you are. Help him with his food; tell him where things are on the plate. Always try to put the same type of things in the same place. Cut his meat for him, butter his bread, then retire quietly unless he needs further help. You can learn to assist him so thoughtfully that visitors will forget that he is blind. This is a moment of triumph he must work to achieve.

Deafness . . .

We may not realize how much of life involves our hearing. To the person who is losing his hearing, the familiar sounds that made him belong to the normal world are vanishing. He is put on the defensive. He watches lips moving, may even pretend he can hear, yet cannot keep up with your words. Even when he has the courage to ask that they be repeated, he cannot get the picture, this leads to uncertainty and withdrawal. The hearing aid can be an answer to the problem, if at all possible. For the person who wants one and cannot afford it, help may be sought and received at the local health office. The patient's sense of shame must be overcome. Outside counsel may be just what he needs. When the hearing aid cannot help, encourage the patient to learn lip reading. He still has his eyes, his hands, and an active mind. He can read; he can build and live a normal life once he is drawn out of his shell.

GENERAL SUGGESTIONS

Reading Aloud . . .

Reading aloud to a patient can be a great source of satisfaction. Read the parts of a newspaper or magazine that he likes best to hear first. If he likes to read the comics first, yield to his wishes. Reading aloud requires some special knowledge. Read distinctly, not so slowly as to unnerve the patient; nor should you hurry along in the style of silent reading. Put some expression in your words without sounding falsely dramatic; show interest in the subject yourself. It is good to practice reading aloud by yourself for voice inflections and mimicries can bring

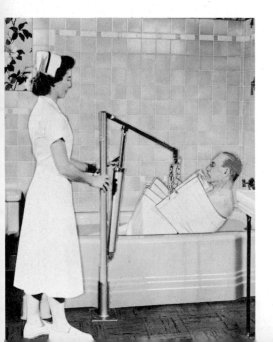

The arthritic patient can be carried from bed to bathtub by a mechanical lift.

PORTO-LIFT CO.

PORTO-LIFT CO.

Many older persons who could not enter a car by themselves are enabled to enjoy a ride by the use of a lift.

laughter to the eyes of a young child and relieve the tediousness of an elderly existence.

How the Family Can Help . . .

When the routine of your home has been disturbed by the illness of one member, you will find that it is the small things that make the difference between a contented patient and a complainer. As a patient, Mother or Grandmother may feel she is a burden, or that she is being left out of family affairs. It helps to have members visiting in turn, carrying the food tray or reading a story. Messages may be carried from friends who are unable to visit at this time. A few minutes spared as soon as family members return from school, work, shopping, or a social event, keeps the patient from feeling neglected. Everyone will find that he can adjust enthusiasm to the mood of the patient. One thought is especially important: Since activity is limited, a big part of any treatment is to keep the patient contented. A cobweb on the ceiling may be very disturbing to Mother, even though it is a source of amusement to Junior to watch it curl in a breeze. You will know what she likes. See that the little things are done her way. Remember that a big supply of loving care and understanding is as good for others as it would be for *you* if you became a bed patient.

"IN OTHER WORDS . . ."

You may use therapy to the same extent that you use your knowledge of home nursing. You will learn how to do many interesting things for the patient. There are many books filled with good suggestions at your school and public library. Watch the effect of an activity. Begin it when the patient is rested; stop before he gets tired. Use an activity to fill any empty spot in the day.

This is what it should mean to you: Learn to feel with your patient what it is to be a hopeful human being, to be able to enjoy life, to work and play again, to accept a handicap and be independent in spite of it. Watch out for things that may cause deformities—tight sheets over the toes, lack of support under the knees. Help to adjust appliances and see that they are used correctly to get the most benefit from them. Protect the patient from infections and accidents. Most of all, build up his self-confidence by encouraging him to help himself.

- What amusing or useful things do you know how to do that would be suitable activities for a child recovering from polio?
- Choose something from the newspaper to read to an elderly man who likes to spend his leisure watching sporting events.
- Have a friend blindfold herself. Lead her around the room, talking quietly, to give her the feel of things.
- Why must you use supporting measures for the body in the illness? What are some of these measures?
- What is the difference between the professional nurse and the therapist?

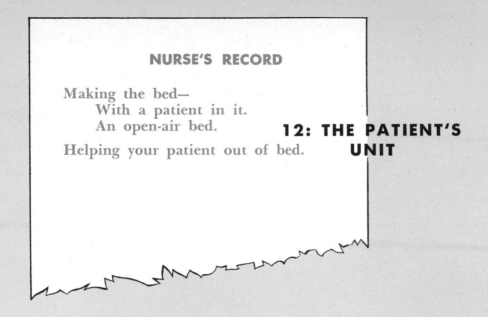

NURSE'S RECORD

Making the bed—
  With a patient in it.
  An open-air bed.

Helping your patient out of bed.

12: THE PATIENT'S UNIT

In the hospital, a wide choice of equipment is on hand. In the home, it must be provided or improvised. Try to secure the equipment required for good nursing care of your patient. *The cost need not be too great.*

No matter where the sick bed may be, the house must have a *patient's unit.* It includes the bed, the furniture, and most of the equipment used for his care. It may be his own room or a room that he shares with someone else. But, even though causing a problem requiring adjustment by another member of the family, it is desirable that the patient be in bed alone, separate even from husband or wife.

The furniture in the unit is the bed, a bedside table, and a chair. Find space for some of his personal belongings. Also, if possible, take care of other needs (telephone, photograph, display, etc.). These are usually in or on the bedside table. To a child who must give up his favorite teddy bear, it is comforting to be able to see it perched in plain view on the bedside table. People may clutter up the table with useless things also, but these may be removed while house cleaning.

The total basic equipment for the long-term bed-patient unit is:

FURNITURE: Bed, bedside table, chair, lamp, overbed tray.

LINEN: Sheets, draw sheet, pillow slips, blankets, spread, cotton bath blanket, face towel, bath towel, washcloth, bedpan cover.

TOILET EQUIPMENT: Wash basin, soap dish, toothbrush container, mouth (kidney-shaped) basin, tumbler for mouthwash, comb and brush, bedpan—and urinal for male patient.

OTHER EQUIPMENT: Rubber or plastic sheet, 36" by 36", water pitcher, drinking glass, thermometer in container, call bell, and a screen or curtain device, if necessary.

Other equipment needed for nursing care should be kept outside the unit, preferably in the bathroom. Treatment trays or thermometer equipment may be kept on the dresser. If everything is kept in its place, it will avoid clutter and very little time will be lost in preparation, thus saving many steps.

MAKING THE BED

As comfort, rest, and sleep are most important in the recovery from illness, special attention should be given to the bed and bedding, and to acquiring the necessary skill in making the bed. Bed making is the "first art" in the practice of nursing.

The bed in the home is usually much lower and broader than the hospital bed, so it is not necessary to make the bed as securely, although this is always desirable. Some adjustments may be made to make the work easier on your back—such as

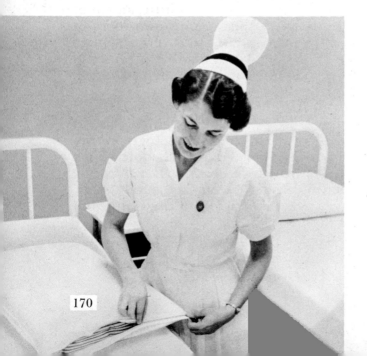

The nonallergic pillow case.

B. F. GOODRICH CO.

170

using blocks to raise the bed so you will not have to bend so low.

Usually two *pillows* are used on the bed—one, small and firm to support the head and shoulders, the other, larger and of softer material for comfort. Kapok, nylon bits, or sponge rubber should be available for patients who are allergic to feathers—or a very light rubberized silk cover with zipper fastenings may be used to protect the allergic patient from the irritating effects of the feather pillow.

A *rubber sheet* is used to protect the lower sheet and mattress, although this may be placed between the mattress pad and lower sheet if your patient is allergic to rubber. In this case, a plastic sheet may be substituted and is really more practical in the home. It is narrower than the cotton sheets and yet long enough to tuck in at the sides of the bed. It must be without wrinkles. Because rubber and plastic prevent access of air to the skin, they delay evaporation and make the patient feel hot and moist at times. Unless your patient absolutely needs the rubber sheet, it may be eliminated entirely—or for certain periods—and replaced by a quilted pad placed under the patient's hips.

The *linen* consists of two large sheets, a draw sheet, a spread, and two pillow cases. The *large sheets* should be strong enough to stand pulling tightly and large enough to tuck in well under the mattress all around. Contour sheets are used

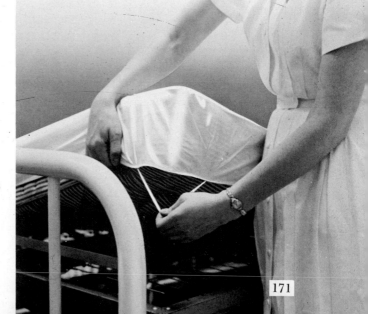

Plastic covering protects
the mattress.

only if the patient is allowed out while the bed is being made. As the name "contour" suggests, these sheets are supplied with corners sewed to fit securely over the mattress, which necessitates lifting the corner of the mattress up and into the corner of the sheet.

The *draw sheet*, which may be made of single or double cotton, must be wide enough and stout enough to pull tightly and tuck well under the mattress. It is called the draw sheet because it is easily withdrawn. The spread should be light and easily laundered. The *pillow slips* should fit the pillows but not so tightly that they distort the shape.

The blankets should be light and warm. They are lighter in proportion to the warmth, depending upon the amount of wool present; a blanket with 60 to 80 per cent of wool is most satisfactory.

EQUIPMENT LIST:

1. Mattress cover
2. Sheets, 2
3. Draw sheet
4. Blanket
5. Spread
6. Pillow cases, 1 or 2
7. Rubber or plastic sheet

Steps In Procedure

1. Bring all necessary linen to bedside.

2. Put on mattress cover with open end at foot of the bed.

Remember

Place chair with sturdy back at foot of bed and place linen on seat in order of use; bottom sheet will be on top, spread and pillow case on bottom.

A quilted mattress pad may be used. Turn mattress weekly to prevent sagging.

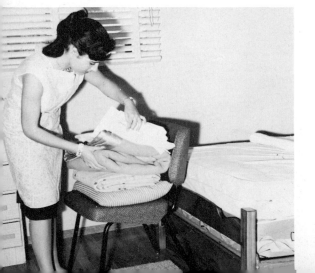

All necessary linen on chair at foot of bed.

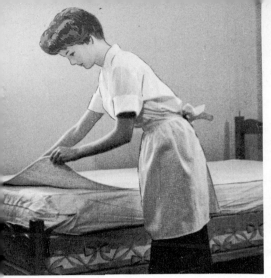
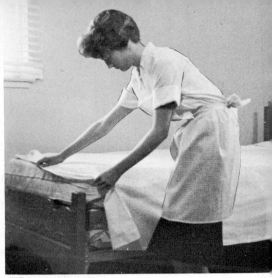

Quilted mattress cover in place. • Bottom sheet.

3. Place the bottom sheet on the bed:

   • With one hem even with the foot of the mattress.

   • With rough side of hem down.

   • Middle fold in center of bed.

   • Allow about 18 inches to fold under head of mattress.

The sheet may not be long enough to tuck under the foot of the mattress, but don't skimp on the folded-under part at the top.

4. Tuck sheets smoothly under head of mattress; miter the corner; tuck sheet under mattress along side from head to foot.

Used top sheet may become bottom sheet when bed is changed the next day.

Sheet pulled firmly under mattress head. • Mitering the corner.

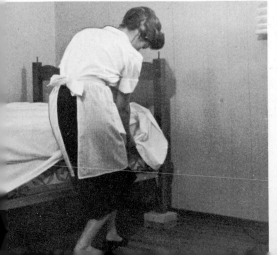
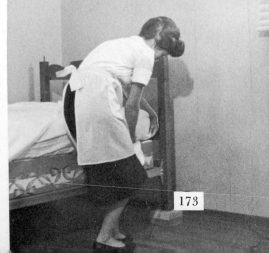

Making a square or mitered corner.

Steps In Procedure

5. Place the rubber or plastic sheet across the center of the bed, with upper edge about 12 inches from head of mattress. *This is not always used.*
6. Cover with cotton draw sheet.

7. Tuck both draw sheets under the mattress at the same time.

8. Place top sheet on bed, so that:
   - Rough side of hem is up.
   - Hem is even with head of mattress.
   - Middle fold is in center of bed.

Remember

Weight of patient's body causes rubber or plastic to slip downwards; be sure upper edge is about 12 inches from head of mattress.

Large sheet may be used, folded once over end to end; place fold toward head of bed and 3 or 4 inches higher than the rubber sheet.

Bottom sheet tucked in along length of bed. • Rubber draw sheet.

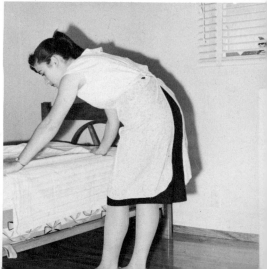

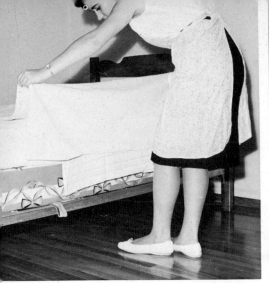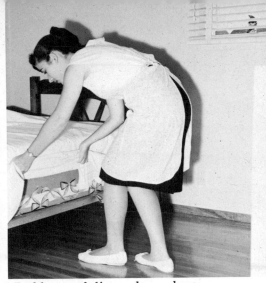

Linen draw sheet over rubber sheet. ● Rubber and linen draw sheets tucked under mattress together for firm base.

● Hangs evenly on both sides.

9. Tuck top sheet under foot of mattress and make square corner on near side.

10. Place blanket, centering, with the upper edge about 6 inches from the head of the mattress.

Blanket must be high enough to cover patient's shoulders.

11. Tuck in at foot and make square corner on near side.

Top sheet in place. ● Blanket.

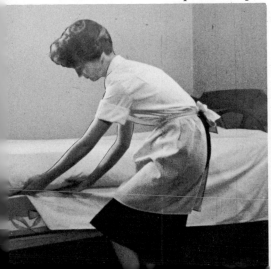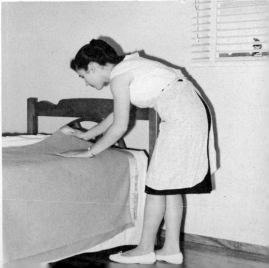

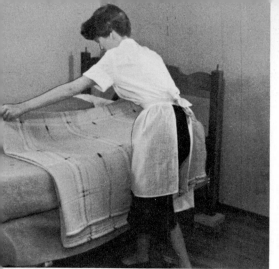
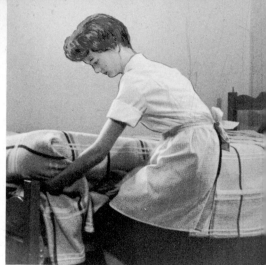

Bed spread. • Spread tucked well under foot of mattress.

Steps In Procedure

12. Center spread and place with upper edge even with the head of the mattress.

13. Tuck under mattress at foot and make square corner on near side.

14. Complete opposite side of bed in same way. Start by folding back everything above mattress cover from side to center of bed. Then proceed with bottom sheet as in Step 4.

Remember

This keeps the sheets and bedding fresh until bed is occupied.

Be careful that the blanket does not hang below spread.

Corner mitered into "triangle hang." • Other side of bed made same way, starting with bottom sheet.

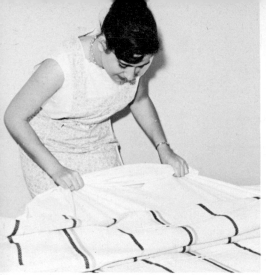
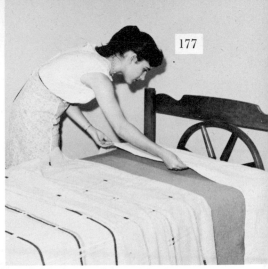

Draw sheet pulled very tight. • Top sheet folded as cuff over blanket.

15. With both hands pull draw sheets taut. Tuck firmly under mattress at center, then at top and bottom.

Brace your thigh against the bed while pulling the sheets tight. Keep your back straight for good posture and efficient body mechanics.

16. With end of sheet, make cuff over blanket. Cover bed completely with spread to keep it neat until use.

17. Put pillow on bed and draw on pillow case.

Grasp one end of pillowcase; push end of pillow through. Pull case over pillow.

18. Lay pillow flat at head of bed, open end of case away from door.

Spread pulled to top of bed. • Pillow placed in case.

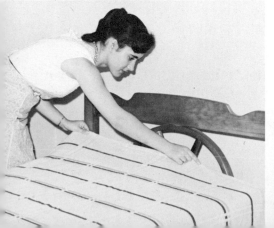
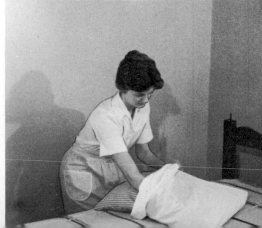

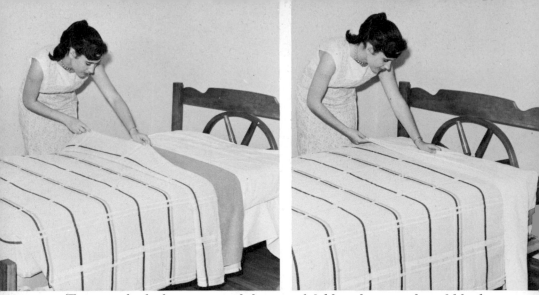

To open the bed, turn spread down and fold under top edge of blanket.

- Turn back top sheet over spread.

To Open a Bed for Your Patient . . .

Do this when preparing the bed for your patient; and you may wish to arrange it like this when he is allowed up for short periods of time.

1. Turn the spread down from the top and fold it under the top edge of the blanket, then turn the top sheet back over the spread. This protects the blanket, keeps it away from the patient's skin, and makes it easier for him to handle the bedclothes.

2. Fold the top covers down in single pleat. Your bed is ready to receive its occupant.

HOW TO MAKE A BED WITH A PATIENT IN IT

You prepare a bed for the patient's comfort—so use a method that will give a comfortable bed. *Review* these important points in making a comfortable bed: Clean linen; tight, smooth lower sheets; top sheet and blanket high enough to cover the patient's shoulders; ample toe space; protection for the mattress.

Always keep the patient's body in *good alignment* as you make his bed. Use *good posture* so as to avoid strains to your own body.

The bed is made in the morning after breakfast or after you give the bath or morning care.

EQUIPMENT NEEDED:

1. Clean linen according to the patient's needs:

   • 1 or 2 sheets

   • Small sheet (commonly referred to as draw sheet) for across middle of bed over bottom sheet, or, bed pad (for mattress protection)

   • Spread

   • Pillowcase, as needed

Steps in Procedure	Remember
1. Arrange clean linen in order of use on the seat of chair.	Avoid shaking dust or lint from bed clothes into the air of the room.
2. Loosen the bedding from under the mattress.	Avoid jarring the patient or shaking the bed.
3. Remove the spread and blanket: • If spread is to be used again, fold it from head to foot and from side to side in half and place it over the back of chair. • Remove and fold blanket in same way.	If the bed is being changed following the bath, the upper bedding will already have been replaced by the cotton bath blanket.
4. Place clean sheet over top sheet. (Bath blanket may be used instead of sheet if patient is chilled.)	Used top sheet may become the bottom sheet, or a draw sheet.
5. Have patient hold upper edge of clean top sheet. Remove soiled top sheet by sliding it out from under the clean sheet.	
6. Remove the pillows; remove the soiled cases and place them with the soiled linen.	Leave one pillow if the patient is uncomfortable without it.
7. Turn the patient toward the other side of the bed.	Guard against the patient turning too far—too near the edge of the bed—and falling.
8. Roll the small sheet up and tuck it under patient's back.	

Steps in Procedure   **Remember**

9. Roll the bottom sheet toward the patient.

10. Lay the clean lower sheet, folded lengthwise, on the mattress, with center fold in the middle of the bed, and high enough to allow for tucking in at top.

    (Used top sheet may be used for the bottom sheet.)

11. Gather the farthest half of the sheet into folds and place the folded portion as close as possible to the soiled sheets.

12. Tuck the clean sheets under the mattress at the top.

13. Make a square corner.

14. Tuck the sheet under, all along the side of the bed.

    If the sheet covers the lower end of mattress, make a corner.

15. Place the small (draw) sheet across middle portion of bed extending from patient's shoulders to midthigh.

    If a rubber or plastic sheet is being used for mattress protection, it is usually used under small sheet. If a folded large sheet is used as small sheet, fold crosswise through the center, hem edges together. Push farthest half against the patient with fold toward the top of the bed. (Single edges are more likely to wrinkle down.)

16. Tuck clean small sheet under mattress; fold the free edge close to the patient's body.

17. Lift the patient's feet over the folded sheets, keeping the body covered.

18. Assist the patient to turn to clean side of bed.

19. Go around to the other side of the bed, pull sheets through. (Place soiled sheets in laundry bag or on chair.) Remove small sheet first, then soiled bottom sheet.

    Soiled pillowcase may be used as laundry bag for soiled linen.

CH. 12: THE PATIENT'S UNIT

20. Straighten bottom sheet, tuck under head of mattress, make a square corner, pull tightly, and tuck in along side of bed.

Brace your thigh against the bed while pulling the sheet tight. Keep your back straight for good posture and efficient body mechanics.

21. Pull rubber sheet (if used) and small sheet together and tuck under mattress.

Tuck in center first, then top and bottom.

22. Put clean pillowcases on one or both pillows; place them under patient's head. Grasp top end of clean case, push end through case to hold one end of pillow. Pull case over pillow.

With your right hand on upper arm near armpit, have patient place her arm around your shoulder, gently lift her head and shoulders; slide pillow into place.

23. Smooth the top sheet, letting edges fall over foot of bed.

If cotton blanket has been used under sheet, remove now.

24. Place the blanket over the sheet, placing it high enough to cover patient's shoulders; let edges fall over end of bed.

25. Make a box pleat in the blanket and sheet together at the center of the lower end of the bed.

Pleat should be loose enough to provide foot room or toe room.

26. Tuck sheet and blanket together under mattress; make a corner.

Holds tighter.

27. Place spread over blanket; adjust it to hang evenly on both sides of the bed and tuck in at the foot. Make a corner.

28. Fold top edge of spread under edge of blanket and turn top sheet over spread to make a cuff.

The turn-under holds the covers in place and protects the blanket.

29. Go to the other side of bed and finish making it following same procedures.

Check toe room after all top bedding is in place.

Steps in Procedure

30. Adjust pillows.

31. Put the bedside unit in order.
    Remove soiled linen.

HOW TO MAKE AN OPEN-AIR BED

Although not frequently used, an open-air bed is still sometimes required for tubercular patients. If the patient is to sleep in the open air, he will need added protection, to keep out moisture, drafts, and cold air; provide lightweight but warm covering; keep the extra weight of the coverings off his feet.

EQUIPMENT NEEDED:

Same as for any bed, with the addition of:

- Extra blankets, according to climatic conditions.
- Rubber sheeting the size of the mattress, or newspapers.
- Cotton blankets instead of sheets.

Steps in Procedure	Remember
1. Put a wool blanket on the upper half of the springs, crosswise.	One edge of the blanket extends up over the headboard.
2. Repeat for the lower half of the springs.	One edge of the blanket is over the footboard. (The two blankets do not meet in the middle.)
3. Cover the springs with the rubber sheet or newspapers.	Five or six thicknesses of newspaper. The bed and springs are now fairly well covered.
4. Place the mattress on the bed; make up the bed as usual.	Use cotton sheet blankets.
5. Place a stiff pillow at the patient's feet.	Must be higher than the patient's toes to take off the weight of the bedding.
6. Place a hot water bottle or heating pad in the bed before the patient gets in.	To warm the bed; leave it in the foot of the bed.
7. After the patient is in bed, place and tuck the top bedding in snugly.	

8. Fold the under blanket from over the foot of the bed back across the lower part of the bed; fold the blankets from the sides over the pillows.

Fold the corners in so that the blankets meet in the center under the chin and lap down the center of the bed.

9. Fasten the top end of the under-blanket to the headboard.

This makes a windbreak for the patient's head.

It is best to make this type of bed indoors so that it is warmed for the patient; it may be pushed to the porch or near the open window. The patient should wear *flannel night clothes* and a *parka* around the head. Gloves may be worn in colder climates. A modern *electric blanket* is very useful, but must be securely tucked. A blanket windbreak is still needed at the head. A *call bell* should be pinned to the bedding within the patient's reach.

HELPING YOUR PATIENT OUT OF BED

The doctor will tell you when your patient may get up. Some patients have to be encouraged to do so, particularly old folks who have had a long illness. Others may try too soon, as in the case of the youngster who is recovering from bronchitis or measles.

The patient should be well rested before attempting to get up, since the procedure itself is somewhat a strain on anyone who has been bedfast for a long time. Decide on the *most convenient time* to try it. He might wish to sit up while visiting with a friend—or he may prefer his "up" time to be reserved for meals. Reassure the patient by soothing away his worries; he may not feel that he is strong enough; he may worry about being chilled. It is only natural to be nervous about the first attempt. You are here to protect your patient. This is how to do it:

1. Keep him out of drafts and protect him by proper clothing.

2. On the first attempt, use fewer clothes and an extra blanket to cover him.

3. Lift or support him as he moves. If the patient is completely helpless, get assistance.

4. Remove loose rugs from near the bed; chose a chair that will not slide.

5. Take his pulse while he is up—the change in position affects the circulation—and watch for signs of fatigue.

EQUIPMENT NEEDED:

- A comfortable chair with arms.
- Pillows, 1 or 2.
- Blankets, 1 or 2, as needed for warmth.
- Bathrobe.
- Slippers.
- Socks, if patient wishes.

Move the chair close to the bed; put a pillow in the seat; cover it with a plastic case if the patient is likely to soil it. Put a pillow lengthwise against the back of the chair. Spread a blanket cross the seat of the chair with top edge several inches above the chair arms. Fold second blanket (if needed) crosswise; place across back of chair with fold at top.

Steps in Procedure:	Remember
1. Bring the patient toward the edge of the bed and help him to sit up.	Standing on the left side of bed facing patient, grasp patient's upper arm near axilla (under arm) with right hand. Have your left arm about his shoulders. Gently pull up, raising him to a sitting position.
2. Swing patient's legs over edge of the bed.	Put one hand under the back, the other under the knees.
3. Put on the robe, socks and slippers.	If the patient is too weak, these may be put on before raising to sitting position.
4. Face the patient. Advance one foot, legs apart, knees slightly bent, for a firm base.	
5. Put his hands on your shoulders, as you take hold of his arms at the shoulders.	
6. Slide him off the bed to his feet.	Give good support to your patient until you are sure he is not dizzy or faint.

7. Support him as you direct him to the chair.	Step sidewise—the patient's back is toward the chair, the chair against the back of his legs.
8. Help him to lower himself into the chair.	Stand close to him, legs apart, one foot forward; bend your knees and hips to prevent strain on your back.
9. Arrange pillows, blankets, and footstool, if used.	Bring the blanket up over the feet, bring the sides across, overlapping. Cover his shoulders with second blanket, if needed.
10. Give patient a magazine or whatever is desired.	If you leave the room, give the patient the call bell.
11. To return patient to bed, reverse the procedure. Bed should be straightened while patient is up.	

• Explain what is meant by the *patient's unit.*

• Little five-year-old Tommy is recovering from the measles; he wants to get up; the doctor isn't due to see Tommy until tomorrow. What do you do?

• Why is a plastic or rubber sheet used under the small sheet? For what reason is a bed pad used?

• Your supply of linen is limited. You want to change the bed every day. Do you reuse any soiled linen?

• Using another student as a patient, demonstrate how to help a patient to a sitting position.

• In what way can you reassure an elderly person who is allowed out of bed for the first time in two months?

13: DIAGNOSTIC AIDS

In medical hospitals, the record or chart is a concise, written account of the health history of the patient and his family, a report of the findings upon examination, the signs and symptoms occurring while the patient is under observation, and the treatment and progress of the disease, if one is involved. Besides all this information, there may be included a certain amount of environmental history that may directly affect the patient's diagnosis and treatment and that is necessary for the identification of the patient and the administration of the hospital or health service.

A record for each patient is also kept by every doctor in his office and by most groups of medical workers associated in any way with medical organizations. Charts have many uses: As an aid to diagnosis and treatment; as a record of data necessary to the administration of a health service; as an aid in teaching medical students; as an aid in legal justice.

The record or chart at home while you are in charge will be of an entirely different type. If, during the severe part of an illness to the sick member, the doctor feels an experienced professional or practical nurse should be called in, then he or she will keep a medical type record. You will not be expected to do so; you will make brief notations concerning the daily treatments prescribed and any medications to be given, and keep a record of temperature, pulse, respirations, and any unusual remark or symptom that will tell the doctor something about your patient you feel he should know. This last is important, because sometimes a patient will think a sign or symptom too minor to bother with; yet it may be important to the doctor. You can't speak out in front of the patient—you might frighten him; let your notes speak for you. Call the doctor's attention to any unusual symptom. Not many home patients have a family nurse thoughtful enough to keep a record; your doctor will appreciate having someone in the home who can take charge.

The patient's chart is the story of the patient—his care and his progress, hour by hour. In the hospital, the doctor will write his orders in the order book or on the order sheet of the record, but, at home, he is more likely to give verbal orders; that is, in conversation. You may buy a form of *bedside notepaper,* but a simple chart of plain paper, divided into several columns for *date, hour, diet,* and *remarks* will serve the purpose of recording the doctor's instructions and patient's records.

Record favorable changes in the patient's condition as well as the unfavorable ones. Keep your notes brief, yet as accurate and complete as possible. If you keep in mind that charting is a part of every nursing procedure, you will find yourself sorting out the important points as you work. Put them down as soon as you finish a treatment. At mealtime or when you are removing the tray from the bedside, notice how the patient has eaten and what particular foods. His *diet* may be an important part of his therapy and the doctor will need this information.

Keep your notes neat and legible; do not use abbreviations.

IMPORTANCE OF OBSERVATION

Observe means to watch or note. Not all people observe in the same way. Ask three people to describe another person and you will get three variations; yet *all may be true.* Some people are naturally better observers than others. Fortunately, you can train yourself to become more observant. One way to improve is by learning *what to observe.* Know what to look for and why certain information is important. For instance, your patient ate only about half of the food on his breakfast tray.

You observed this when you removed the tray from the room. You must go on to school, but you can leave instructions for the patient to receive a snack at mid-morning; if he will be alone for a time, leave some juice or milk in a vacuum bottle at the bedside.

Understanding Symptoms . . .

The patient *tells* the doctor only a small part of the information that is available about him, such as whether he feels hot, dizzy, can't sleep, or is unable to eat. These are called the *subjective* signs of illness. You must be aware of the other symptoms, the *objective* kind, that you observe as you give nursing care. To *observe* and *report*—the two go hand in hand.

Understanding what to look for will help you give better nursing care. These are points to cover:

PHYSICAL SIGNS

1. **Facial expression:** Interested and alert or does he show fear, anxiety, worry? Does he show contentment or dissatisfaction? He may be unusually expressionless, or pale, or flushed.

2. **The eyes:** Tired looking, sensitive to light. The eyeballs may be sunken or stand out. The eyelids may be red, rimmed, swollen, heavy, or drooping. Are the pupils too small or too large? Is the white part of the eye stained? Are there any tears or discharge, puffiness under the eyes? Or are they especially clear and fresh?

3. **Nutrition:** The patient may be over-/or underweight; his face may be twisted in signs of digestive disturbance. Does he express a desire for food? Is his skin healthy?

4. **Posture:** Note whether he lies on his back comfortably or, from weakness, slides down from the pillows with signs of difficult breathing; lies with the body curled or twisted in such a position as to relieve pain in a certain area. Does he lie, sit, walk as if he feels *strong?*

5. **Movements:** Is the patient quiet and at ease—or restless, tossing, turning from side to side (as in hemorrhage) or in severe pain (as in colic)? Does he have difficulty in turning? Can he control his muscles, or does he have tremors, muscle spasms?

6. **Condition of the skin:** Dry or parched? Cracked about mouth? Is it moist, cold, or clammy? Is it hot or discolored? Do you find new bruises, scratches, rashes, or sores? Is redness more noticeable over bony areas?

7. **Mental state:** Is he wide awake when he should be, dull, in a coma or stupor? Does he talk sensibly? Is he depressed, or over-excited? Can he hear and see as well as normally? Does he know where he is? Indications of mental illness are very significant; steps may have to be taken to prevent injury, and specific treatment may be needed. The patient does not always realize that he has changed. Observation is important.

8. **Pain:** Pain is Nature's way of telling us something is wrong with the body. Tender spots indicate something wrong that may not be observable. Describe a pain in the patient's own words as nearly as possible; it may be sudden, sharp, knifelike, dull, aching. Some patients try to hide their pain; others will exaggerate their symptoms. Still others will complain when there is no cause that can be found. Your understanding of the person will aid you greatly.

Patient's Attitude . . .

You will learn much about how a patient feels about his lot by watching his actions and listening to what he says. Is he a chronic worrier? Is he co-operative, unreasonable, fearful? Notice anything that seems peculiar to you, but may have a definite explanation. He may not be able to give an understandable reason for a certain action but when he tries to tell you, write it down in the patient's own words. It may contain a clue to his behavior and important information for the doctor.

Sleep . . .

How many hours does he sleep each day? Is he restless; does he awaken often? Does he take naps in the day time? Is he drowsy most of the time? Does he sleep less than he thinks he does? Is there a *change* in his sleeping habits?

Food . . .

What kinds of food does he favor today? Is his diet agreeing with him? Does he eat as though he enjoys the act or does he have to be encouraged to eat? Does he complain of soreness in the mouth? Does he have dentures? Do they fit comfortably? Does he have difficulty in swallowing? Food habits will tell of an impending body disorder: Difficulty in taking food may be a sign of stomach disorders; poor teeth or badly-fitted dentures; mouth infections; mental disorders (such as fear of being poisoned); constipation; diarrhea.

HOW TO ASSIST WITH AN ADULT PHYSICAL EXAMINATION

With the emphasis on *prevention* of illness and disease, much thought is given to the periodic health examination, which has an important part in keeping us well. Naturally, if nothing abnormal or disturbing shows up in this periodic examination, the individual has a feeling of well-being and freedom from worry.

If the health examination is to fulfill its purpose as a preventive measure, it should be complete. It should include inspection of the entire system. Special attention should also be given to problems of the individual. Of course, you go to the doctor's office for your yearly examination. When he is called to the home to see a patient, there is usually a specific reason. Remember your last examination and do everything you know how to make your patient comfortable throughout his examination at home.

You may arrange bed covers, hand equipment to the doctor if he asks your help; he may work right from his medical bag, but if he knows you can help, he will make use of it. If the patient's temperature has not been taken, you may do so. The doctor will examine the eyes, ears, the nose and throat, the mouth, the teeth and the tongue, the neck, the arms, the hands, the chest section, and the abdomen; he will listen to the heart and the lung sounds; he will examine the legs and the feet. He may examine the groin section. The patient will lie flat on his back with one pillow under his head for most of the examination; if able, he sits up while the doctor examines his chest. The doctor may also want him to stand so that he can check his posture and spine.

The Doctor's Bag . . .

The general practitioner's medical bag usually carries all equipment needed for a simple physical examination. He also carries a prescription pad and drugs for treatment of common ailments. If he knows beforehand that he will be concerned with a specific problem, he will bring the special equipment he needs.

EQUIPMENT NEEDED:

- Cotton blanket or single sheet.

EQUIPMENT FROM DOCTOR'S BAG:

- Flashlight.
- Tape measure.
- Tongue depressor.
- Ophthalmoscope (instrument to examine eyes).
- Otoscope (instrument to examine ears and sometimes, nose).
- Blood pressure apparatus.
- Percussion hammer.

If the doctor wants to examine the pelvis section, he will have:

- Rubber gloves.
- Lubricant.
- Vaginal and rectal instruments.

Steps in Procedure	Remember
1. Remove patient's gown, or use gown that opens up front.	Easy to remove and adjust.
2. Put patient on his back with one pillow under his head.	Keeps the patient in normal position.
3. Put the cotton blanket or sheet over the patient; fold the top covering back to the foot of the bed.	
4. Hand doctor equipment.	If he has placed his equipment out for you to assist him.
5. If doctor desires darkened room for eye examination, turn off light.	Turn it on after examination.
6. Cover the patient's chest with a towel when the abdomen is examined. (See page 192.)	Give patient paper tissue to hold over mouth—tell him to turn his head when he coughs.
7. (Woman) Hold the towel over the breasts when patient sits up for chest examination.	
8. Turn the lower half of the blanket up to expose legs.	Tuck it under the thighs.

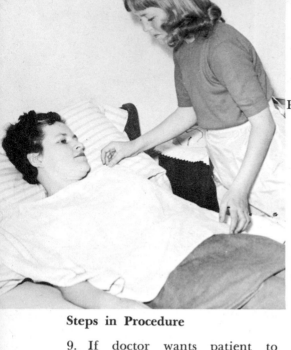

Place towel over patient's chest during abdomen examination.

Steps in Procedure	Remember
9. If doctor wants patient to stand, place a paper towel on the floor.	Adjust gown first; hold bath blanket around patient.

When the examination is over, straighten the gown and draw up the bed covers. Remove the blanket. Make the patient comfortable. If he wants another pillow under his head, and the doctor consents, give it to him.

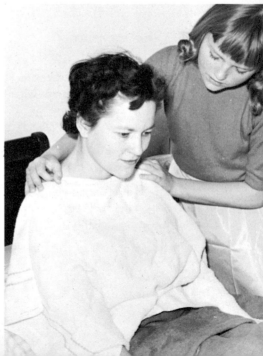

Hold towel in place when patient sits up. Pillow under back provides support.

192

Pelvic Examination . . .

The purpose of the vaginal examination, of course, is to examine the organs of the pelvis and lower abdomen. The vaginal canal is dilated or separated by a special instrument known as the vaginal *speculum;* the vaginal wall, the cervix, and lower portion of the uterus are observed. The appearance of these parts—whether they are swollen, purple-colored, glistening-white—can be very important in diagnosis. Besides the speculum, rubber gloves and a lubricant or oil are needed.

Allow the patient to wear her gown. Ask her to come as close to the side of the bed as possible; have her flex her knees, placing the feet flat on the bed. This relaxes the abdominal muscles. The blanket is placed crosswise across the abdomen. Bring the ends of the blanket down to cover the legs, wrapping one corner about the foot to hold it in place. Raise the middle portion between the legs to the groin only when the doctor is ready for the examination. Protect the patient at all times from unnecessary exposure.

Lubricate the speculum, when doctor is ready, by dropping a small amount of lubricant about the size of a quarter on the top part. When the examination is completed, hold out a paper towel for the speculum and take it to the bathroom; rinse under very hot water. Wash in warm, soapy water; rinse, dry, and give to the doctor.

He may want you to wash his gloves if he has completed his examination, or he may wrap them to return to his office for special care. Assist him to pack his bag, or pack it for him while he talks to the patient.

Rectal Examination . . .

Turn the patient on his left side; flex the right knee against the abdomen; flex the left knee slightly. Cover patient loosely with cotton blanket. Lubricate the rectal speculum (slightly different from the vaginal speculum but made along the same basic lines). Assist the doctor in obtaining specimens if he is going to take any. When he has completed the examination, take speculum in a paper towel to the bathroom, pour cold water over it while holding it over the stool. Be very careful not to drop it. Wash in warm soapy water, rinse, and dry; return to the doctor. Take care of gloves and bag as above.

If a specimen was taken, label a small piece of paper and wrap it around the tube; keep it in place with a tightly wrapped rubber band. The label should have on it the patient's name, address, kind of specimen, date, and the doctor's name. Give it to the doctor to place in his bag. He will take it to his own or the hospital laboratory.

ASSISTING WITH THE EXAMINATION OF AN INFANT OR CHILD

The same equipment is used for examining a child as for an adult. Gaining the child's co-operation is another thing. If he is too young or too ill to understand, then you will have to restrain him for certain parts of the examination. (Ask the doctor's advice on how you can be of service.) To hold down the knees, one arm across the legs just above the knees

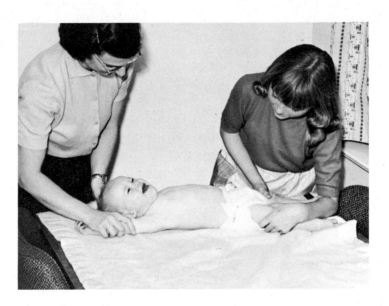

gives a firm and effective hold. The child's arms may be raised above the head or held at the sides by placing his hands palm down on the bed; your hands go one above the elbow on either arm. For examination of the spine, hold him upright, one of your hands behind his head, the other supporting the lower end of his spine, his head leaning against your shoulder.

Remember to explain every move to the youngster, since fear may be allayed if he knows what is going to happen. Many times, restraint is not necessary if time is taken before the examination to explain that the doctor needs to examine him in order to help. Do your best to gain cooperation without restraint.

OBSERVING BODY WASTES AND SAVING SPECIMENS

Urine Analysis . . .

The kidneys separate waste liquid products from the blood and send them out through the excretory system. From the kidneys, they are carried through the ureters to the bladder and then expelled through the urethra.

The average output every day averages from a pint to 2 quarts, depending on the amount of fluids taken into the body, age, diet, temperature, and general condition of the patient. To keep a water balance, at least six to eight glasses of fluid are required every day. If this amount is supplied and other conditions are normal, between 1 quart and 1½ pints of urine will be the normal output. The output for a child will be less than that for an adult.

Usually a doctor requires an examination of the urine in a medical laboratory at the beginning of an illness or pregnancy or with the physical examination. Later, he will want an analysis for treating and watching the progress of the disease, as in the use of antibiotics (crystals show up in the urine) and diabetes mellitus (color tests show the severity of the disease).

Except for a few simple tests, it takes a skilled technician to examine the urine. Freshly voided urine is transparent and light amber or yellow in color. The different wastes in the urine give it its color. Blood will tinge it reddish. There should be a

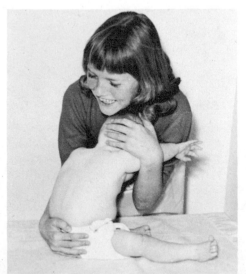

Holding an infant for spinal examination.

very small number of blood cells in the urine; a large number definitely means something is wrong.

Normal, fresh urine has a characteristic odor. As it stands, it changes and takes on an ammonia odor. Any change affects the results of tests, so it is sometimes necessary to add drugs to prevent change until the urine can be taken to the laboratory. The specimen that is not going to be examined right away should be kept in the refrigerator.

Nursing procedures in connection with urine are observing, collecting specimens, measuring the amount, and recording it. Every elimination is important for helping the doctor treat the patient. Also you must know when the urine is to be measured and when a specimen is required. Be sure not to dispose of it before it has been measured. Even if the patient can go to th bathroom, have him use the bedpan or urinal instead of the toilet. Always save a specimen that is in any way unusual.

How to Collect a Specimen . . .

The doctor may ask for specimens at different times of the day, but, if he just asks that a specimen of urine be saved for laboratory examination, save the first urine voided in the morning. If a patient is menstruating at the time, give her a basin of warm water, soap, and towel, and have her bathe the genetalia before collecting the specimen. Remember to tell the doctor about this, since a few blood cells will be in the urine. Use a small jar—a 4 to 6 ounce one will do—with a tight screw cap. Wash it out with hot soap and water, scald, and dry by turning it to drain over a paper towel.

EQUIPMENT:

- Specimen bottle.
- Label.
- Bedpan or urinal.

Steps in Procedure	Remember
1. Place the patient on the bedpan or give urinal and instruct to void.	If the patient feels that her bowels might move, ask her to urinate first. Remove pan, empty specimen and return pan to her.
2. Remove the bedpan or urinal when patient has voided.	

196

3. Pour at least 4 ounces of urine into specimen bottle.

It is important to have enough urine for all of the tests.

4. Label the bottle with the date, patient's name and the doctor's name.

A piece of paper fastened around the bottle with a rubber band is better than a sticky label that might come off.

5. Wipe outside of jar, screw lid on tightly and place in refrigerator until doctor comes for it.

The doctor may ask that it be delivered to his office or laboratory.

Observing the Feces . . .

Feces are the waste products left of the food we eat. The amount of feces expelled at any one time is called the stool or bowel movement. The process of expelling the feces is called defecation; the common term is to say the bowels move. Of course, bowels is another name for intestines.

The movements or "waves" of the intestines move the material along until it reaches the rectum. By this time, the feces is a soft mass; when it enters the rectum, it presses on the nerve endings in the wall and this stimulates the desire to defecate. Most patients feel this stimulus in the morning after breakfast. One bowel movement daily is normal but some people may have several a day or one every other day. The individual rate of digestion and removal of waste products affects a person's habit.

Normal feces are soft but formed. The matter is greenish brown, due to coloring from the bile. Yellow or light colored stool shows that the normal amount of bile is lacking. This may mean the liver is not working right or it may mean—especially in infants—that the bile is flowing into the blood stream instead of into the digestive tract, causing *jaundice*. This lends a yellowish tinge to the skin and eyes. Light colored stools may also mean *undigested* fat in the stool. When the stool is dark or "tarry," it may mean bleeding from the stomach or in the upper portions of the intestines; bright red means bleeding in the rectum or the lower portion of the intestines. The bright blood from the lower bowel will be on the surface of the stool, whereas the blood from the upper bowel and stomach will be mixed.

Both the color and the odor vary with different foods eaten, and are also affected by various drugs. Although the odor of the stool is generally characteristic, any unusual odor should be noted. It is important to notice *anything* unusual about the stool: Pus, mucus, worms, curds, or undigested food. They all are important to the doctor's treatment. Any stool that appears too unusual should be saved; he may wish to have laboratory testing done.

How to Collect a Specimen of Feces . . .

EQUIPMENT

- Clean bedpan.
- Glass jar and cover or scalded cottage cheese container.
- Wooden tongue blade or old spatula; aluminum foil may be wrapped around knife.
- Paper bag for used tongue blades or foil.

Steps in Procedure	Remember
1. Have him defecate in bedpan.	Every stool may be important.
2. Remove the bedpan to the bath- room.	
3. Put a small amount of the feces in the container; cover tightly.	Use tongue blade or spatula to transfer feces to container. Cover tightly to keep specimen moist.
4. Label with patient's name, type of specimen, date, and doctor's name.	
5. Keep warm until doctor comes, or take to his office.	

It is important that stool specimens are examined while still fresh. However, since the specimen must wait for the doctor to pick it up—unless he asks you to bring it to his office—it should be kept as near body temperature as possible. The container holding the specimen may be set in a bowl of hot water or placed on a shelf above the stove to be kept warm until it can be sent to the laboratory.

Vomiting as Part of Diagnosis . . .

Vomitus is not an illness but is a symptom. Its appearance and odor will tell something about the cause. Notice whether it contains undigested food; is odorless or has a sour smell; is liquid or in chunks. Does it contain mucus or pus? Does it have a greenish or yellow color? If so, this is material forced back into the stomach from the small intestines after bile has entered. If it has a fecal odor, it has come from even lower in the bowel and may be evidence of an intestinal obstruction. Vomitus the color of coffee grounds contains digested blood and means bleeding somewhere in the digestive tract—usually in the stomach.

There is a difference between vomiting and spitting up, which a baby *may do in* small amounts of milk after feeding. A child actually may vomit in an effort to get attention; some nervous patients bring food up after eating. An old or semi-paralyzed patient may hold food in the mouth for a while and then spit it out if his spirit is low or the effort of swallowing discourages him.

When vomitus contains anything unusual, a specimen should be saved for the doctor to inspect. Note the total amount, if you can. For the official specimen, use a small container with a tight lid and label as you would a urine or feces specimen.

Care of Patient . . .

If the patient is lying down, help him by raising his head slightly and holding a small basin under his chin. The curved emesis basin is used for this in the hospital but any small basin will do. Turn his head to the side, for complete draining, to prevent blocking air passages. If the patient is sitting up, hold the basin for him and support his head by placing your hand

Aiding a vomiting patient.

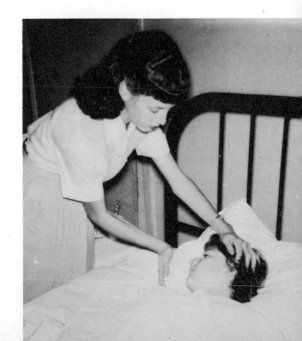

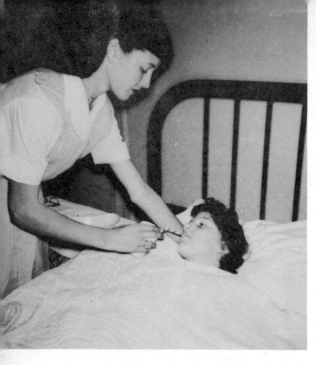

Make patient comfortable after vomiting.

on his forehead as he leans over the basin. A towel under the basin helps protect patient and bed but there may be no time for this. Of course, if your patient vomits frequently, you should put a plastic cover on the pillow before the pillow slip.

Remove soiled linen, if necessary. Wash patient's face and hands; rinse his mouth with water and a soda mouthwash or antiseptic solution. Make him comfortable. Open the windows to remove any lingering unpleasant odors.

THE USE OF X-RAYS

X-rays help to locate unusual tissue and bone conditions. Hard bone tissue contains mineral salts that the X-ray does not penetrate easily, so the shape is the main feature on the photo film. In order to show soft parts of the body, it is necessary to coat that part so that the X-ray will not penetrate it. To X-ray stomach or intestines, barium is generally used, mixed with water or milk, which the patient drinks. Films are taken at intervals thereafter to trace its progress through the bowel. It may also be given by rectal enema for examination of the rectum and lower intestine.

There are many forms of X-rays and fluoroscopy (instant X-ray; no permanent film). If you or a member of your family needs X-ray studies, the doctor will tell you how to prepare for them. For stomach or any intestinal studies, he will ask

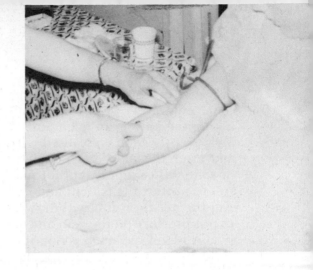

Inner forearm near elbow is the usual place for a blood sample.

that you eat nothing after dinner the evening before. For a broken bone, there is no other preparation than to support the affected part until you arrive at the hospital, clinic, or office. This will be discussed further under emergency care.

BLOOD ANALYSIS

Examination of blood cells under the microscope detects any variation from normal and the effects of disease or drugs. In diseases of the body such as anemia, some of the blood cells will change in size and shape. Also, a disease organism is found in the blood, such as with syphilis and malaria.

A full specimen of blood is obtained by inserting a needle into the vein of the patient and withdrawing the amount of blood necessary into a syringe. If only a few drops are required, the ear or finger may be pricked with a needle and a small amount touched to a glass slide.

Blood is usually taken from the inner forearm near the elbow. The veins here are close to the surface and easy to see, although other areas may be chosen. The patient lies on his back comfortably or may sit on a chair with his arm resting on a smooth surface. A tourniquet is applied around the upper

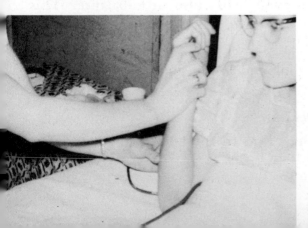

Patient bends arm to stop bleeding.

201

arm, tightened, and secured by a slip knot. The tourniquet prevents the blood from flowing back, and helps the vein become enlarged. More blood may be forced into the vein by asking the patient to open and close the fist several times. The area over the vein is cleansed with alcohol on cotton both before and after the needle is inserted. A protective sheet of plastic or some other moistureproof material may be placed under the arm to protect the patient and bed covers. A gauze sponge is laid over the needle as it is withdrawn, and the patient bends the arm to put pressure on the vein and stop the bleeding.

A blood specimen is obtained from an infant or very young child by puncturing the jugular vein in the neck. For a sick patient, the doctor or laboratory technician will come to the home to collect the blood specimen. Usually all that is necessary is for you to stand by to loosen the tourniquet or hold the specimen tube or bottle. He will probably have his own method of labeling, but ask him if you should prepare the label. The syringe and needle should be rinsed immediately, but the person withdrawing the blood should take care of this.

TEMPERATURE

The body produces heat when it "burns" nutrients; it gives off heat through the skin, lungs, and body discharges. When heat is produced and lost in proper balance, the body temperature is normal. If the temperature goes higher or lower, it means that the balance is upset.

Changes in Temperature . . .

Water intake, weather, clothes, activity, food, and emotions affect the body temperature. The body uses the water to regulate the heat. If you perspire, heat is lost because perspiration cools the body as it evaporates. If heat is lost rapidly, the body becomes chilly. If too little heat is generated in the body, the *normal heat loss* is great enough to cause an imbalance. This happens when a patient takes very little food and still loses heat through ordinary body processes.

The body temperature varies during the day; it is usually highest in the early evening and lowest about 4 o'clock in the morning.

Respiration and Temperature . . .

Food will not produce heat in the body without oxygen.

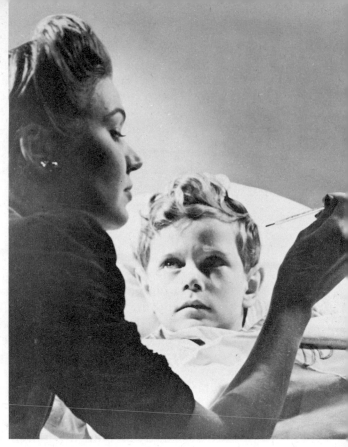

BECTON, DICKINSON AND CO.

Read the thermometer accurately, and be most cautious with children.

Oxygen is inhaled and carbon dioxide, excess heat, and other waste products are exhaled. Because of this definite relationship between the body temperature and respiration, they should always be considered together.

Abnormal Temperature . . .

Normal oral (mouth) temperatures vary slightly, from 97° to 99° F. Abnormal temperatures range from low grade fever at 100° to high fever at 103°-105° F. or over. The heat in the body rises to the fever range when the heat-regulating centers are stimulated. The most common cause of fever is the body's defense against infection and poisons. Treatment does not center on the fever but rather on the causes. The general nursing care of a patient with fever consists primarily of keeping him quiet and comfortable, by the use of ice bags, sponge baths, and plenty of fluids.

Fever may increase gradually or it may develop suddenly; it subsides the same ways. If the temperature falls very suddenly, it is called the *crisis*. It may cause shock, so the patient must be watched closely and heat applied if signs of shock appear.

Subnormal Temperature . . .

Oral temperatures below 98.6° F. are subnormal, caused by shock or loss of fluids through diarrhea, perspiration, vomiting or bleeding.

The general care is applying heat with blankets and hot water bottles; giving hot fluids.

Measuring the Body Temperature . . .

You measure the body temperature with a *clinical thermometer*. The temperature desired is of the body interior uninfluenced by clothing, outside moisture, or air; the thermometer is placed where it will be enclosed by body tissues, in the mouth, the rectum, the axilla (underarm), or the groin.

The most accurate is rectal. The mouth is the most convenient; there are large veins under the tongue that contribute free circulation of blood near the surface. However, in some conditions the mouth temperature is neither reliable or safe. *Never* take a mouth temperature if the patient is unable to keep his mouth closed, if the mouth is parched, inflamed, injured; or if the patient is unconscious, delirious, or mentally ill. It is not a safe method for *children*.

Take an axillary or groin temperature if the case prevents better methods. Naturally, you will consider the best and safest way to take the most nearly accurate reading.

The Thermometer . . .

A thermometer has a bulb, a stem through which the column of mercury flows, and the tip end. Pick up your thermometer by the tip end; hold it horizontally. The tube is hollow; the bulb is filled with mercury. Long lines show degrees from 94° to 110° F.; only even numbers are printed, since there is not enough room for all. Short lines show 2/10°. A red arrow marks normal temperature—98.6° F. Odd numbers and tenths are marked only in lines.

Read the thermometer; the mercury appears on the ridge between the numbers and the lines. Hold the marked side toward you; turn the instrument very slowly until you see where the mercury stops; note the number.

Clinical thermometers showing different types of bulb. The lower two are used in the mouth; the upper one is for rectal temperatures.

The mercury stays at the last reading until it is shaken down. Stand away from any furniture. Grasp the tip firmly. Shake with a snap of your wrist, till the reading drops to 95°.

Cleanse the thermometer, holding it by the tip, bulb down. Moisten a small piece of cotton or tissue with antiseptic solution; wipe toward the bulb and over it. Discard the cotton. Now repeat the cleansing, using plain water. It is now ready to take your patient's temperature. Always wait ten minutes if the patient has just had something hot or cold to drink.

"Clean" and "careful" are important words when using the thermometer.

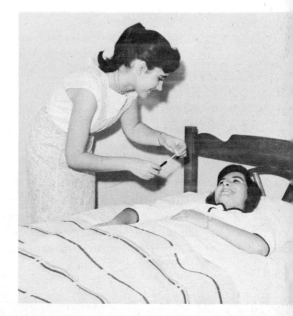

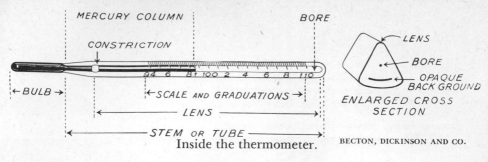

Inside the thermometer.   BECTON, DICKINSON AND CO.

HOW TO TAKE THE TEMPERATURE BY MOUTH

Steps in Procedure	Remember
1. Place the bulb of the thermometer in the patient's mouth well under the tongue, the glass tube coming out near the corner of the lips.	Tell him to close his lips but not bite down—to prevent injury from broken glass or poisonous mercury in a broken thermometer.
2. Leave the thermometer in place 3-5 minutes. Count pulse and respiration while taking temperature.	
3. Remove the thermometer.	
4. Wipe from top toward bulb with dry cotton or tissue; discard wipe in wastebasket.	Always wipe the thermometer before reading it.
5. Read thermometer.	Note the whole number and tenths. If there is doubt in your mind, shake the instrument down and take again.
6. Wipe the thermometer with cotton or tissue moistened with antiseptic and put it in container.	Prevents spreading infection; the thermometer is ready for use next time and in a safe place.
7. Record the temperature on your patient's record.	

HOW TO TAKE THE TEMPERATURE BY RECTUM

A rectal thermomter is like a mouth thermometer except for the bulb, which is chubby and shorter. Lubricant is used for rectal temperature so that the thermometer will slip into place without irritation; petroleum jelly is suitable. The normal temperature by rectum is about 1° higher (99.6°) than if taken by mouth.

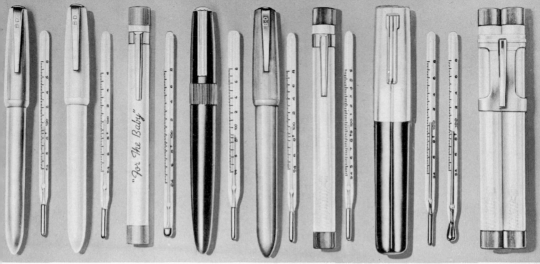

Several styles of thermometers and cases.

Steps in Procedure	Remember
1. Turn an adult patient on his side; turn an infant or small child on his abdomen.	So that the anus is visible.
2. Lubricate the thermometer.	Put the lubricant on a piece of clean tissue—never dip the thermometer into the jar of lubricant.
3. Insert the bulb about 1 inch, carefully.	Do not try to insert the bulb without first seeing the anal opening.
4. Hold in place for 3-5 minutes. Count pulse and respirations while taking temperature.	Some patients may be able to hold the thermometer in place.
5. Remove the thermometer.	
6. Wipe clean from top to bulb with clean dry cotton or tissue.	Always wipe thermometer before reading it.
7. Read thermometer.	
8. Wipe the thermometer with cotton or tissue that has been moistened with a disinfectant and put it in container.	Be sure to wipe thermometer clean of grease and fecal matter before cleaning and disinfecting.
9. Record the temperature on your patient's record.	

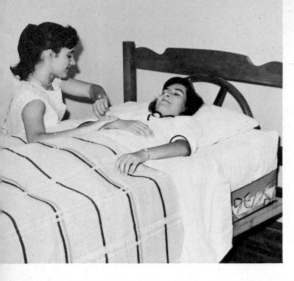

Take the pulse and the temperature together.

HOW TO TAKE AN AXILLARY OR GROIN TEMPERATURE

Temperature by axilla (underarm) or groin is necessary when it is difficult or impossible to take the temperature by mouth or rectum. The method is less reliable, so it is important to follow directions carefully. Normal temperature by axilla or groin is about 1 degree lower than by mouth .

Steps in Procedure	Remember
1. Explain to patient what you are going to do.	
2. Dry the underarm or groin by wiping with a soft, dry washcloth or towel.	
3. Place the bulb in the center of the armpit with the opposite end slanting toward the chest.	Be sure that thermometer is not touching gown or clothing.
4. Bring the arm close to the body. In the groin method, flex the thigh on the abdomen.	To insure as closed cavity as possible. If necessary, hold thermometer in place.
5. Leave thermometer in place for 10 minutes.	
6. Remove thermometer; read.	
7. Record the temperature on your patient's record.	Write "A" or "G" after temperature to show where it was taken.
8. Cleanse and store thermometer.	

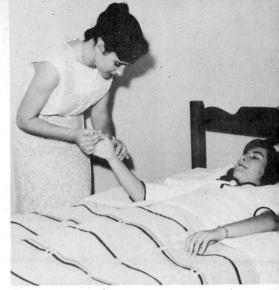

The pulse is usually taken in the wrists, using the radial artery.

THE PULSE

The pulse of the arteries is caused by the wave of blood flowing through as the left side of the heart contracts. Every beat sends a new wave toward the capillaries. Under this repeated flow and spurt system, the arteries expand laterally with each spurt. This feels like a slight vibration, which is the pulse. To take a pulse, place your fingertips over large arteries that lie close to the skin, across a bone with very little soft tissue around it. There are several points where the large arteries lie near the surface of the body:

Temporal—just in front of the ears.
Mandibular—on the lower jawbone.
Carotid—each side of the neck.
Femoral—in the groins.
Radial—in the wrists opposite the base of thumbs.

The radial artery is the one most commonly used to count the pulse, since it is conveniently located.

Anything that affects the action of the heart and blood vessels will affect the pulse. Heart disorders, activities, emotions, infection, hardening of the arteries, or hemorrhage will bring about pulse changes. The observations you make about the pulse give important information about the patient's condition. They are concerned with the *rate*, the *strength*, and the *rhythm* of the vibrations.

The Rate . . .

The pulse tells how *often* the heart beats. There are several factors that affect the rate: The size of an individual, the weight, and whether male, female, infant, child, or adult. The normal rate for an adult man is from 60 to 80 beats a minute. It is slightly higher for the woman—from 75 to 90. The infant pulse rate varies from 120 to 140 beats a minute and the rate for the child will be between infant and adult rates, according to size and age.

The pulse rate will increase with activity, such as violent exercise and physical work. Excitement, anger, and fear increase the rate. Some drugs increase it, as will fever or body misfunction. It increases in proportion to temperature rise—up 10 beats for every one degree. Most of these conditions raise the rate of the pulse only temporarily; an abnormal or continual rapid pulse may be a sign of heart disease, heart failure, hemorrhage, or other serious disturbances. If the pulse rate is chronically above normal, the condition is called *tachycardia,* which simply means "quick heart."

A continuously slow pulse rate is known as *bradycardia.* It may occur in convalescence after a long, feverish illness. In this case it is a serious sign, since it could mean brain pressure, cerebral hemorrhage, or heart block.

Some drugs decrease the pulse rate and are used in treatment of heart conditions.

Pulse Strength . . .

The strength of the pulse changes with the amount of blood in the arteries (volume), the strength of the heart contractions (beats) and the elasticity of the blood-vessel walls. It may be described as large, big, full, bounding; or small, weak, feeble, thready. The pulse may have both strong and weak beats within a minute; then the strength is said to be irregular.

Pulse Rhythm . . .

A normal rhythm has the same timing between beats. When the pulse sometimes skips a beat, it is called *intermittent.* The pulse also may be regular in rhythm but irregular in strength; that is, every other beat is weak. Sometimes you may be able to feel these weak beats; at other times they may be so weak as not to be felt at all. This may be very serious in heart conditions when the patient is on the drug digitalis. That is why you must practice to perfection the firm hold needed to feel a pulse, and give extra attention to the act in caring for the sick member suffering from a heart condition.

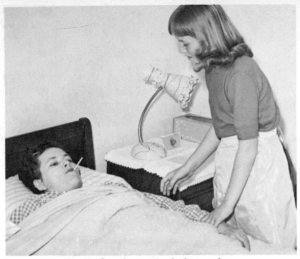
Press firmly to feel the pulse.

The Pulse Tells Us Much . . .

You can see why recognizing and recording qualities concerning the pulse are important. The pulse is a guide to the condition of the heart and circulation; in health and illness the pulse shows how well the heart is functioning. No variation is too slight to report. The doctor notes these signs and makes plans for further investigation to find the cause of the difficulty, because the pulse is only a symptom, not a disease.

TAKING THE PULSE

The only equipment you need to take the pulse is a watch with a second hand and a calm, quiet attitude. Some patients who are nervous anyway become very apprehensive at having the pulse taken.

Steps in Procedure

1. See that the patient's arm is resting in a comfortable position.

2. Place the tips of three fingers on the artery on the inside of the wrist just below the thumb and locate the pulse.

3. Press the fingers firmly enough to feel the pulse.

Remember

Do not hold the patient's arm up or flex the arm; this affects the pulse.

Never use your thumb, as it has a pulse of its own which may be confused with that of the patient. Place the forefinger between the tendons and the wrist bone to find the pulse.

Steps in Procedure	Remember
4. When the pulse can be felt plainly, look at the second hand on the watch and count the beats for one full minute.	This will give you time to note the quality of the pulse. Count again if you are not sure the first time.
5. Record the pulse on the patient's record.	Make notation for doctor if there is anything unusual about the pulse.

RESPIRATION

Respiration is the process that brings oxygen into the body and gets rid of carbon dioxide waste. It is a characteristic of all living things in one form or another. The body can live without food for quite a while, but for only a few minutes without oxygen. Oxygen is needed to keep the body cells alive; carbon dioxide accumulation kills them. Therefore it is most important to observe the respirations for any possible interference in the breathing process. The respiratory center in the brain controls and regulates the respiration in accordance with the amount of carbon dioxide in the blood. Injury to this center or to the nerves leading from the lungs will affect respiration; too little or too much carbon dioxide in the blood affects it. Any misfunction of the chest muscles and diaphragm will also affect breathing.

Normally, this process is automatic; you breathe without thinking about it. Of course, you can control your breathing to a certain extent by taking deep breaths occasionally.

The Rate . . .

The rate of breathing for an adult while sitting is from 14 to 18 times per minute; women have a more rapid rate than men. For the infant, the rate is about 40; for children it varies from 25 to 30 per minute. Excitement, exercise, pain, and fever increase the rate. It is characteristic in such conditions as pneumonia, heart disease, hemorrhage, and kidney inflammation. Certain drugs will increase the rate. Rapid respiration means that the body is trying to adjust to the cause in maintaining the right balance between oxygen and carbon dioxide. The body also tries to adjust by taking deeper breaths.

If a patient takes in and breathes out small amounts of air, the respirations are said to be *shallow*. When a person is making a definite effort to gasp in more oxygen and get rid of carbon dioxide, his breathing is *difficult*. Normal exertion may make breathing difficult for some people. There are various terms to describe the wrong kinds of breathing, but these will be sufficient at present.

Taking the Respiration Rate . . .

The only equipment you need is a watch with a second hand. The patient should be at rest. It is best to take the respiration after you have recorded the pulse; you can then keep your fingers on the patient's wrist and count the respirations without the patient knowing it. Breathing may be difficult for the patient if he knows his respirations are being counted.

Observe the rise and fall of the chest or abdomen. Count the respirations for one minute. Record the rate and anything unusual you might have noticed. Counting respiration is just as important as taking temperature and pulse. You may be the very first one to notice a change in the breathing rate which may be very important to your patient.

BLOOD PRESSURE

Because the heart forces blood into the circulation, there is always a certain amount of pressure in the arteries. The pressure depends upon the rate of the heartbeats and the ease with which the blood flows into the smallest vessels. The pressure is highest in the arteries nearer the heart, because they are few in number and feel the full force of the beat. The pressure in the *arterioles* is less because they are farther from the heart and less affected by its beat.

The pressure is at its height when the heart is contracted; this is called the *systolic pressure*. The pressure reduces as the heart relaxes and is at its lowest just before the muscle starts to contract again. This is the *diastolic* pressure.

Both pressure readings give important information. Normal systolic pressure for a man at rest is about 120, the diastolic about 80. Blood pressure increases gradually with age; this is probably due to the loss of elasticity and thickening of the blood vessels. Any pressure that is too far above the normal may indicate difficulty in the circulatory system.

Measuring Blood Pressure . . .

Blood pressure is measured by an instrument called the

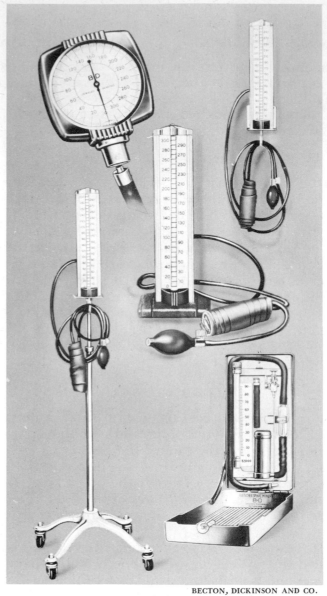

Different types of blood pressure apparatus. Manometer gauge is at upper left.

sphygmomanometer, more commonly referred to as the blood pressure apparatus. It is a cloth-covered bag, or cuff, with two rubber tubes extending from it. One tube is connected to a rubber bulb air pump; this bulb has a valve that can be opened and closed. The other tube is connected to a glass tube of mercury, the *manometer,* which is closed at the top and marked for blood pressure readings. The manometer is fastened securely in the case. Blood pressure is rated by listening to the heart-beats with a stethoscope, placed over the artery inside the bend of the elbow.

You may never be called upon to do this, but if a member of your family were suffering from high blood pressure or circulatory disturbance, knowing how to take the pressure might be valuable. When rating a blood pressure, you do two things at the same time: (1) listen to the heartbeat through the stethoscope and (2) watch the manometer. You listen for the first sound to appear while gently adjusting the screw on the air bulb so that the air will be released slowly. Then as the column of mercury falls, you listen for the change in the sound; it may be a definite hushing or it may be a gradual fade-out of the loud sound. You note the reading on the manometer at both these points; they are the two pressure readings.

Student nurses practice taking blood pressure while instructor watches.

BECTON, DICKINSON AND CO.

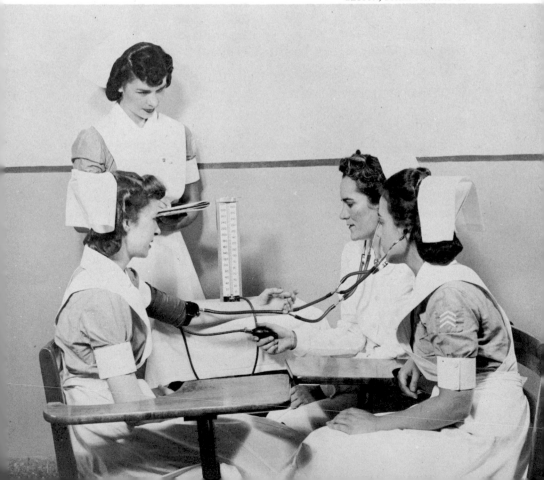

Take the pressure when the patient is at rest and quiet; physical exertion or emotional disturbances will cause a false reading. Prepare the patient, especially if a child, by explaining that the cuff on the arm may be tight for a second or two. Rest the manometer on the bedside table and have the patient move to the near side of the bed. Extend his arm, palm up, resting on the bed. Wrap the cuff, tubes down, around the upper arm. Wrap snugly but not too tight—about 2 inches above the elbow so that the area over the brachial artery is exposed. Close the valve of the air pump. Put the stethoscope tips in your ears; hold the bell in your left hand and place it over the artery. Press tightly, for it must be airtight in order for you to hear properly. With your right hand, pump air into the cuff by squeezing the bulb; do this until you cannot hear the pulse beat, and the column of mercury is at 160. You may have to go higher but this is usually where to start; listen and watch! Open the valve slowly—watch the column of mercury. The sharp, tapping sound will be the systolic pressure; the duller and softer sounds will be the diastolic. After you are certain of your reading (do the task over if you are uncertain), release all the air from the bag, loosen the cuff; remove, fold, and place it in the case. Record the blood pressure readings on your patient's chart.

- Five-year-old Tommy is going to the doctor's office for a pre-school physical. How would you explain this to him? List brief ideas.
- Little sister is just recovering from diarrhea; her morning stool has red specks in it. What will you do?
- Practice taking one of your classmates' temperature, pulse, and respiration. Why are these taken together? What association have they?
- Discuss the breathing process and the parts of the body involved, as well as the chemical exchange.
- When might you have to know how to take blood pressure?

NURSE'S RECORD

Morning care.

Evening care.

Changing body positions.

The back rest.

Relieving pressure areas.

Mouth care.

Baths.

The back rub.

Fingernails, toenails, and hair.

Bedpan and urinal.

Braces and other supports.

The hearing aid.

14: COMFORT AND HEALTH SKILLS

You carry out many nursing procedures for the patient's health and grooming and to make him comfortable. Many of them are done together, but each is complete in itself. Some procedures are grouped together because they are performed at the same time of day, though actually separate.

MORNING CARE

Early morning care is given before breakfast: Washing the hands and face, brushing the teeth, giving the bedpan and urinal, straightening the bed linen, taking the temperature, pulse, and respiration rate, and setting up the tray for breakfast.

Later morning care consists of bathing the patient, making the bed, caring for the hair, nails, dusting or tidying the unit

217

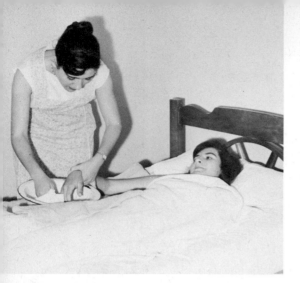

Wash patient's hands before breakfast.

and caring for the flowers (Chapter 5). Your patient's particular desires are given attention at this time, too.

EVENING CARE

Evening care, given for personal health and comfort, prepares the patient for supper and also for the night. Some procedures are done before supper, some afterward. Combinations include washing the face and hands, brushing the teeth, the back rub, combing or pinning the hair, giving the bedpan or urinal, changing the patient's position, adjusting the bed and bedclothes, adjusting the bedside table or tray.

There are other combinations which you will learn as you go along. You can see that you must learn to do these procedures separately first if you are to give satisfactory care. Know them well, so that your nursing care will not be spotty or uneven. You may be responsible for the entire, around-the-clock care of your patient. This book will try to prepare you for that responsibility.

How to Wash Your Patient's Face and Hands . . .

Wash a patient's hands and face before breakfast, with a bath, and before supper. It is also done at other times for sanitation and comfort.

EQUIPMENT NEEDED:
- Wash cloth.
- Face Towel.

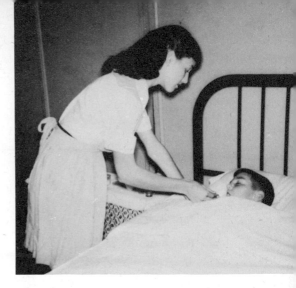

Spread towel under patient's chin.

- Soap.
- Basin with warm water.

Steps in Procedure

1. Bring all articles to bedside.

2. Spread the face towel beneath the patient's chin.

3. Wet and wring out the wash cloth; wrap it around the fingers.

4. Wash eyes gently from nose toward hairline.

5. Wash face, forehead, nose and cheeks.

Remember

Encourage the patient to help himself, if he is able.

Use separate corners of the washcloth for each eye. (Use no soap).

Use an S-motion around mouth and chin. Soap as desired. Use long firm strokes to stimulate circulation.

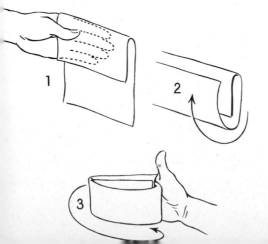

Easy way to wrap the wash cloth securely around the hand.

Steps in Procedure	Remember
6. Rinse in same order.	Be sure to rinse off all soap, since it tends to dry the skin.
7. Dry in same order.	Wrap section of towel around hand to prevent dragging.
8. Wet and soap cloth; wrap it around hand to wash neck and ears.	Wash far ear, front of neck, and near ear, using one continuous stroke.
9. Rinse cloth, as before; follow up with drying, as before.	
10. Put the basin and the soap dish next to the patient; put his hands in the basin. Wash, rinse, and remove basin. Dry.	Putting fingers in water is refreshing. Clean nails gently.
11. Apply lotion or oil, if desired.	

CHANGING BODY POSITIONS

Have you ever spent a few days or a week in bed? If so, what parts of your body began to get stiff or sore? You found that if you lay on your back too long, the muscles of the upper back and neck became stiff; the elbows became irritated from constant rubbing against sheets; the heels became numb and the legs felt tingly.

You change the patient's position for several reasons: to prevent muscle deformities, from lying in one position too long; to relieve pressures and strains to certain parts of the body; to stimulate circulation—particularly of the arms and legs—and for special procedures such as the back rub. If the doctor specifies a certain position, follow his order exactly; it may be a part of the therapy. Never use mechanical aids such as a board under the mattress, rolls, rings, or pads unless you have checked first with the doctor. These may be irritating and are reserved for special conditions.

Points to remember in changing the patient's position are:

Keeping the body in good alignment (no awkward positions to produce harmful strains).

The safety of the patient.

Resolving the patient's fears.

Proper handling to prevent pain or injury.

Your posture, in order to proceed effectively without undue strain to yourself.

Ask for assistance in aiding helpless or heavy patients.

If the patient can help, explain the exact procedure to him. Reassure him that he will not hurt himself if you act together. Think of your own posture. Standing close to the bed, advance one foot, for correct balance. Keep your back straight and bend forward from the hips. Most beds in the home are low, so, from necessity, the knees may also be flexed. However, be sure to keep the back straight, so that you use your strong thigh and hip muscles instead of putting the strain on the muscles of the back. Review postural stances in Chapter 2.

Below is a list of the equipment you will need for keeping the body in good alignment in the different positions that the patient assumes in bed. Specific mechanical supports are listed, too, but remember to check first with the doctor before using any.

Pillows—large and small.
Bed boards for a sagging mattress.
Rolled cotton blankets.
Folded towels for pads.
Cotton doughnuts for pressure (reddened) areas.
Rubber rings.
Sandbags.
Bed cradles (a wire frame to hold the covers off the feet).

HOW TO TURN THE PATIENT TOWARD YOU

Steps in Procedure	Remember
1. Stand on the side of the bed to which the patient is to be turned.	Advance one foot; shift your weight from the leg in front to the other as the patient is turned.
2. Firmly, but gently, grasp the far shoulder with one hand, and the hip with the other.	Keep your back straight.
3. Turn the patient slowly toward you.	
4. Move the pillow to a comfortable position under the head and shoulders.	

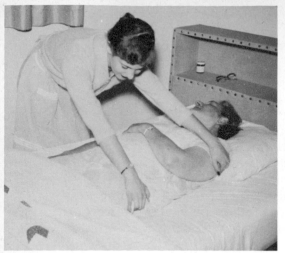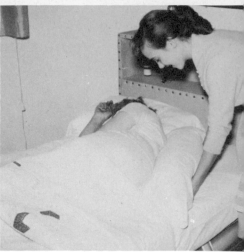

Proper stance and grip for turning patient toward you (STEPS 1 AND 2).

• Put pillow under head and shoulders (STEP 4).

Steps in Procedure	**Remember**
5. Flex the patient's upper arm and support it with a small pillow if this is comfortable for her.	
6. Flex the patient's upper leg and support it with a pillow. Leave the lower leg extended.	
7. Support the back with a pillow.	Protect the pillow with a plastic case, if necessary.
8. Support the abdomen with a small pillow, if desired.	This is especially helpful to the patient who has had recent surgery to the abdomen.
9. Leave the call bell within patient's reach.	

Support flexed upper leg with pillow (STEP 6).

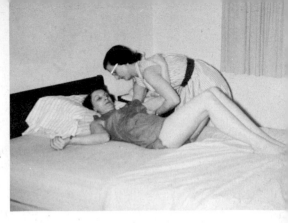

Preparing to turn patient away from you (STEP 2).

HOW TO TURN THE PATIENT AWAY FROM YOU

Steps in Procedure	**Remember**
1. Assist patient to flex knees.	Explain to patient, allowing him to help as much as possible.
2. Slide one arm under patient's back until the hand is beneath far shoulder blade.	
3. Place other hand as far as possible under patient's hips.	
4. Drawing arms toward you, gently roll patient away from you to a comfortable position on side.	His back will be toward you.
5. Pull lower buttock (hips) toward you and support back with a pillow.	

HOW TO MOVE A PATIENT UP IN BED

Steps in Procedure	**Remember**
1. Remove all but one pillow.	Never try to lift a heavy patient alone. Seek assistance.
2. Move remaining pillow up to head of mattress.	Explain to patient what you are doing and how he can help.
3. Ask patient to flex knees and press feet firmly against the mattress. Ask him to grasp hold of the head of the bed with both hands.	The more the patient flexes his knees, the further he will be moved up in bed.

Steps In Procedure

4. Stand with one foot advanced and face the head of the bed.

5. Place one arm under patient's neck and shoulder; place your other arm under his thighs.

6. Give the signal, "Now." Patient pulls with arms, pushes with feet, while you help him to lift toward the head of the bed.

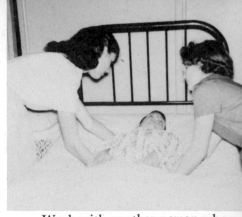

Work with another person when gentle movement is necessary.

If the patient is extremely heavy or unable to help himself, another person works with you:

Steps in Procedure	Remember
1. One person stands on each side of the bed, facing the head.	
2. Place one foot ahead of the other so that the weight may be shifted as the patient is moved.	
3. Place one arm under the patient's neck and shoulder and the other arm under the thighs.	Keep the forearms on the bed so that the weight of the patient is not shifted.
4. Have your helper in the same position and, at the signal, "Now," slide the patient gently toward the head of the bed.	Always work *in unison*.

The Bed . . .

The Gatch bed is the standard hospital type bed. It has a mechanical back rest, knee and foot adjustments. These may be rented from hospital and surgical supply houses for use in the home. The bed is higher, making it easier to give adequate nursing care and service. Because of expense, substitutes may be used for movable parts.

Back rest made of 2 three-quarter pillows with 2 regular pillows laid across them.

THE BACK REST

Your patient may be permitted to sit up for short periods; this does not always mean that he is allowed out of the bed, but he may be raised into a sitting position with adequate support. Using the Gatch bed, you merely turn the bed crank. The knees may also be raised slightly to help the body assume its natural curves, lessening strain and fatigue.

Substitute back rests are: A triangular pillow, canvas stretched over a frame, a card table, or even a cardboard box, cut to fit into the angular space at the head board. When none of these is available, pillows will do: Place two pillows crosswise, one on top of the other; place two more pillows lengthwise, reaching from the headboard top to a comfortable position against the patient's back. The *knees* may be supported with a rolled cotton blanket or pillow.

Specific Parts of the Body . . .

Many patients lie on their back most of the time; some stay in this same position through long illnesses. It is important that they be protected against developing body deformities. To prevent backache, or spastic muscles from developing in the legs, a small pillow supports the lower or lumbar part of the spine; two pillows support the head and shoulders; a pillow or a box at the foot of the bed supports the feet in normal position by pushing the toes forward.

Parts of the body may be elevated or lowered to improve circulation, to relieve congestion, or to stop bleeding. Pillows are used to elevate a leg or arm. If the treatment includes moist heat or cold compresses, the pillows are protected with rubber or plastic covers. Sandbags are often used for firm supports, when required. The patient will help indicate when such extra firmness will give him relief.

Methods of elevating parts of the body.

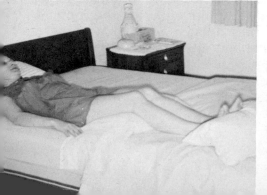
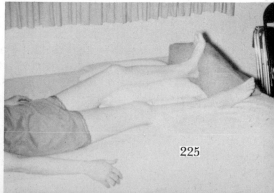

The inflated rubber ring.

B. F. GOODRICH RUBBER CO.

The arm or leg is supported along its whole length when being moved. It is moved slowly and gently. *Phlebitis,* or inflammation of a vein, usually occurs in the leg. *Move the leg as little as possible* to prevent dislodging the blood clot from the inflamed area. If the clot should become dislodged and obstruct an artery that supplies a vital organ—the lungs, heart or brain—it could bring almost instant death.

RELIEVING PRESSURE AREAS

Continuous pressure on any part of the body over a long period of time makes a patient uncomfortable; besides producing a fatiguing effect, pressure hampers the circulation and may cause sores, called *decubiti.* They occur most frequently at the base of the spine, the elbows, heels, shoulders, hips, knees, and back of the head. In short, they appear wherever bones are prominent under the skin. Very old or very feeble patients, or others with impaired sensation, are most likely to become sore at pressure areas, because they go unnoticed.

How to Use Rubber and Cotton Rings . . .

The doughnut-shaped cotton ring is used to help relieve pressure on various parts of the body. It must be made to fit the part for which it is intended, for if bulky or too loose it gives little support. Rubber rings inflated with air or sponge rubber pads are also used. These aids must never take the place of good nursing care to the back. Smooth, dry sheets, frequent back sponging with alcohol or cream rubs, and turning the patient at intervals are the key answers to relieving pressure areas; such care should not be neglected.

The Rubber Ring . . .

EQUIPMENT NEEDED:

- Rubber ring.
- Pillowcase.
- Air pump or small piece of gauze.

Steps in Procedure

1. Loosen the metal valve.

2. Pump or blow air into the ring until it is one-third full.

3. Tighten the valve.

4. Put the ring into the pillowcase and fold excess under the ring.

5. Take to bedside. With one hand under the patient's lower back, help him to raise the hips, then slide the ring under him, so that:

   • The pressure area is over the hole in the ring.

   • The metal valve is at the side of the patient.

   • The pillowcase is tight and smooth.

Remember

Use air pump if available, or cover the valve with two layers of gauze and blow air into the ring.

Rubber is irritating to the skin and causes perspiration. Never use ring without a cover.

If the patient is unable to lift himself even with your assist-

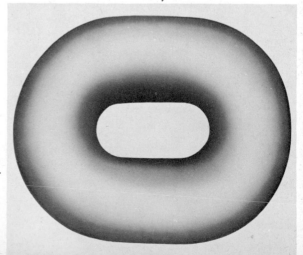

Latex foam cushion.

B. F. GOODRICH RUBBER CO.

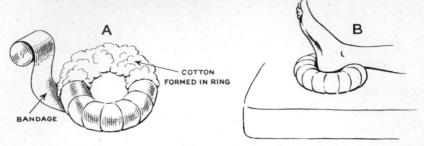

COTTON FORMED IN RING

BANDAGE

A

B

ance, help him to turn toward you so that he is on his side; place the ring in position and roll him onto it. Then the hand may be slipped under his lower back and the pillow easily adjusted into correct position. Using the ring for the first time may tire the patient; for this reason, it is wise to keep a record of both the *time the ring is in use* and the *appearance of the pressure area* for the doctor.

The Cotton Ring . . .

EQUIPMENT NEEDED:

- Cotton.
- Bandage, 1 or 2 inch.
- Adhesive tape.

Steps in Procedure	Remember
1. Make a firm roll of a length of cotton (about 1 inch in thickness)	
2. Shape the roll into a ring the size you will need. Overlap the ends of the cotton to hold it firmly.	The cotton ring is used under the patient's heels, elbows, head, or shoulders.
3. Fasten the overlapping ends with adhesive tape.	
4. Wind bandage smoothly around the ring, taking the roll of bandage through the hole each time as you wrap.	
5. When ring is completely covered with bandage, fasten end of bandage with a piece of adhesive tape.	
6. Place the ring, or "doughnut," in position by slipping it under the sore or pressure area.	The spot should be over the hole and lifted from the area of friction.

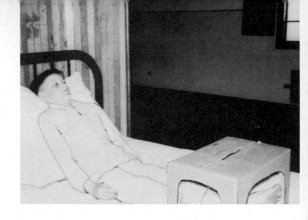

Bed cradle made from cardboard box.

Although making the cotton ring as described here assures you of the desired size, a *quick ring* may be had by rolling a sock all the way to the toe.

The Bed Cradle . . .

The bed cradle is a frame used to keep the bedclothes from touching all or parts of the patient's body. The most common is the wire cradle. The *narrow cradle* is used over an arm or leg, or both legs. The *wider or longer cradle* is used for the whole body. A temporary home cradle may be just a suitably shaped cardboard box or carton from which the top and two ends have been removed, or *chicken wire* shaped as a tunnel over the part.

A cradle is used in the treatment of fractures, burns, or wounds. Some cradles, to supply heat to certain parts of the body, have attachments for electric light bulbs. *Safety note:* Care must be taken not to touch the connections with wet hands, and to protect the patient from contact with the cord.

Since the cradle holds the bedclothes away from the body, the patient may become chilled. In this case, arrange a cotton blanket loosely over the part inside the cradle; if the cradle is used over the legs, make the foot of the bed first, tucking the top covers firmly under the mattress, making a square corner. This holds the warm air in and protects the patient from drafts.

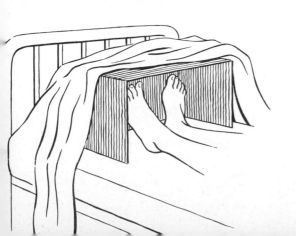

Make cradle high enough to avoid cramping.

MOUTH CARE

The patient's teeth should be brushed before breakfast and after each meal. If he does not have the energy or interest to brush his own teeth, it is up to you to see that this important feature is not neglected. Many disease organisms enter the body by the mouth. Food particles lodging in the crevices between the teeth cause decay and breath odor. Dental authorities tell us that fermentation occurs more rapidly and much sooner than supposed, with sugar being turned into acid a few minutes after it has been eaten. So if teeth cleaning is to be effective, it must be done immediately after eating—no matter when or where we eat. Poor teeth and other mouth conditions which interfere with eating habits are harmful to a person's health as a whole. Good habits established as part of a routine during illness will stay with your patient after he is well.

If the patient can brush his own teeth, be sure that he knows *how* to do it. Consider his choice of dentifrice and mouthwash, since some tastes may be nauseating to him. The accepted toothbrush by most dentists consists of two rows of medium stiff bristles, six tufts to a row, widely spaced so they enter all depressions. The brushing surface should be flat and the handle straight.

A child's brush should have a smaller handle than an adult's and five pairs of tufts instead of six. If your patient is a child who is just learning how to care for the teeth, here is an opportunity to teach him the right method:

1. First brush the biting surfaces of the back teeth. In this way the stiff brush can reach the crevices before the bristles are softened.

2. Place the sides of the bristles against the gums, pointing away from the biting surfaces. Roll the brush so that it sweeps from the gums to the biting surface—three to six strokes at each location. Brushing across from left to right or right to left will not reach the crevices and cannot clean effectively. It may cause wear of exposed tooth surfaces and make the teeth sensitive at the gums.

3. Be systematic. Get into the habit of brushing the various groups of teeth in the same order each time, so you won't miss any.

4. The *best times* to brush your teeth are right after eating, before bedtime, and on arising.

5. Keep your toothbrush in a dry place, clear of other

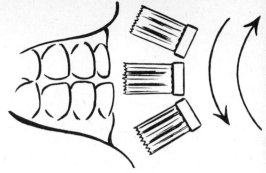

Toothbrush position.

brushes. Bristles will keep drier and stiffer if you have two brushes and alternate them in use.

How to Brush the Patient's Teeth . . .
EQUIPMENT NEEDED:

- Small basin.
- Face towel.
- Toothbrush.
- Cool glass of water.
- Dentifrice.

Steps in Procedure

Remember

1. Spread the towel under the patient's chin if he is unable to sit up.

Adjust the patient's position as allowed. Encourage him to brush his own teeth if he is able.

2. Turn the patient's head to one side and place the basin under his chin.

3. Moisten toothbrush and add the dentifrice; give to the patient. Assist him to brush the teeth.

Instruct him as necessary.

4. Raise the patient's head; give him a mouthful of clear water.

Hold the basin close to the chin so that he may spit the rinse water into it. If *mouthwash* is used, caution him against swallowing.

5. Repeat step 4 until the mouth is well rinsed.

6. Remove the basin, wipe the mouth and chin.

Allow patient to do this if he is able.

7. Rinse the toothbrush under running water, rinse equipment.

Mouth Care for the Very Ill or Helpless Patient . . .

High temperatures, mouth breathing, malnutrition, and other conditions may accompany illness and tend to cause cracking and drying out of the lips which, in turn, may lead to infection. Discomfort and more serious conditions can often be avoided by good nursing care. The mouth should be kept moist by frequent cleansing and rinsing. Drying of the lips can be controlled by applying emollients, such as mineral oil or petroleum jelly, which are common household articles.

EQUIPMENT NEEDED:

- Tray.
- Two face towels.
- Heavy tweezers.
- Cut gauze.
- Basin (curved, if available).
- Stick swabs.
- Glass with equal parts of mouthwash and water.
- White oil, cold cream, or petroleum jelly.
- Small glass covered with gauze.
- Spatulas.
- Drinking tube, if possible.

Steps in Procedure

1. Adjust patient's position with head to side, unless otherwise indicated.

2. Protect patient's chest and pillow with face towel.

3. If a toothbrush cannot be used, make a swab of gauze with edges turned in and wrapped around tweezers.

4. Moisten with mouthwash and clean around teeth, gums, roof of mouth, and under tongue.

5. Have patient rinse mouth with mouthwash, if he is able to use drinking tube.

Remember

Gauze swab can be used (STEP 3).

6. Apply lubricant to lips with a stick swab.

7. Discard soiled articles and re-stack tray.

8. Boil basin, tweezers and glasses every day.

9. Tray may be kept on the bed-side table or on top of dresser.

Cleanse mouth at least three times a day.

Care of the Mouth When Patient Wears Dentures . . .

Many people are sensitive about wearing dentures; treat this as though it were natural, and give them privacy if they desire to care for their dentures alone. When the dentures are left out of the mouth, put them in a container with enough water to cover them and place them out of sight—in the bed-side table or dresser drawer.

If your patient is in the habit of taking out his dentures frequently, be careful when fluffing pillows for giving treatments lest they fall to the floor; dentures are expensive. If you find that they are not worn constantly, look for irritated areas in the mouth; the dentures may fit poorly. Poor-fitting dentures often result in poor nutrition. The person neither eats the proper foods nor chews well the food he does eat.

Encourage your patient to keep his dentures fitted and to care for them intelligently. Food particles lodging beneath them cause disagreeable odors as well as being detrimental to the health. If he is able to care for them himself, he will want to do it in the bathroom where they may be washed and rinsed under running water. If your patient is bedridden then you take over care of the dentures and mouth.

EQUIPMENT NEEDED:

- Basin.
- Hard toothbrush.
- Dentifrice.
- Glass with mouthwash and cold water.

Steps in Procedure   Remember

1. Give the patient a piece of tissue; ask him to remove his den-

Steps in Procedure   **Remember**

tures and place them in the basin.

2. Wash the dentures under running water with a firm brush and dentifrice, giving care to crevices.

   Avoid washing dentures over sink with a wide drainage outlet, since they may slip from fingers and fall into drain.

3. Rinse in cold water.

4. Place the dentures in a piece of tissue or a glass of cold water until ready for use.

5. Return to bedside and assist patient to rinse mouth with mouthwash or water.

6. Give dentures to patient.

   Always moisten dentures before patient puts them in his mouth, if they have been in tissue.

- You have been caring for your grandmother who has recently returned from the hospital after pneumonia. She is crabby and does not want to move off her back. Explain to her the reasons for changing body position.

- Your small brother had his tonsils removed yesterday morning and does not want to brush his teeth today. What substitution can be made here?

- What is a decubitus? How may you help prevent it? Demonstrate how to make a cotton ring.

- Place a book on the desk; pretend you are moving a patient up in bed, using the book on the desk for weight. How do you place your feet? Are you bending from the hips? If the desk is low, are you remembering to bend the knees?

- Using a cardboard box, make a back rest for a youth bed.

- How would you care for a partial dental plate? Suppose your patient repeatedly removed his dentures, what would you do?

BATHS

The main purpose of any bath is cleanliness, but to the sick person, the bath is much more than this. It adds to his general comfort; it stimulates circulation, thereby promoting muscular relaxation and adding to mental good feeling. There are three kinds of cleansing baths: The tub, the shower, and the sponge bath in bed. The patient's condition decides which kind is safest and best for him.

How to Give a Tub Bath . . .

A tub bath can be very important to the patient who has spent a long period in bed. It is a highlight showing that he is gaining strength and independence in another step toward being well. It should not be rushed; should be given when most convenient for the patient and the family. Always get the doctor's permission to give a tub bath when you have been giving bed baths to your patient. If you are in doubt about any condition, consult him; if your patient shows excessive exhaustion, a skin rash, or pain, call it to his attention.

It is up to you to judge how much help your patient needs with the tub bath. With small children, you must remain throughout, but some adults or teenagers may feel embarrassed by having someone standing by; you may have to remain just outside the bathroom door. In this event, remember—although the bath is for the patient's comfort, you are responsible for his safety. It is better not to try the tub bath until the patient can *safely* carry on alone.

EQUIPMENT NEEDED:

- Bath towel.
- Washcloth and soap.
- Bath blanket (cotton).
- Bath mat (or towel).
- Bathrobe and slippers.

Steps in Procedure	Remember
1. Check the temperature of the bathroom.	See that it is free from drafts.
2. Place chair beside the tub. Place all equipment on chair; mat on floor.	
3. Fill the tub one-third full of warm water.	Temperature of the water should be approximately 105° F.

Steps in Procedure   **Remember**

4. Help the patient to put on bathrobe and slippers and walk to bathroom.

   Place mat or heavy towel on bottom of tub.

5. If necessary, help patient undress and step into the tub.

   Use bath blanket to protect from drafts or chilling.

6. If necessary, give assistance to bathe (especially back).

   If you leave the patient to bathe himself, call or check frequently. Never lock the bathroom door!

7. Help patient from tub and assist with drying as necessary.

   Keep covered with bath blanket to prevent chilling.

8. Assist in putting on gown, bathrobe, and slippers.

9. Assist patient back to bed. Make comfortable.

   Always provide for rest after bath. If patient is chilly, give a warm drink.

10. Clean tub, remove soiled clothing, and return articles used; this is a courteous consideration and precaution if other members of the household use the same bathroom facilities.

The Shower Bath . . .

When the patient is allowed to have a shower bath, prepare and assemble all needed articles near the shower. To be safe, the shower should be equipped with a floor mat, a wall soap dish, and a hand rail. Caution the patient against standing on one foot. Place a small stool in the shower if necessary; if he gets tired or weak, he may sit down. Regulate the temperature of the water before the patient steps into the shower and always stay within calling distance. Be ready to assist as needed.

How to Give a Sponge Bath to a Bed Patient . . .

The bed bath is usually given after breakfast, but when the patient is in his own home, a time should be chosen when it will be convenient to the patient and to the family. Although most of the activity is centered in the bedroom, you will need access to the bathroom to replenish your supply of water and for emptying your basin. The bath is given in such a way as to give desired effects with the least amount of exertion to the patient, without chilling. Some patients do not look forward to the bed bath because of embarrassment or because they are afraid to move. It is up to you to reassure your patient that he will be covered with a bath blanket, the door of the room will be closed, and you will help him move slowly and gently. His refreshed feeling after the bath should help influence him.

There are times when even the bed bath may be harmful— as in cases of bleeding, after certain operations (back conditions), or when the patient is in a weakened condition. Under the guidance of the doctor, decide what the patient can do and when, thereby sparing him extra motion. Try to make him as comfortable as possible throughout the procedure; for instance, if he wants two pillows under his head and an extra blanket for covering, comply with his wishes.

EQUIPMENT NEEDED:

- Bath basin containing hot water.
- Bath blanket.
- Bath towel.
- Face towel.
- Washcloth.
- Patient's gown.
- Extra bath towel.
- Soap.
- Rubbing alcohol.
- Talcum powder.
- Clean linen, as necessary.

Before starting bath . . .

1. Give mouth care.
2. Offer bedpan.
3. Determine what clean linen is needed.
4. Tell the patient about the bath.
5. Check the temperature of the room; close windows if necessary.
6. Place a straight back chair beside the bed for linen.
7. Clear the bedside table and cover it with newspaper for protection.
8. Fill the bath basin with warm water slightly more warm

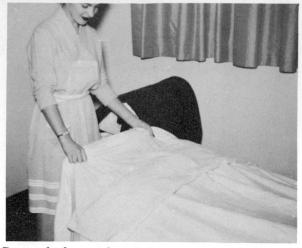

Proper bed procedure before sponge bath (STEP 1).

than for bath since it will cool slightly while you are readying patient. Place it on bedside table, with soap and other toilet articles.

Steps in Procedure	Remember
1. Remove spread and blanket; fold over back of chair over clean linen. Put bath blanket over patient. Go to foot of bed and pull out sheet.	
2. Move patient over to near side of bed; remove gown or pajamas.	Do not allow patient to chill.
3. Remove all but one pillow, unless this is uncomfortable for patient.	
4. Place towel across patient's chest.	
5. Have patient wash face, neck, and ears, if he is able.	Encourage patient to help himself, but do not insist. Watch for signs of fatigue.
6. Uncover the arm nearest you. Place towel lengthwise under it. Wash, rinse, and dry.	Make a mitten of washcloth.
7. Do other arm same way.	Allow patient to put his hand in basin of water, as in washing.

8. Put the towel over the chest; fold the bath blanket down. Wash, rinse and dry the chest.

With women patients, check the areas under the breasts for irritations. Wash well around to the back.

9. Put towel over chest; turn back bath blanket to waist. Wash, rinse, and dry the abdomen, working so as not to expose the patient.

Wash well around to the back, over pubic area, and upper thighs. Patient may be able to do this.

10. Allow patient to rest while you change bath water.

Cover patient well to prevent chilling.

11. Turn the patient on his side or stomach; turn the bath blanket back; put towel around the back. Wash, rinse, and dry back.

Turn him away from you. Tuck the towel against the back to protect the bed, from the hairline to the buttocks.

12. Rub the back. (See page 241.)

Give attention to pressure areas.

13. Turn the patient back.

14. Put the towel under the leg nearest you; wash, rinse, and dry the thigh and leg.

Tuck the blanket back to the fold where the thigh meets the abdomen, careful not to expose the patient.

15. Put towel under the foot; place basin on towel and place foot into basin; wash foot, remove basin, and dry foot.

Put newspaper under towel in case water spills over.

Washing chest and abdomen (STEPS 8 AND 9).

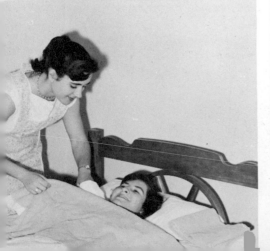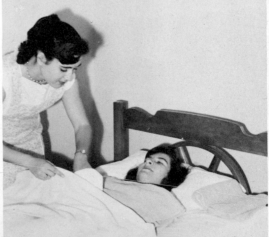

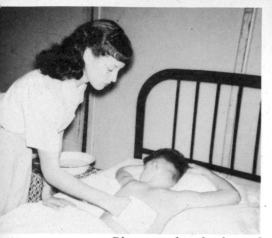
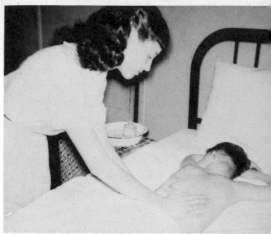

Place towel on back; wash (STEP 11). Rub back (STEP 12).

Steps in Procedure	Remember
16. Repeat for the other thigh, leg and foot.	
17. Put the towel under the buttocks. Wash the genitalia if patient is unable to.	The patient may do this if he is able. Place the basin, soap and cloth within reach. Leave the room if he wants you to do so.
18. Remove the bath towel.	
19. Help patient into gown or pajamas.	
20. Comb hair, protecting pillow with towel.	
21. Trim nails as needed.	
22. Make bed.	
23. Remove and clean all equipment; return to straighten bed unit.	

Washing leg and foot (STEPS 14 AND 15).

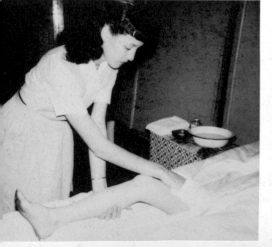
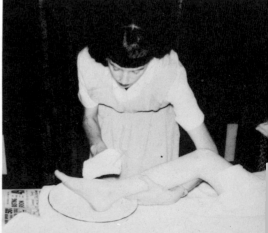

Patient in position for back rub. Notice two large towels sewed together to serve as cotton blanket.

Partial Bed Bath . . .

The patient should have a partial bed bath on days when he does not have a complete bath. It consists of bathing the face and hands, the underarms, the back and buttocks, and the genitalia. If he is able to do this for himself, assist where needed. Make sure he has privacy; check the temperature and change water as needed.

THE BACK RUB

After bathing and drying the back, it should be massaged or rubbed. A back rub is refreshing, relaxes tired muscles, and stimulates circulation, so it is especially helpful over pressure areas to prevent sores. Rub the back with the morning bath and as a part of the evening care, but you may add this touch to the final part of any treatment, giving comfort and relaxation. Warm your hands and the alcohol to prevent chilling the patient. Be sure your nails are trimmed and heavy rings removed to rub effectively without scratching.

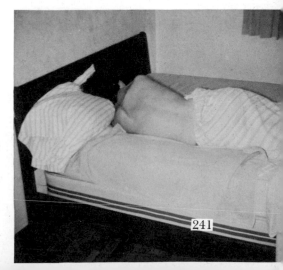

Position on the side is also acceptable for back rub.

241

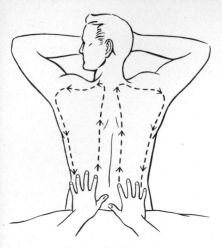

For the greatest benefit, massage as the arrows indicate.

Steps in Procedure	Remember
1. Help the patient to turn on side with back toward you and the body near enough to the edge of the bed so that you can reach comfortably.	If patient lies on the abdomen, a pillow under woman's hips relieves pressure on breasts and favors relaxation.
2. Remove the gown or roll it up over the shoulders.	Stand with one foot advanced, bending the knees slightly. Massage evenly, using the palms of your hands in a stronger stroke in the upward motion. Rub dry.
3. Pour a small amount of alcohol on your hands and apply it to the back.	
4. Dust powder on your hands. Continue massaging motion.	Now exert firm pressure about neck and shoulders, using a circular motion—move the muscles under the skin.
5. Give special attention to reddened or pressure areas.	Observe and note any skin condition.
6. Replace or adjust the gown; adjust bed, straightening bottom sheets to check sheet wrinkles. Make patient comfortable.	Always leave bedclothes neat.

FINGERNAILS, TOENAILS, AND HAIR

Care of the Fingernails . . .

Nice hands are pleasant to see as well as a health protection.

Brittle, broken nails may be the result of improper diet or fever. Emotional tensions may cause nail biting. A torn cuticle is a site for infection which may be transferred to the mouth. Dirty fingernails also carry germs.

Essential daily care consists of cleaning beneath the nails and pushing back the cuticle. The best time to do this is after the morning bath when the cuticles are softened. Soap and water loosen dirt and soften the cuticle temporarily. A daily application of an emollient or oil to the nails and cuticles will help keep them soft and in good condition. Use an orange stick to clean under the nails and push back the cuticles. The stick is blunt and smooth and is less likely to injure the nails than a metal file. Trim hangnails with cuticle scissors.

If your patient is able to care for his own nails, encourage him to do so and prepare for him the following; stand by to assist if needed:

Small basin one-third full of warm water.
Soap.
Hand towel.
Nail brush.
Orange stick.

Care of the Toenails . . .

Although cutting nails is not always advocated, if the patient's toenails are thick and hard, it would be better first to cut them, then file them smooth. Cut them straight across; this prevents scratching of the other leg and snagging on the bedclothes. It prevents ingrown toenails. If the corner of the nail shows a tendency to grow into the skin or causes painful pressure, force a small piece of cotton under it. When you notice corns or callouses, apply a small amount of cold cream or petroleum jelly to soften them; gradually scraping off the dead skin will remove them entirely.

Caring for finger nails is important for health, and it helps keep the patient pleasantly occupied.

Sometimes a patient will start an infection by cutting at a corn or callous with a razor blade. Should you notice an infection of one of the toes, cover it with clean gauze and call it to the doctor's attention.

Care of the Hair . . .

Brushing and arranging a woman's hair is a pleasant part of the daily care for her. To the chronically ill patient, appearance is all important especially if her condition is such that she can do little for herself. It stimulates the circulation and distributes oil so as to give it a sheen. It keeps the hair in good condition, makes her feel better, and gives you a chance to note the condition of the hair and scalp.

It is not necessary to spend long periods of time fussing with your patient's hair, but it is important to arrange it becomingly and in a manner that will not become disarranged immediately. For instance, long hair may be braided; short hair may be bound with ribbons. If your patient is able to comb her own hair, encourage her. This is good for her morale and will keep the muscles of the neck and shoulders in tone.

The Shampoo . . .

The patient should have his or her shampoo in the bathroom. Choose a chair or stool low enough that the head rests against the rim of the bowl. The patient may lean back against the bowl or face it, bowing well forward. If he chooses this latter position, give him a towel to hold over his eyes. The most convenient method is to use a spray; adjust the temperature and test before using; proceed as for usual shampoo. If the patient becomes faint, stop the procedure immediately, wrap his head in a towel, and get him back to bed. After he is rested, finish with a bed shampoo. You will need help for this! Instructions are omitted here because "experience is the best teacher."

BEDPAN AND URINAL

To Give and Remove a Bedpan . . .

You can help to establish regular health habits by offering the bedpan at certain times every day. The best time for bowel elimination is after breakfast but, if the patient already has an established habit, keep the time convenient to his needs. Assure the patient of privacy; protect the bed to avoid soiling.

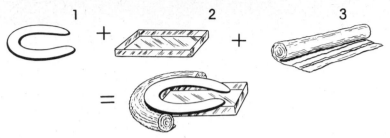

You can make a bedpan from a toilet seat, a deep cake tin, and a towel rolled and placed under the seat to keep it in raised position. This device requires extra care when removing, to prevent tipping.

EQUIPMENT NEEDED:

- Bedpan (warmed with hot water and then dried).
- Bedpan cover.
- Protective cloth.
- Toilet paper.

Steps in Procedure	Remember
1. Turn back the bedclothing at the side.	
2. Put protective pad or towel under patient's hips.	If bed protection is necessary.
3. Put the bedpan beside the patient. Instruct the patient to	Raise head of bed or place pillows in manner comfortable to patient.

To give the bedpan, turn back bedclothes; place pan beside patient. (STEPS 1 AND 3).

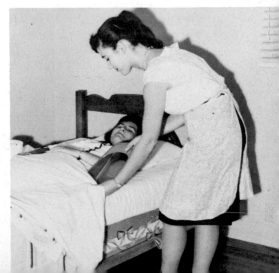

Steps in Procedure   **Remember**

  draw up the knees; put one hand under the hips and help him lift; slip the bedpan under him with the other hand. Adjust it in comfortable position; replace bed covers.

4. Put the toilet paper and call bell within patient's reach.

Tell patient to ring immediately when he is finished. Stay within hearing distance. Never leave a very ill patient alone.

5. Return when patient calls; cleanse patient if he is unable to do it.

6. Remove pan and cover it.

7. If necessary, turn patient on side to complete toilet.

8. Straighten top bedding, make patient comfortable.

Bring equipment to bedside for patient to wash hands. Leave him clean, dry, and comfortable.

9. Note contents of the bedpan before emptying. Empty, wash thoroughly, and return pan to proper place.

To Give and Remove a Urinal . . .

The urinal is used for the male patient. There is also a wide-mouth type of urinal used for the female patient who is unable to move her hips frequently, such as when an elderly woman suffers a fractured hip.

Cover it as you do the bedpan when bringing it to the patient's unit. Help the patient place it, if necessary. If condition permits, elevate the head slightly, advise the patient to flex knees a bit to prevent tipping the urinal. Place equipment for handwashing before leaving the room. After use, rinse the urinal first with cold water, then with hot water. Before pouring out the urine, notice if there is anything unusual about it.

The Commode . . .

Some patients have great difficulty in using the bedpan or

Portable toilet or commode.

urinal. If such a patient is able to go to the bathroom, the doctor may permit him to do so, or a commode may be placed at the bedside or brought into the patient's room when needed. The same precautions for getting a patient up should be observed when assisting a patient to use a commode. Stay with him if he is in a weakened condition. Provide for cleanliness afterward.

BRACES AND OTHER SUPPORTS

When supports of metal framework or plaster are made removable by the use of adjustable straps or other devices, they are called *braces*. They are made for, and adjusted to, the individual person. Braces are used in treatment of patients who have had polio, fractures, and other bone problems. Once the doctor or the brace maker has shown you how to correctly adjust and remove, put the brace on and off correctly, be sure to follow instructions to the letter. Never adjust a screw or buckle without instruction.

When you put on or remove a brace, give the necessary support to the part of the body affected. Handle the brace carefully; if you bend or twist it out of line, it may injure the patient. Keep the brace clean; be careful if the brace has straps that you do not get them wet, for they could dry out and crack. Inspect all parts before use to make certain the brace is in good shape and safe; see that it gets repair if needed. As the patient progresses, the braces may need adjustments; call these to the attention of the doctor. If the patient has a weight gain or loss, it will affect the brace.

If the patient is able, encourage him to put on his own brace. Watch, and give assistance when needed. See that he does not "favor" the injured part, as this sometimes creates other conditions. If he balks against wearing the brace, explain that caution and following instructions now may pay off later on. If you are unable to convince him, call it to the attention of the doctor.

THE HEARING AID

A hearing aid operates on an electric battery connected to a small sound magnifier inserted into or behind the outer ear. This magnifier can be regulated to "tune in" the sounds. Modern hearing aids are small, inconspicuous, and easy to wear. Some people are sensitive to being made conspicuous by this wonderful aid, so proceed cautiously if you are aware that your patient feels this way. Older patients, unwilling to try new "contraptions," may have to be persuaded anew each time the hearing aid is brought out. Arrange the hair, if patient is a woman, so that it is well covered. Persist in encouraging the patient.

When caring for a hearing aid, follow the manufacturer's instructions. Keep the instrument clean, but be careful not to get any of the connections wet. If the aid needs adjustments or a new battery, take it to the agency from where it was bought, if possible. Be sure that the ear is clean before inserting the hearing aid, as wax may cause an impaction. Report anything unusual to the doctor.

- What is included in the patient's daily cleansing care?
- Your patient is feeling better today. She thinks she will take a tub bath rather than let you give her a bed bath. What will you do?
- You have been nursing your mother back to health from a bad attack of flu. Her hair is quite oily and smells musty; she has been out of bed for one-half hour yesterday and today. Should you give her a shampoo?
- Why do we use an emery board for the nails?
- What are the benefits of a bath? What types are there? Describe each.
- What does a back rub do for your patient? What does a reddened area tell us? What precautions should be taken?
- Before proceeding with the bed bath, what should be done?
- Why is it important to observe the contents of the bedpan and urinal? If the urine has a tinge of red, will you call the doctor immediately or wait until his next visit to tell him? Should you save the urine for him to see?
- When are braces used? What special precautions should you observe in their handling and use?
- Discuss the practical use of the hearing aid.

NURSE'S RECORD

Heat applications.

Cold applications.

Enemas and other rectal treatments.

Protective nursing measures.

Surgical supplies.

Drugs and administration.

Antiseptics and disinfectants
in common use.

The antibiotics.

The antihistamines.

15: TREATMENTS AND MEDICATION

HEAT APPLICATIONS

Heat applications are used frequently to treat disease and to relieve aches and pains. You are familiar with use of heat for the comfort of the patient; when your patient is chilly, place a hot water bottle, hot brick, or electric pad by his feet. Since heat must be fairly intense to produce reasonable effects, there is danger of burning the patient. Most of the time, other than for immediate relief for yourself or a sick member of the family, you should have permission from your doctor for prolonged applications of heat. That is, you may apply heat as emergency treatment to raise the temperature of the body for chills and shock, but you do not apply a hot water bottle to relieve a pain in the abdomen without first consulting your doctor. Since one of the uses of heat when applied locally is to soften and accumulate pus, it might result in a ruptured appendix, if infected.

Heat to the Body . . .

Heat dilates the blood vessels in the skin, resulting in more blood and warmth to the area. It stimulates the circulation and the sweat glands, thereby helping to remove poisons from the body. It relaxes tense muscles (spasms) and stimulates relaxed, inactive ones (as with polio). It may be used to promote softening the pus in an abscess and to bring blood from another area by applying it to a local part. For example, applying heat in the form of a foot bath draws blood from upper areas of the body.

Precautions . . .

Precautions to prevent burns from uses of heat are necessary for these reasons:

• The nerves of the skin are easily numbed and, after repeated or prolonged periods of heat, the patient may not feel the pain of a burn.

• Some parts of the body are especially sensitive to heat, such as the inner surfaces of the arms and thighs.

• Lowered body resistance makes the body more sensitive to heat.

• Infants, small children, and elderly people with thin, fair skin are more sensitive to heat.

• Semi-conscious or feverish patients cannot always tell you when heat is too intense.

• If he has circulatory trouble, the patient may be unaware of too much heat. This is true in diabetics.

The action of heat depends upon whether it is applied moist or dry, the temperature, how long it is applied, the part of the body to which it is applied, and the condition of the patient.

Dry Heat . . .

Think of all the reasons why he might be sensitive to heat. Decide what degree of heat is safe. You will not want to use the same degree of heat for baby brother that you would for mother's feet during a cold. Use heat enough to accomplish its purpose but within the safety range. It is recommended that you check all water temperatures with a *bath thermometer;* while this is not common in the home, you may use an oven heat gauge or make the water just bearable to your fist. Check on the heat application frequently; if you find that the skin is too reddened, adjust the temperature.

How to Apply a Hot Water Bottle . . .

A hot water bottle is used to relieve aches and pains, to increase the circulation, or to warm an area. Since some people can stand more heat than others, tell your patient that you have tested it, but he must tell you how it feels to him. Never put a hot water bottle against the skin directly; wrap it in some heavy cloth, such as flannel or a bath towel.

EQUIPMENT:

- Hot water bottle.
- Towel for cover.
- Pitcher of hot water.
- Thermometer, if available.

Steps in Procedure	Remember
1. Pour hot water into pitcher.	Boiling or hot water poured directly into the bag ruins the rubber.
2. Test the temperature of the water in the pitcher.	Temperature should be from 120° to 130°, or make the water bearable to your fist.
3. Pour water into bottle until it is about one-third full.	Bottle that is more than one-third to one-half full will be heavy and uncomfortable.
4. Expel air by squeezing the upper half of the bottle.	

Expelling air (STEP 4). Hold the neck at an angle.

251

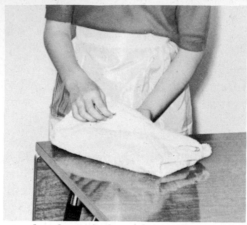

Cover the hot water bottle entirely with a soft towel before applying it.
(STEP 8).

Steps in Procedure	Remember
5. Screw in the stopper securely.	Inspect the washer before screwing in stopper.
6. Wipe bottle dry.	
7. Turn it upside down for leaks.	
8. Wrap in towel and pin.	Never apply bottle without a cloth or towel.
9. Apply as ordered.	With pins and neck away from patient's body.

Return to your patient frequently to test the heat of the bottle and the appearance of the skin under the bottle. When the bag is no longer needed, empty it and hang upside down to drain and dry. Put the stopper where you can find it, or tie it to the bag. When the bag is dry, screw in the stopper, allowing air in the bag to keep the sides separated. Store it in its usual place.

Hot bricks, potatoes, or salt bags heated in the oven can be used effectively. The salt bag retains heat well, is light, and can be used on the softer parts of the body. Of course, the heat of these substitutes will have to be regulated by the towels used for wrapping.

The Electric Heating Pad . . .

There is an advantage to using the modern electric heating pad. It can be controlled to a certain extent. For prolonged use, this affords more danger of burning if the skin becomes numb and insensitive to heat. Also, if the electric wiring gets wet, it may cause a short circuit in the pad. Most pads are now available with rubber covering; *never use moist dressings with an ordinary heating pad.*

Before you apply the pad, connect it to the electrical outlet; turn the switch to *high* to see if it heats promptly. Turn it off and disconnect it from the outlet. Cover it with a towel—not a light pillowcase—connect it to an outlet near the bed, adjust to proper temperature, and apply. Check it and the area beneath it frequently for overheating.

Moist Heat . . .

Moist applications heat the skin more quickly than dry applications, since water is a better conductor of heat. Wring hot water packs or compresses out firmly. Because moist compresses soften and weaken the skin, use them for promoting drainage—for example, to bring a boil "to a head." This means the pus and infectious materials are softened enough to be removed. Moist heat is more penetrating than dry heat, so is more effective to relieve pain in the deeper tissues.

Gauze compresses, wool or flannel packs, poultices, and baths are used to apply moist heat. You may also use old toweling cut into small pieces. The doctor prescribes the kind of application and how it is to be used. It may be for long periods or short periods with frequent changing to keep them hot. He may prescribe a mild antiseptic solution, such as salt or boric. The compress should be large enough to cover the affected area; it need not be sterilized unless there is a break in the skin.

Before you lay the compress on, explain to the patient that it loses heat from the time it is wrung out until it touches the skin. Explain also that you apply it gradually to remove any fears he may have about being burned.

EQUIPMENT:

- Basin containing prescribed solution.
- Electric plate.
- Compresses of suitable size.
- Two clamps or tongs.
- Cotton applicators.
- Petroleum jelly.
- Oilcloth or plastic wrapper.
- Paper bag for wastes.

Steps in Procedure	Remember
1. Put solution in basin on hot plate; heat.	Heat until it steams.
2. Apply petroleum jelly to the area to be treated with the applicators, as a protection against burning.	
3. Wring solution out of compresses with tongs or clamps.	Wring as dry as possible.
4. Apply the compresses to the area.	Apply gradually.
5. Lay the piece of plastic or oilcloth over it immediately.	
6. Change every 2 to 3 minutes, to keep uniform heat.	
7. Remove compresses at end of prescribed time.	Usually applied for 20 to 30 minutes.
8. Dry the skin.	Leave towel over area for a few minutes to prevent chilling.

NOTE: You can make a small, hand wringer from a pair of large, wooden spoons and a piece of canvas or pillow ticking, about 16 inches long and 10 inches wide. Make a 2-inch hem at the ends of the canvas or ticking, and run the handle of a spoon through each hem.

To use this wringer, place it over a bowl. Lay the compress in the center of the wringer. Pour hot solution over the compress; then squeeze out excess fluid by turning the spoons end-over-end in opposite directions, with enough outward pull to keep the wringer taut.

How to Give a Hot Foot Bath . . .

A foot bath may be given to relieve congestion in the head and to stimulate the circulation. It naturally affects other parts of the body by drawing excess blood from those parts. That is why a hot foot bath—usually a mustard type—is given to ease painful menstruation or headaches and to relax muscles. The doctor will prescribe the temperature and the length of treatment. Use either plain or salt water. If mustard is used, the temperature of the water should not be above 105°, because mustard increases the action of heat on the skin.

The patient may be sitting in a chair, supported in a sitting position in bed, or in a lying position. The room should be at a comfortable temperature. If cool, see that the patient is protected from chilling.

EQUIPMENT:

- Foot tub or basin.
- Pitcher.
- Bath thermometer, if available.
- One or two bath towels.
- Rubber or plastic protective sheet and cover.
- Cotton blanket.

Steps in Procedure

1. See that your patient is in a comfortable position.

2. Fill the tub or basin about ¾ full of hot water or solution ordered.

3. Check the temperature of water with a bath thermometer. Water should be slightly warmer than body temperature.

4. Take basin to bedside where other materials are all ready.

5. Cover the patient with the cotton blanket; fold the bedclothes back to the foot of the bed.

6. Adjust the protective sheet under the tub.

7. Flex the patient's knees, support with folded pillow, so that patient's feet will be flat in the tub.

8. Put the tub on the bed be-

Remember

Explain to patient what you are going to do.

Slip your arm beneath the ankles;

255

Steps in Procedure

yond the patient's feet. Lift the feet into the tub.

9. Cover the legs and tub with blanket, to hold the heat in.

10. Bring hot water to bedside and add to tub if needed.

11. When the soak has lasted the required amount of time, remove feet from the tub.

12. Remove the tub from the bed; dry the feet and wrap in cotton blanket to keep the heat in for a while.

13. Remove the protective sheet. Pull up bed clothes.

14. Remove and clean equipment.

15. If a chart is being kept, record treatment and length of time, or any unusual reaction, such as dizziness or nausea.

Remember

slide the tub up. Lower the feet gradually.

Pour hot water near the edge of tub; keep your hand between steam and patient's foot.

Lift as before; straighten the legs and rest the feet on a towel.

How to Give a Sitz Bath . . .

The Sitz bath is given to relieve abdominal or pelvic congestion, for retention of urine, and to relieve pain after rectal surgery. At home, it is given in the bathtub; the patient sits in the tub with the water covering the thighs. The temperature of the water is about 105° to 120° F., depending on the patient. The bathroom should be comfortably warm to prevent chilling. Also a shoulder towel or small blanket should cover the upper part of his body during the bath. If he becomes uncomfortably warm during the bath, an icecap or cold compresses may be applied to the head. Watch him carefully, so that he may safely be helped out should he become excessively tired—especially after surgery.

Remove the patient from tub at end of the prescribed time and clean up the bathroom.

The Steam Inhalation . . .

The steam inhalation provides warm, moist air for breathing. Medications are added to the water because they are sometimes soothing to inflamed membranes of nose and throat. Steam inhalations relieve swelling, congestion, inflammation, and pain of the throat and the upper respiratory tract. Tincture of benzoin or menthol are the medications most commonly used.

Some means of concentrating the steam on the patient is necessary. Also provision must be made to keep the solution steaming hot. In the home, a tea kettle with a rubber tubing and a funnel attached to the spout, and an electric plate, may be used. A pitcher containing hot solution, with a paper bag slipped over the top, may be substituted. Cut a hole in the bottom of the paper bag for the patient's nose and mouth. The patient sits in bed and holds the pitcher in his lap in a basin. You may slip a large towel over his head and the pitcher, to enclose the steam. Hot solution must be added if the inhalation is longer than ten minutes.

COLD APPLICATIONS

Cold is applied to contract the blood vessels—to relieve pain, as in a headache, or to lower a person's temperature. Cold slows up the activity of bacteria in infections and directs the blood to another part of the body.

Used over long periods of time, it can burn the skin. Cold should be removed for intervals to prevent this. If the skin looks white, spotty, or the patient complains of numbness, remove the application. Cold is applied by icecaps, compresses, and baths.

A paper bag with the end cut out carries steam medication to the patient.

• Large towel over the patient's head retains the vapors.

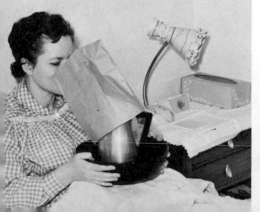 

How to Fill and Apply an Icecap or Collar . . .

You may apply an icecap in an emergency, such as for a nosebleed, but its use is usually prescribed by the doctor.

An icecap is a flat, oval, or round rubber bag with a leak-proof, screw-in top. An ice collar is a narrow rubber bag curved to fit or tie easily around the neck. These bags are used after surgery on the throat, mouth, or teeth to check and prevent bleeding. The regular ice bag may be applied to the abdomen to calm intestinal movement as for appendicitis, to relieve pain in engorged breasts, to relieve swelling, and somtimes to relieve pain over the heart area in heart disorders.

EQUIPMENT:

- Icecap or collar.
- Towel to cover, and safety pins.
- Crushed or chipped ice.

Ice collars.

B. F. GOODRICH RUBBER CO.

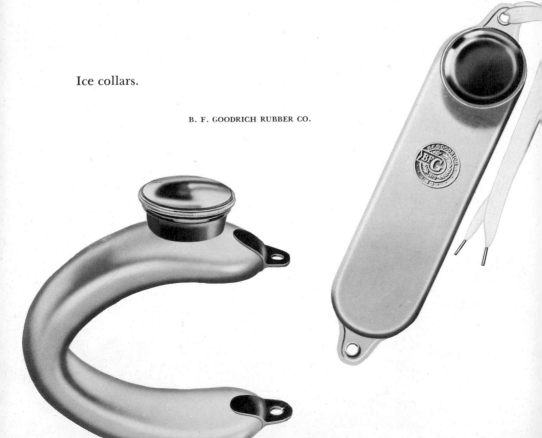

Standard icecap.

B. F. GOODRICH RUBBER CO.

Steps in Procedure	Remember
1. Fill icecap or collar half full with crushed ice.	Pieces of ice should not be bigger than size of walnut.
2. Press out air with one hand and screw on metal cap with other.	Flatten the icecap and push down on it to expel air.
3. Wipe cap dry.	
4. Test for leaks.	
5. Wrap in towel; pin.	Never apply icecap without cover.
6. Apply to affected part with metal part turned away from patient's body.	Icecap is never applied to skin constantly hour after hour. Watch the skin for bluish-white effect.
7. Remove as prescribed. Remove cover, drain, dry. Fill with air before screwing top on for storing.	

B. F. GOODRICH RUBBER CO.

English round icecap.

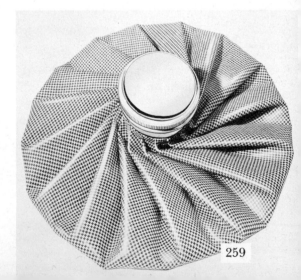

How to Apply Cold Compresses . . .

Compresses should be made of something light and porous such as gauze. If the solution prescribed is other than plain water, then a small bowl of that solution may be put into a larger basin of ice. *If it is applied to stop infection,* each compress must be discarded after it is removed.

EQUIPMENT:

- Basin of water and pieces of ice.
- Compresses.
- Paper bag for wastes, if any.
- Protective sheet or covering.

Steps in Procedure

Remember

1. Put compresses in basin of cold water.

Use two compresses, to have a cold one ready each time.

2. Wring out and apply.

Wring out with hands; apply quickly but carefully. Do not cover; the heat of the body will warm the compresses rapidly.

3. Wring out next compress; remove the last one and apply the new one. Change about every two minutes.

4. Remove the compresses when the prescribed time is reached, usually from 20 to 30 minutes.

5. Make the patient comfortable.

6. Remove and care for equipment.

7. Record treatment and time required on patient's chart.

How to Give a Cold Sponge Bath . . .

A cold sponge bath is given most commonly in the home to help reduce fever. When you call the doctor for a sick member of the family, you should always have the temperature to report. In the case of infants and children, he may prescribe a cold sponge until he can arrive. He will tell you the solution (usually water, but sometimes a small amount of alcohol, is added to stimulate evaporation on the skin), how long to give it at one time, and how often it should be repeated. He may ask that the sponge bathing be continued until the temperature drops to a certain degree. If the patient develops a weak, rapid pulse, bluish lips and nails, and chills, stop the procedure at once and apply heat.

Explain the procedure to your patient. Explain how rubbing the skin and cool water will cool his blood and will make him more comfortable.

EQUIPMENT:

- Basin of water from 70° to 85°.
- Basin of chipped ice.
- Bath thermometer, if available.
- Cotton blanket.
- Face towel.
- Bath towel.
- Two washcloths.
- Hot water bottle and cover.
- Icecap with cover

Steps in Procedure	Remember
1. Cover the patient with cotton blanket; fold top covers back to foot of bed.	
2. Remove patient's gown.	
3. Add ice to the water and bring it to prescribed temperature, usually from 70° to 85°.	
4. Take the temperature, pulse and respiration.	Check the pulse frequently throughout the bath; watch the color of the skin.
5. Place the hot water bottle at the feet; the icecap to the head.	
6. Sponge the face and dry it.	

Steps in Procedure	Remember
7. Rub the arm briskly, to bring the blood to the surface.	
8. Sponge the arm.	Plenty of water on the washcloth. Begin high on the neck and go down the outer surface of the arm; begin in the axilla and go down the inner surface of the arm.
9. Sponge the other arm.	As above; rub first.
10. Sponge the chest and abdomen.	Keep changing the cloths as you work.
11. Sponge each thigh and leg.	
12. Turn the patient; sponge the back.	
13. Replace gown. Tuck cotton blanket about patient; draw up top covers.	
14. Remove and care for equipment.	
15. Take the patient's temperature.	It may be as high as when you began; reaction may not have set in as yet.
16. Record on patient's chart.	Note duration of bath.
17. Take patient's temperature ½ hour later.	This is the "drop" temperature. If the temperature is still high, call the doctor and report it.

There are certain conditions that discourage reactions to the cold sponge bath. Persons who are *exhausted* or *excessively nervous* react unfavorably. *Old people* who have hardening of the arteries should be watched carefully. Sometimes *children* react unfavorably, especially if there is a rheumatic tendency.

ENEMAS AND OTHER RECTAL TREATMENTS

Enemas are given to remove fecal material from the colon and rectum, to relieve intestinal distention, to give medications, or to supply the body with fluid or nutritive materials.

The cleansing enema is given to cleanse or wash out the larger bowel before and after surgery, delivery, X-ray examinations, or to relieve constipation. The *habit* of taking enemas to relieve constipation is not recommended, since this condition should not be allowed to occur in the first place. The enema serves as an artificial stimulus. Roughage in the diet and plenty of fluids will help do away with enemas for elimination purposes.

How to Give a Cleansing Enema . . .

The most common solution for the cleansing enema is warm water to which a small amount of soap has been added. You can make a solution of soapsuds by swishing a cake of mild soap around in the water until the solution takes on a milky appearance, or you may add mild soap flakes. The suds on top of the solution should be removed so that no air bubbles will be drawn into the bowel. The amount of solution will be prescribed by the doctor, along with the type and method of administration.

Combination hot water bottle and home enema bag. • Rubber enema bag, tubing with clamp, enema tips and douche nozzle.

B. F. GOODRICH RUBBER CO.

 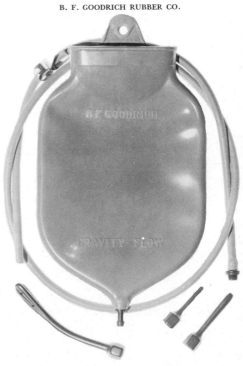

The most common device used in the home is the combination *enema bag* and fountain syringe. It consists of a rubber bag with a bottom outlet. It is made in one piece without seams and has a wide opening at the top for easy filling. It has about 3 feet of rubber tubing that may be attached to the bottom of the bag, and a rectal tip which is attached to the end of the tubing. A metal clip turns the flow of solution on and off. For infants, the small enema bulb with hard rubber tip is also used. More recently, for modern convenience, the *disposable plastic container* attached to a smooth plastic rectal tube has been devised. The rectal tube is soft enough to eliminate the danger of piercing the rectal lining and just long enough to place the solution into the rectum for good retention, insuring complete cleansing.

Technique Using Fountain Syringe . . .

EQUIPMENT:

- Fountain syringe, tubing, rectal tip, clamp.
- Solution as prescribed.
- Jar of lubricating jelly.
- Protective sheet and cover.
- Pole with hook for hanging bag. (May be floor lamp, wall hook, or hanger over edge of door.)
- Toilet paper.
- Bedpan and cover.
- Cotton blanket.
- Paper bag for wastes.

How to Prepare the Equipment . . .

Steps in Procedure	Remember
1. Close the clamp of the tubing; check bag, tubing and tip for leaks.	
2. Prepare the solution about a temperature of 105° F.	It will feel slightly warm when poured over the wrists; prepare about 1½ pints; more if necessary.
3. Place a small amount of lubricant on a piece of tissue for use at the bedside.	Never dip the rectal tip in the jar of lubricant.

How to Prepare the Patient . . .

Steps in Procedure	Remember
1. Explain to the patient what you are going to do.	The cleansing enema is to make him comfortable; to make the bowels move; the warm solution runs into the rectum and softens the feces.
2. Reassure the patient.	The solution is warm; you will give it slowly; he can tell you if it runs too fast.
3. Encourage his co-operation.	The effect will be better if he holds the fluid for from 5 to 10 minutes, he will be on the bedpan so there is no danger of accidents.
4. Cover patient with cotton blanket; fold back top covers.	
5. Turn the patient on his left side near the edge of the bed, with the right knee flexed.	
6. Slide the protective sheet and cover under the hips.	

The Enema . . .

Steps in Procedure	Remember
1. Hang the enema bag about 18 inches above the bed level.	
2. Lubricate the rectal tip about 3 inches.	Place used piece of tissue in bag for wastes.
3. Open the clamp; allow a small amount of fluid into the tube to clear out any air; close the clamp.	Air interferes with the effects of the enema as well as giving pressure.
4. Lift the upper buttocks with the left hand; insert the tip into the anus.	Tell the patient what you are doing; insert the tube slowly.
5. Open the clamp; allow fluid to run in slowly.	If the solution flows too fast, regulate flow by pinching off tube with thumb and finger.

Steps in Procedure	Remember
6. When the required amount of solution has run in, close off clamp; pinch off tube near patient's body and remove tip.	If patient complains of pain or cannot hold solution, pinch off tubing to stop flow for a minute or two.
7. Disconnect the rectal tip and place it in the waste container.	Keep soiled tip from contaminating other equipment.
8. Put patient on bedpan; place toilet paper and call bell within reach.	Raise to sitting position; make comfortable. If doctor gave permission to use bathroom, patient may do so.
9. Care for the equipment.	Rinse the bag and tubing; rinse the rectal tip in cold water and wash in warm, soapy water.
10. When the patient has finished expelling enema, assist with use of toilet paper if necessary.	Be alert for patient's bell in case he becomes fatigued.
11. Empty bedpan, cleanse and store.	Notice contents.
12. Wash patient's hands; make him comfortable; open window if necessary, to air room.	
13. Record the treatment on patient's record. Record time and type of enema, the form and color of feces, and the patient's reaction.	

If your patient is unable for some reason to lie comfortably on his side, he may lie on his back or abdomen. If he is unable to retain the solution, he may be placed on the bedpan for the enema.

Using Disposable Plastic Container and Rectal Tube for Self-Enema . . .

1. Lubricate the flexible rectal tube with the enclosed lubricant, or petroleum jelly.
2. Remove cap from container and attach tube.
3. Assume the knee-chest position or lie on the left side.

4. Gently insert the tube into the rectum.

5. Squeeze container to expel solution.

6. Retain the solution until the urge to defecate occurs; a minimum of retention time is five minutes.

7. Discard tube and container.

8. Go to bathroom.

The Flatus Tube . . .

The rectal tube is sometimes used to help the patient to expel excess gas in the lower bowel. A hard rubber tube should be used. Insert the tube as for an enema; then place the outer end in a container of some kind to prevent soiling of the bedclothing. A jar with a paper towel or hole in the lid will be satisfactory. Remove the tube at the end of the prescribed time— usually 10 to 20 minutes. Note the results on the patient's record.

How to Insert a Rectal Suppository . . .

A medicated suppository is a cone-shaped or long, slender object with a base of cocoa butter or glycerin. When a suppository is inserted into the rectum, the heat of the body melts it. The medication is absorbed through the rectal mucosa. Medicated suppositories are used to soothe the rectum and to relieve pain, as with hemorrhoids.

Soap and glycerin suppositories are used to stimulate the bowel, especially for infants.

Steps in Procedure

1. Lubricate the suppository with petroleum jelly.

2. Carry it to the bedside in a folded tissue or piece of gauze.

3. Wrap the tissue or gauze around the index finger and insert the suppository into the rectum as far as your forefinger will reach; less with an infant or child.

4. Hold the buttocks together.

5. Wash your hands with hot, soapy water.

The Enema for a Child . . .

An infant or a very young child may not be able to retain the enema, so you must have the crib protected with a protective pad and a small basin—the curved basin is convenient—to catch the fluid. If it is necessary to hold the child, ask another member of the family to assist you. When using the enema bulb, give the solution slowly; use plenty of petroleum jelly on the tip of the bulb; have a container of fresh solution handy so that you will not have to step away from the child. Usually a cup of solution is sufficient, but the amount depends upon the age and the condition for which the enema is given.

PROTECTIVE NURSING MEASURES

Some of the ways of protecting yourself and others from infection are: Good health practices; immunization against communicable diseases; avoiding contacts with people who have communicable diseases; special procedures to prevent contacts with infectious organisms.

Nursing measures that prevent spread of infection are isolation, disinfection, and sterilization. Isolation keeps disease germs from spreading; disinfection and sterilization destroy germs. These are called aseptic procedures. *Asepsis* means freedom from poisons; *antisepsis* means preventing sepsis or poisoning; an *antiseptic* is an agent used to destroy harmful germs.

Medical aseptic technique is carrying out procedures to control and prevent contacts with disease organisms and to destroy them after they leave the body; *surgical septic technique* is carrying out procedures to make and keep articles sterile.

Sterilization and Disinfection . . .

Sterilization means to destroy harmful organisms by exposing them to heat or chemical disinfectants. Some germs are harder to destroy than others, yet boiling destroys most organisms. Chemical disinfectants are so powerful that they may not be used for some articles. You sterilize articles in the home by boiling them on the kitchen stove. The water must cover them completely for the required time; always use a container with a lid. Boiling for 10 minutes makes contaminated articles safe.

Disinfectants will not always kill organisms but will check their growth. Soap and water, sunlight, and fresh air are good disinfectants. Fresh air and summer sunlight will sterilize most articles in about 6 hours.

SURGICAL SUPPLIES

Surgical supplies include dressings, cotton balls, towels, and bandages that are used in surgical and nursing treatments. They are prepared for sterile or unsterile use, depending upon the treatment. You can buy them and sterilize them later in the oven, or you may buy them individually packaged and sterilized.

These materials are expensive, so they should not be used needlessly. Clean squares of a soft, white cotton cloth are a satisfactory substitute for professional dressings.

Gauze . . .

Gauze dressings are made up into various sized sponges, compresses, and pads, of folded gauze, usually four thicknesses. Bandages come in different sizes and qualities. The firmer gauze with the tighter mesh weave is best because it covers the dressing better and stays securely in place. *Muslin bandages* may be used—are really better when added strength is needed, such as to hold a splint in place.

Cotton . . .

Cotton comes in different grades. Some are finer and more absorbent than others. A good grade of cotton is used to make tipped applicators and cotton balls. The coarser grades are used for pads.

Cellucotton, used in pads for incontinent patients, usually has a backing of insulating paper. A substitute is a plastic sheet sewed to a piece of toweling.

Applicators . . .

Applicators are slender sticks or toothpicks tipped with cotton. They are used to apply medications or to cleanse areas that are too small, or recessed (such as the throat) to be reached with a sponge. They are also used to cleanse infant nostrils and ears. A small piece of cotton is twisted on the end of the stick and rolled so that all edges are tucked in. The cotton must be thinned out on the end so that the final twist will go securely around the stick to anchor it. Otherwise, the tip may slip off in a cavity and be difficult to recover.

Ready-to-use sterile applicators are recommended.

269

Adhesive Tape . . .

Adhesive is used to hold dressings and splints in place or to support parts of the body, such as the lower back or side. It can be purchased in different widths. It can also be bought in colors and plastic-coated.

Ready-made Supplies . . .

Ready-made supplies may be purchased in drugstores; the *adhesive pad* and oval *eye pad* are examples of dressings available ready to use. They are more expensive over long periods, but are best for an occasional dressing and can be bought in small amounts. The *woven* or *elastic bandage* is sometimes used for supportive bandaging. It holds its elasticity when washed and used over and over.

Preparing Articles for Sterilization . . .

Dry surgical supplies are sterilized in covered glass, plain metal, or enamelware containers. *Heavy wrapping paper* may also be used to wrap sterile goods. A moderate heavy grade in two thicknesses can be used over again for approximately 5 to 7 wrappings, as long as the inside does not become soiled or stained. A double thickness of *unbleached muslin* makes a good heavy wrapper.

The wrapper must be large enough to cover the article with plenty of overlapping. When pins are used to fasten the covering, make sure the head of the pin is the only part of the pin showing on the outside. If both head and tip show, it means the tip will contaminate the sterile pack when it is pulled out.

(1) Never touch sterile articles with unsterile ones, and (2) discard an article if you should happen to contaminate it. Every movement in aseptic procedure is a link in the chain of asepsis; if you break one link by contaminating something, the chain is broken, and you open the door to infection.

You can handle sterile articles with a sterile pair of tongs from your kitchen. Keep them in a container—a pint fruit jar will do—filled with alcohol or Lysol solution.

Applying and Disposing of Dressings . . .

The doctor prescribes the treatment and instructs how to apply the dressing as well. No ointments or medicines other than those he has ordered should be used with dressings.

Steps in Procedure	Remember
1. Wash hands thoroughly before starting.	
2. Remove old dressing.	Place it in a paper bag so that it can be burned.
3. Holding cotton ball with tongs, moisten it with alcohol and cleanse wound. Repeat.	Never go back over wound with same cotton ball. Once over is all.
4. Apply any special medication with applicator.	
5. Pick up clean dressing with tongs and place over wound. Use several thicknesses.	Dressings must be large enough to cover the entire affected area—according to the drainage on the last dressing.
6. Attach the dressing with several strips of adhesive or bandage, to anchor and to keep dust out.	
7. Remove old adhesive marks with acetone or fingernail polish remover. Wash the skin afterwards with cool water.	
8. Remove wastes. Make patient comfortable.	

If you are going to need dressing preparations over a long period, it will be more convenient to keep all material used for surgical dressings separated from household supplies, in a covered tray or a box with a cover. A covered tray may consist of two large cake tins, inverting one over the other.

How to Take Care of a Bedsore . . .

Bedsores are caused by pressure on the parts of the body that are not well protected by pads of fat or other tissue. Prevention is the best treatment. The skin is more likely to break down if it is constantly moist or is not clean. Anyone who has had a long rest in bed will be susceptible to pressure areas over bony prominences such as at the shoulder blades and the end of the spine.

Rubbing reddened areas, keeping the skin dry, removing wastes from the skin when caring for incontinent patients, and changing the patient's position to relieve pressures are good preventive treatment.

DRUGS AND ADMINISTRATION

Drugs are given for general effect of the body as a whole or for special effects on one organ or one kind of body tissue. *Active principles* are the substances to which the drug owes its effect. Although drugs are very useful, they can be dangerous. Only the attending doctor knows your patient well enough to prescribe a medicine and how it should be used. There is no such thing as a harmless medicine, since each individual has a different body make-up. For instance, the dosage of aspirin sufficient to relieve your headache may cause disturbing ringing of the ears in your younger sister. The age, weight, and the sex all have to be considered when drugs are given. Some persons are *allergic* to common drugs.

When a patient has been using a drug over a long period, the drug will eventually lose its effect unless the dosage is increased constantly; sometimes it may lead to a craving or habit. This is what happens when a person takes *amphetamine* or "happy pills" for a lark. Some young people are led into experimenting with these dangerous drugs, which can spoil their lives.

Normally, drugs are eliminated from the body very quickly, some more quickly than others. Others may be thrown off so slowly that, if given over a period of time, they tend to pile up in the body and give undesired reactions. These drugs are said to have a *cumulative effect*. Drugs of this type are digitalis, given in heart conditions, and the bromides, given as a sedative. When you give or use this type of medication, you look for signs of cumulative effects.

Sources of Drugs . . .

Drugs may be chemicals, such as sodium bicarbonate; substances obtained from animals, such as insulin; substances obtained from plants, such as iodine; and more recently, substances obtained from molds, such as penicillin and aureomycin. These later discoveries as well as artificially produced drugs have led to startling developments in the treatment of disease in the last half century.

How Drugs are Given . . .

The effect of a drug will depend to a large extent upon its method of entrance into the body. Drugs act more quickly when given directly into the blood stream; with decreasing rapidity if injected into the muscles by the following methods: Under the skin (*subcutaneously*), by mouth, by inhalation, by rectum, and by rubbing into the soft areas of the skin (*inunction*).

Drugs are prepared as medications in the following forms: Liquids, powders, pills, capsules, tablets, plasters, suppositories, and ointments.

The form of drug, its properties, and the desired effect will influence the method for giving it. Combinations of drugs are given sometimes because together they produce more desirable effects than if one is given alone.

The doctor prescribes the drugs for your family; he also prescribes the amount and frequency of dosages. The pharmacist makes up your prescriptions; the druggist sells drugs and drug preparations. The pharmacist may also be the druggist, but all druggists are not pharmacists.

Safety Rules for Giving Medications . . .

One of your responsibilities in giving medications is to know, recognize, and follow certain rules so thoroughly that you can teach the other members of your family how to be careful and avoid any mistakes that may be harmful, if not fatal. Once a drug is taken, it begins to act. There is no way of getting it back that is as easy as not to make the mistake in the first place. Antidotes may help in some cases, but in others, may prove more harmful.

The following are **safety guides** in measuring and giving medications:

• Be certain you understand the doctor's order clearly.

• Read the label on the container three times—when you take it off the shelf, when you remove the cover, and when you put it back on the shelf.

• If you are not sure about the drug (when it has been on the shelf for an unknown length of time), the dosage, or how to give it, consult the doctor.

• Always know a medication by its label; many times you keep it in the same spot on a particular shelf, but check the label to be sure.

• Never use a medication ordered for one member of the family to treat another member with similar symptoms.

• Never give a medication from an unmarked container.

• Never give a medication to a semi-conscious or delirious patient.

• Give medications on time.

• If you should make a mistake in measuring and giving a medication, waste no time in calling and reporting to the doctor.

• Always think *why*, when you give a medication and recall the signs of an unfavorable reaction.

How to Give Medication by Mouth . . .

More medications are given by mouth than by any other way. Liquids may be given full strength or diluted with water after they are measured. Most are followed by a drink of water. Some helpful guides are as follows:

TYPE	METHOD OF ADMINISTRATION
Liquid	Full strength or diluted with water after measuring.
Powder	Dissolved in water or other liquid as ordered; may be put in capsules.
Pill	Given as they are, with water; may be ordered crushed and dissolved in water.
Capsules	Given as they are, with water.

Some medications may need mixing at the bedside, such as effervescent liquids; give while they are still foaming.

When possible, offer the patient a simple explanation of the reasons for giving a specific medication; the mental or "psychological" effect is sometimes equally important as the effect of the drug.

ANTISEPTICS AND DISINFECTANTS IN COMMON USE

Antiseptics prevent the growth of organisms; disinfectants kill them. An antiseptic may become a disinfectant if used in greater strengths, or if applied longer and at a higher temperature. Unfortunately, these drugs, if used in strengths powerful enough to kill organisms, also destroy body tissue.

Carbolic Acid . . .

Carbolic acid, or phenol, is an antiseptic that may injure the tissues even though used as a very dilute or weakened solution. Taken internally, it can cause great tissue damage and be fatal. Strong solutions of phenol are disinfectants, for articles such as fabrics, metal, and wood. Alcohol dissolves phenol, can be used as a rinse for anything that has been disinfected in phenol; alcohol can remove phenol from the skin or mucous membrane.

Cresols . . .

The cresols, obtained from phenol, are more effective in killing germs, cheaper, and more widely used. However, they are poisonous also. Cresols are mixed with green soap and and sold under various trade names such as Lysol, Creolin, Sanatol, and so on.

Iodine . . .

Iodine is very penetrating, effective as an antiseptic, but is also a skin irritant. If the solution stands for some time, it becomes concentrated and is likely to cause a burn; it is unsafe to use. Alcohol will remove iodine from the skin surface.

Alcohol . . .

Seventy per cent ethyl alcohol is an effective antiseptic. Stronger solutions are not as effective because alcohol needs a certain amount of water to destroy germs. It can be used to disinfect the skin or for sickroom articles. It is also used in rubbing compounds.

Mercurochrome . . .

Mercurochrome is a moderately effective antiseptic which is not irritating. It is used to disinfect the skin and as an antiseptic in some types of infections. It may be mixed with alcohol for more effective use, although the common solution found in most homes is the aqueous solution, meaning mixed with water. Chlorinated soda solution will remove the red stains of mercurochrome.

Merthiolate . . .

Merthiolate is the trade-name of a mercury preparation

that is less poisonous than the stronger bichloride of mercury. It is used in wounds as a disinfectant or as an irrigation. It is also used as an antiseptic in weaker solution. Metaphen is another trade-name preparation used in treating infections and disinfecting equipment.

Other Preparations . . .

Hydrogen peroxide is only a mild antiseptic because its action is so short. It is used to cleanse wounds. *Sodium perborate* releases oxygen when combined with water and counteracts acid conditions; it is used as a dusting powder and as a mouth wash. *Potassium permanganate* is a mild disinfectant with some deodorant powers; strong solutions are irritating and may cause burns. When it has lost its effectiveness, it turns brown and should not be used.

Boric acid is a very weak antiseptic but does check the growth of bacteria; solutions can be used on delicate membranes, since boric acid is non-irritating. In weak solution, it is commonly used as an eyewash.

Normal mucous membranes, the linings of body cavities, produce their own antiseptic secretions as a natural defense against invading bacteria. Constant use of antiseptics in medicated mouth washes, douches, and nose and throat sprays may interfere with these functions. Antiseptics are beneficial when used properly, but are definitely harmful otherwise.

THE ANTIBIOTICS

Antibiotics sound like magic. You hear that the little girl down the street did not have to have her appendix operation last night after all; she recovered miraculously with antibiotics.

Although antibiotics sound like magic, there is nothing mysterious about them. They come from common earth. They are not made by man, but by molds, the simplest form of plant life. The mold that forms on stale bread is only one of the many thousands. They produce and give out poisons which kill their enemies. These poisonous chemicals are called *antibiotics,* which means "against life"; that is, against the enemies of the mold's life.

Louis Pasteur, who discovered germs, knew that many of the enemies of man were also enemies of mold which had learned how to poison them. He suggested that man might one day borrow the mold's weapon against a common microbial enemy, but the clue was neglected in favor of other investigations into the world of germs he had uncovered.

Penicillin . . .

That is why Alexander Fleming, a British bacteriologist, was not surprised, when in September, 1928, a mold wafted through the open window of his laboratory killed the staphylococcus germs he was growing on an agar plate. Staph germs were bad for humans, so why not cultivate the mold which seemed to know how to kill them, he reasoned? He systematically collected the mysterious juices they gave out and injected mice infected with different kinds of disease germs. In June, 1929, he was able to report that the product of the penicillium mold, "may be an effective antiseptic for injection into areas infected with penicillin-sensitive microbes." Fleming did not develop penicillin any further, but he kept the plant thriving.

By 1943, private American pharmaceutical companies had invested millions of dollars, besides the three million of the government's, getting penicillin into mass production. The war was on, and thousands of soldiers were dying of infections which penicillin might combat.

Penicillin meant the saving of many lives on the battlefield. Off the battlefield, it opened a whole new door to treatment of pneumonia, boils, diphtheria, bacterial endocarditis (a heart infection), food poisoning, gas gangrene, meningitis, scarlet fever, strep throat, tetanus, and many other infections. Of course, there were diseases that penicillin didn't cure: Tuberculosis, urinary tract infections, dysentery, undulant fever, and others such as typhus, polio, and yellow fever caused by a *virus* or their big brothers, the *rickettsias*. The antibiotic of penicillin didn't touch them; there are thousands of molds in the earth, most of which have their own brand of antibiotic medicine. These would be hunted down to poison the enemies of man that penicillin couldn't touch.

The Mycins . . .

The ground soil hunt went on to the following discoveries: Streptomycin (good for tuberculosis) in 1944; chloromycetin in 1947; aureomycin in 1948; terramycin in 1950. These are called "broad spectrum" antibiotics because they attack most of the diseases destroyed by penicillin and many others. Penicillin cured 25 diseases; aureomycin is used in more than 50. In 1953, achromycin was produced from its sister drug, aureomycin, and has proved as effective as other broad spectrum antibiotics in fighting a wide range of diseases but with almost none of the uncomfortable reactions which sometimes follow administration of the older preparations. It has proved especially effective against mixed infections following childbirth and has played a large role in making childbirth safer.

The wonder drugs have not limited their effectiveness to the human race. Since aureomycin is produced by the fermentation process, there are large quantities of mash left. Researchers, seeking a use for this by-product, discovered this mash, when processed, makes a remarkable feed supplement that stimulated animal growth. This supplement is now used by commercial manufacturers of feeds for hogs, chickens, turkeys, and dairy calves.

THE ANTIHISTAMINES

The antihistamines control the release of histamine. See discussion of allergies, Chapter 9. *Benadryl* is useful in treating hives, hay fever, and serum reactions. *Pyribenzamine* is also an effective antihistamine, but both of these drugs are likely to cause side-effects such as dizziness, sleepiness, nausea, and sometimes excessive nervousness.

You will find various cold remedies selling under trade names which are antihistamines. As increasing use has led to greater experience, the antihistamines have been found to be effective for a greater range of disorders than originally assumed. Often an antihistamine will be given along with a medication which would produce an allergic reaction if used alone. Previously, where long drawn-out desensitization was necessary in respiratory and skin disorders, the antihistamines have proved a powerful substitute.

Although almost all of the antihistamines produce side effects, *chlortrimeton* takes us a step closer in overcoming this threat. It is also rapid acting, bringing relief from allergy attacks as quickly as 30 minutes. Other such drugs are being brought into use now.

The field of antihistaminic therapy is continually broadening by research and clinical experience. One of its more recent advances is its use in dentistry; progress is being made for its use on stomach and intestinal disorders.

- Discuss how you would make surgical dressings for an abdominal wound. Would it be easier to buy them? Why do you think this?
- Who decides when an enema should be given? Name the various types of enemas.
- Why is care needed to expel the air from the tubing before inserting the tip for an enema? What do you do if your patient cannot control the anal muscles?
- What should the temperature of the foot bath be? How would you measure this if you do not have a bath thermometer?
- Why do you always wrap a hot water bottle or an icecap?
- What is the temperature of water in a hot water bottle? Why is the bottle only partially filled? How would you test for leakage?
- How often do you fill an icecap or ice collar?
- Is the icecap applied hour after hour constantly? Explain.
- What are some of the antiseptics or disinfectants found in your home? When are these solutions harmful?
- Do you have any self-medication habits? Discuss.

NURSE'S RECORD

Home safety.

Accident prevention.

The do's of first aid.

Bandages and binders.

How to stop bleeding.

First aid for nose bleed.

Fainting.

Removing foreign body from the eye.

Removing foreign body from the nose and throat.

How to treat a minor wound or cut.

The ideal first aid kit.

Violent emergencies.

16: MEETING EMERGENCIES

HOME SAFETY

According to the United States Public Health Service, "there is no place like home—for accidents." Every nineteen minutes someone is killed and every eight seconds someone is disabled in the home. In the United States in one year, 4,127,000 people were either injured or killed in the home by accidents that could have been prevented.

As an example of one state, in Massachusetts in one year, 1,040 people were killed by home accidents. For every death about four permanently disabling accidents occur. As true in the whole United States, the majority of accidents in Massachusetts happen in the age groups under 14 and over 65.

NATIONAL SAFETY COUNCIL

Check List for Home Safety . . .

What are the causes of home accidents? It is found that they fall into three main groups: (1) Environmental factors; (2) human factors; and (3) a combination of both.

Environmental factors mean those conditions in your surroundings which may contribute to the number and severity of accidents. These we are able to do something about.

DO YOU SEE IT?

1. Do you look for tripping hazards—toys left around, mops and brooms, other clutter—and put them away?

2. Do you light your way ahead of you into rooms, up and down stairs?

Wise use of closets can prevent many tripping accidents. • Stop fires before they start. It may save your home and your life.

3. Do you look at the label before taking any medicine?
4. Do you seek out fire hazards—rubbish in attic or basement, bundles of oily rags—and clear them out?
5. Do you watch for cleaning supplies—insecticides, medicines, matches left where children can get at them—and put them away?
6. Do you look to see that all the window screens and guards are fastened securely?
7. Do you see that cigarettes and matches are really out?
Is your kitchen safe from fire? Are storage spaces free of flammable materials?

Constant care is needed to keep harmful objects away from children. • Window and screen security may prevent broken bones.

DO YOU PRACTICE IT?

1. A fairly universal rule of fire prevention is NO SMOKING IN BED. Do your family members always observe it?

2. Do you always disconnect electrical appliances when not in use?

3. Do you always provide adequate ventilation in any room where portable gas or oil heaters are used?

The safety points in this check list are important, but there is a more important fact about home safety: You must be alert, aware, and safety conscious.

Human factors in home accidents mean the mental, emotional, and physical states of the individual bringing on the

Be sure cigarettes and matches are extinguished after use. Disconnect electrical appliances when they are not in use. Little precautions like these prevent big trouble.

accident. Among these human factors are age, sex, emotional stress, and physical disability. An adult may use with safety an appliance which would be unsafe in the hands of a child. An adolescent may, without great risk, climb a ladder to a height that would be dangerous for his grandfather to attempt. Adults and youngsters alike, when emotionally upset or tired, are more prone to accidents.

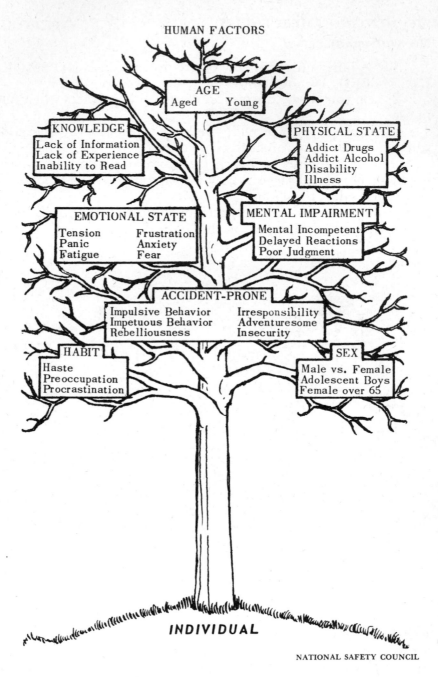

HUMAN FACTORS

AGE
Aged   Young

KNOWLEDGE
Lack of Information
Lack of Experience
Inability to Read

PHYSICAL STATE
Addict Drugs
Addict Alcohol
Disability
Illness

EMOTIONAL STATE
Tension   Frustration
Panic   Anxiety
Fatigue   Fear

MENTAL IMPAIRMENT
Mental Incompetent
Delayed Reactions
Poor Judgment

ACCIDENT-PRONE
Impulsive Behavior   Irresponsibility
Impetuous Behavior   Adventuresome
Rebelliousness   Insecurity

HABIT
Haste
Preoccupation
Procrastination

SEX
Male vs. Female
Adolescent Boys
Female over 65

INDIVIDUAL

NATIONAL SAFETY COUNCIL

First Aid . . .

You do not run to the doctor for every minor cut or burn—nor is it necessary. It is important to know the difference between a serious and minor injury, to know when medical attention is needed, and to give proper first aid treatment for any injury. Your quick and intelligent action in some emergencies may save a life.

The American Red Cross has long seen the need for the teaching of first aid. Courses are offered in most communities to give this service. Courses are being taught in the high schools and to the Boy and Girl Scouts as a part of their achievement programs. The dangers of atomic warfare bring about special instruction of civilians in the first aid technics to use in case of an atomic bomb attack. Many schools have "defense drills" as well as fire drills. There is a course available to every citizen in the country. Your parents, your brothers and your sisters—besides yourself—should enroll in the Red Cross and the civilian defense courses as a means of self-protection.

ACCIDENT PREVENTION

It goes without question that many accidents could be prevented. First aid instruction should go hand in hand with information about prevention. State and local governments provide public protection by means of highway regulations, fire laws, and industrial safety precautions. The National Safety Council and the state safety councils carry on a never-ending campaign for safety, through publications, talks, and films.

Emergencies and Nursing Care . . .

Accidents occur, however, and it is important to know the proper thing to do if first aid measures are necessary. This part of the book is not intended to serve as a substitute for a complete course in first aid, but it will fill you in enough to meet some of the more common emergencies.

The Right Attitude . . .

Sometimes the less you do, the more helpful you will be to the victim. If you can remain calm, half the battle is won; you may not have to worry with the victim as much as with those around you. For example, sister may become faint when she sees baby brother bleeding from a cut on the finger. Your attitude will calm others. You must make up your mind quickly what you are going to do; your attitude and knowledge of first aid will put you in command of the situation.

THE DO'S OF FIRST AID

It is always easy to follow directions when you can have a specific set of rules. Unfortunately, although emergencies may resemble one another, each is different and there are no cut and dried rules to follow. However, there are a few basic principles. Your reactions when an accident happens should be almost automatic if you know the principles of first aid.

1. **Look the situation over.** Is it serious enough to require a doctor? Gushing blood, a large area burn, a leg in awkward position, or an unconscious victim is serious enough. Keep excited people out of the way by giving them something to do; ask one of them to call the doctor at once; send another to bring blankets. This will keep them occupied and out of the way while you give your whole attention to the patient.

2. **Look the patient over.** Although in minor accidents this will be accomplished very easily—little Sally shows you her thumb that got too close to the heater—you still want to be sure of the nature of the injury. Ask her to tell you how the accident happened and look for bumps, scratches, or marks on other parts of the body, if necessary.

3. **Make the patient comfortable.** Move him as little as possible. In most emergencies, it is best to keep the victim lying down; moving may do more damage to an injured or broken limb. Keep the patient warm.

4. **Give the necessary first aid treatment.** Sometimes, this is all the treatment the victim needs, but in serious conditions, you give emergency treatment until the doctor arrives.

5. **Watch for follow-up signs.** Even though an injury appears to be only slight, certain signs may show up a few hours or a few days after the accident. A person who shrugs off a bump on the head as nothing may begin vomiting later, have blurring of vision, headaches, or other symptoms.

Family Emergencies and Medical Aid . . .

There may be times when an emergency condition exists and all efforts to reach the doctor fail. Of course, if little Mary steps on a nail or cuts her finger between the hours of 8 a.m. and 5 p.m., you may find the doctor in his office; but, chances are, if you are unable to reach him by phone, he will be either making other house calls, at the hospital, or otherwise unavailable at the moment.

Medical aid is always available for emergencies at the hospital. This department, formerly called the "dispensary," is now referred to as the "emergency room" or "outpatient department." The emergency room is equipped to handle almost every type of emergency from a small cut needing several stitches to delivering a baby. A registered nurse is on duty at all times and resident staff doctors are on call. A record of the accident and treatment is kept on file or sent to your family doctor.

BANDAGES AND BINDERS

A bandage is a piece of material used to hold dressings or splints in place, to give support or to supply pressure. When applying bandages, there are a few reminders that will help you:

1. Apply firmly but not so tight as to cut off the blood supply to the part. Remember that after injury, body tissues swell in order to protect themselves; check the bandage and loosen it if necessary.

2. Always use the square knot, because it will not slip.

3. If possible, leave the tips of the fingers and toes free so that you can check the nails. If the blood supply is being cut off, the nails will become blue or purple.

Roller Bandage . . .

Roller bandages of gauze or muslin come in several widths suitable for bandaging the various parts of the body:

Fingers and toes	1 inch width
Head and foot	2 or 3 inch
Arms and legs	2 to 6 inch
Trunk	4 to 6 inch

This type of bandage can be applied neatly and snugly on the arms and legs, but each turn must be as firm as the one ahead of it. Too much pull on the roll will tighten the bandage and cut off circulation; too loose a pull will give a loose bandage and it will fall off. If you allow for swelling, then the bandage can be anchored with strips of adhesive tape, or you can split the end, carry the two ends around opposite sides, and tie a square knot.

This bandage is most often used in the surgeon's work. For the average person, unless only a simple circular bandage is being used, it is not too satisfactory.

First Aid Methods
Bandaging

GENERAL BIOLOGICAL SUPPLY HOUSE, INC.

A. Triangular bandage
1. Triangular bandages from 40″ square of muslin cut diagonally
2. Fold in triangular bandage to make cravat
3. Two styles of cravat bandage

B. Triangular bandage on hand
1. First fold
2. Finished bandage

C. Open head bandage
1. Cross ends of triangle
2. Tied in front, tucked in at back

D. Cravat bandage for cheek or ear
1. Tied above the ear
2. Looped bandage at side of head

E. Triangular bandage as arm sling
1. Open bandage in place
2. Sling with ties at back of neck
3. Arm sling under one shoulder

F. Cravat and triangular bandages on shoulder
1. Point of triangle looped under cravat
2. Cravat tied at back—triangle tied at arm

G. **Open bandage for chest**
1. Point of bandage at shoulder
2. End looped under arm at waist
3. Completed bandage from front
4. Completed bandage from back

H. **Cravat bandage for ankle**
1. Bandage looped under arch, then crossed at back of ankle
2. Ends of bandage pulled forward
3. Ends looped under side straps
4. Ends crossed again at back, returned to front and tied

I. **Roller gauze bandage for finger**
1. Winding finger, one end left at wrist
2. Gauze crossed at knuckle, returned to wrist, crossed again and tied

J. **Cravat bandage of elbow**
1. Tied at front

K. **Four tailed bandage for nose.**
1. Gauze or muslin strip 3 feet by 4 inches
2. Bandage tied at back of head and base of head

Triangular Bandage . . .

The triangular bandage is the most valuable type of band-age, as it ties on well without adhesive tape and is very easy to

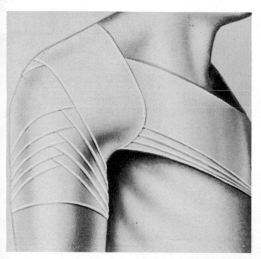
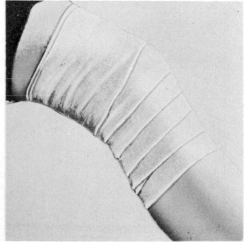
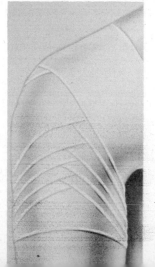

Elastic bandages.

BECTON, DICKINSON
AND CO.

First Aid Methods
Splints

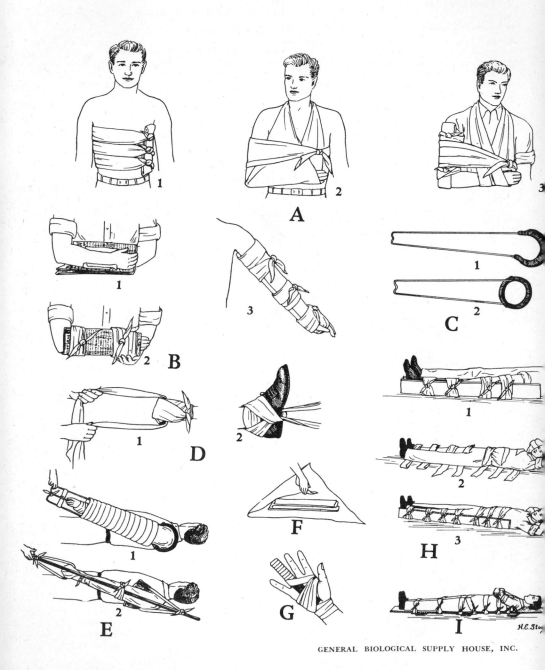

A

B

C

D

E

F

G

H

I

H.E.Stow

make from any kind of cloth—piece of shirt, old sheet, or large handkerchief. The bandage is made from a piece 36 inches or 40 inches square, the larger for use on adults. Fold for a triangle, or cut the square diagonally for two bandages.

The *cravat* type is made from a triangular bandage by bringing the point to the middle of the base. Then this bandage is

Elastic bandages.

BECTON, DICKINSON AND CO.

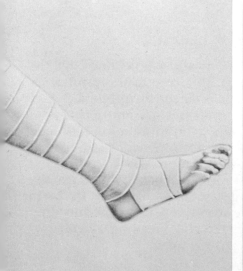

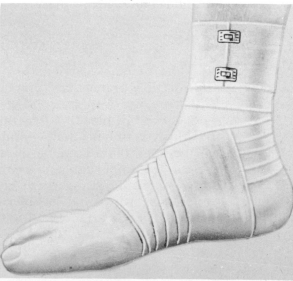

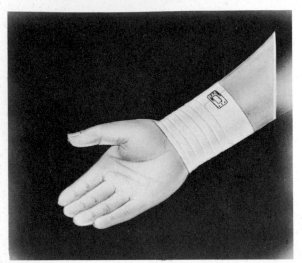 

Elastic bandages.

BECTON, DICKINSON AND CO.

divided by being folded lengthwise along the middle until the desired width is reached.

The Elastic Bandage or Binder . . .

Elastic bandages roll evenly without need of reversing, and fit all parts of the body comfortably, allowing free ventilation to the part. They exert a firm, constant pressure which may be varied to suit the condition. They are made of a balanced weave of rubber threads and long-staple cotton yarn; they may be laundered frequently when soiled to restore elasticity which becomes lost with use. They are used primarily to give support and hold bandages in place.

HOW TO STOP BLEEDING

The blood is carried throughout the whole body by the arteries; they branch, and branch again, down to the capillaries. When any one of these blood vessels is cut or torn, blood is lost. The amount of bleeding depends upon the size and location of the blood vessel injured. Although a large amount of blood will be lost from a large vessel, severance of smaller vessels will present the same dangers—hemorrhage and shock. The next most important thing, then, is to treat shock, which usually comes from injury and loss of large amounts of blood, by keeping the patient warm. Do not give stimulants until the bleeding is controlled, because they will make the bleeding worse.

Bleeding can be controlled by pressure directly over the bleeding spot, or by shutting off the blood supply to the part by applying pressure to the artery. Pressure at the right spot will control venous bleeding in most injuries on the outer surface

NATIONAL SAFETY COUNCIL

6 PRESSURE POINTS TO STOP ARTERIAL BLEEDING

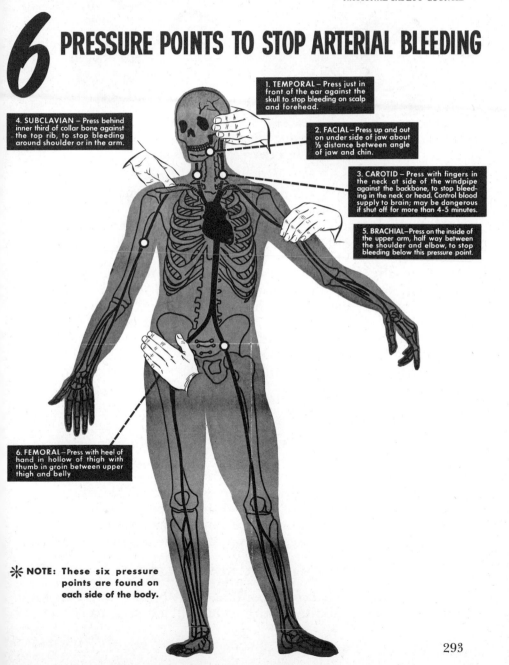

1. TEMPORAL — Press just in front of the ear against the skull to stop bleeding on scalp and forehead.

4. SUBCLAVIAN — Press behind inner third of collar bone against the top rib, to stop bleeding around shoulder or in the arm.

2. FACIAL — Press up and out on under side of jaw about ⅓ distance between angle of jaw and chin.

3. CAROTID — Press with fingers in the neck at side of the windpipe against the backbone, to stop bleeding in the neck or head. Control blood supply to brain; may be dangerous if shut off for more than 4-5 minutes.

5. BRACHIAL — Press on the inside of the upper arm, half way between the shoulder and elbow, to stop bleeding below this pressure point.

6. FEMORAL — Press with heel of hand in hollow of thigh with thumb in groin between upper thigh and belly

✳ NOTE: These six pressure points are found on each side of the body.

293

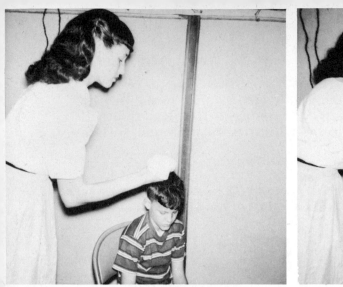
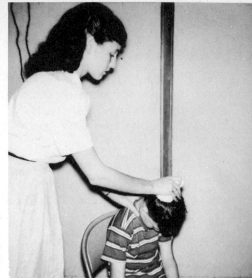

Proper way to control bleeding from a head injury. If no bandage is available, use a clean cloth. Press firmly.

of the body. Apply a clean dressing, folded to make a pad, to the bleeding area; you can use a clean handkerchief or other cloth if you do not have a dressing. Press the dressing firmly on the bleeding area; then apply a firm dressing to hold it in place. Be sure the circulation is not shut off.

Normally, the blood flows through all the channels that are open; if some channels are shut off too long, permanent damage may be done and blood will never flow through them again. When an area has no blood to supply its needed oxygen, the tissues die. This is why we stress not applying a tourniquet, for you can see that if a tourniquet is left on too long, it may cause death of the tissues. This is also true of the bandage that is too tight.

Pressure Points . . .

You can tell by the flow whether the bleeding comes from an artery or a vein; blood from an artery comes in spurts; it comes from a vein in a steady flow. Pressure on a large artery supplying blood to the injured part will control bleeding; the artery must lie close to the bone so that there is a firm surface to press against. The six main pressure points are shown in the accompanying poster, released by the National Safety Council.

FIRST AID FOR NOSE BLEED

Nose bleeds may occur spontaneously, be caused by an injury, or by a medical disease such as high blood pressure.

Always keep the patient upright; bending over only brings more blood to the head and increases the bleeding. Loosen anything tight around the neck; place a cold wet compress over the bridge of the nose. Press the nostril on the bleeding side against the bridge of the nose; this usually gives the clot time to form within several minutes. If this treatment does not check the bleeding within 15 minutes, call the doctor. Pack a piece of sterile gauze into the nostril gently. Cotton is not a good thing to place in the nose because the tiny wisps become soaked and may become embedded in the clot and so be hard to remove.

Watch the patient with the severe nose bleed for signs of fainting and shock. Keep him upright for several hours after the nose bleed and tell him not to blow his nose, since this may loosen the clot and start the bleeding again.

FAINTING

People faint when they are tired or hungry or are in crowds and do not get enough air; an emotional shock or the sight of blood may produce fainting. If he does not recognize the symptoms soon enough, the patient may fall and injure himself.

Fainting is caused by an insufficient amount of blood in the brain. The signs are dizziness, nausea, blackness before the eyes, pallor, and perspiration. The victim loses consciousness, his pulse is weak, and his breathing is shallow. If he recognizes these symptoms and complains, immediately bend his head forward between his knees so that his head will be lower than his heart, to bring more blood to the brain. If he has fallen, keep him lying down and place something under his feet—a coat or blanket; loosen tight clothing. Smelling salts, or aromatic spirits of ammonia, under the nose will help restore

To stop nose bleed, place a cold, wet compress across the bridge of the nose. Apply gentle pressure.

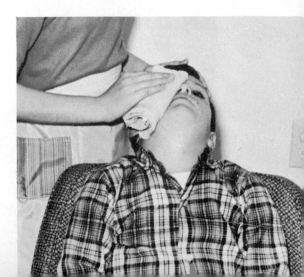

Bending the fainting person's head forward brings needed blood to the brain.

consciousness. Do not allow him to get up until he has recovered completely; then get him up slowly—first, to a sitting position, then standing, before he attempts to walk.

REMOVING FOREIGN BODY FROM THE EYE

Frequently, foreign bodies—particles of dust, ash, or an eyelash—lodge in the lining of the eyelids or become imbedded in the eyeball. You must never try to get out a particle that is embedded. Tears—nature's way of trying to dislodge a foreign body—will remove nearly anything, and lessens irritation. In no case should the eye be rubbed; this may scratch the eye and set up an inflammation.

To remove a foreign body that is not embedded:

1. Pull down the lower lid to see if the body is on the mucous membrane; if so, you may lift it off gently with the clean tip of a handkerchief or with a cotton-tipped applicator.

When fainting persons fall, they should be kept lying down until fully recovered. Elevate the feet slightly.

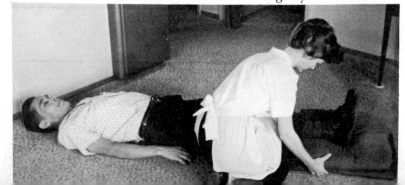

Always moisten cotton before applying it to the eye; tiny dry whisps may cause more irritation.

2. Grasp the lashes of the upper eyelid with your forefinger and thumb; ask the patient to look upward, pull the lid forward and downward over the lower eyelid. Usually this dislodges the body and the tears wash it away.

3. Flush the eye with boric acid solution (one-half teaspoon of powdered boric acid to a cup of boiled water) or some other mildly antiseptic eyewash. You can do this with a medicine dropper.

4. If the eye looks irritated, apply a drop of castor oil, mineral oil, or olive oil.

If none of these measures is successful, then you must send the patient to the doctor. The longer a foreign body remains in the eye, the greater is the danger of infection. Reassure young children that you are covering the eye only until the doctor can check it.

REMOVING FOREIGN BODY FROM THE NOSE AND THROAT

How often do you hear that a child has put a bean or rock into the nostril and forgotten it? The warning is when a sudden temperature comes on and a runny nose suggests a cold.

Unless the object is clearly seen and at the end of the nostril, you must not try to remove it with a finger. Any vegetable product in the nostril—a pea or bean—is likely to swell, so you can put a few drops of olive or mineral oil into the nostril to prevent the swelling from taking place. You may be able to pick it out with a tweezer, but you must be careful not to force it up farther. It is safer first to attempt its removal by asking the child to blow the nose—with *both* nostrils open.

Objects often become stuck in the throat; children put coins and safety pins into their mouths; small pieces of food become lodged in the throat or esophagus. Do not attempt to loosen or take out any foreign body with your fingers unless it can be dislodged easily; if you can't see the foreign body and the child is able to breathe all right, send for the doctor or take the child to the hospital emergency room. Watch the youngster's color to see if he is breathing all right; you can tell by the color of the skin. If the patient becomes blue and distressed, hold him upside down and slap his back sharply. Have an adult lean over from the waist. Sometimes breathing aid is necessary even after the body is dislodged.

Never attempt to dislodge a foreign body in the ear. You may drive it farther down and injure the hearing. Call a doctor immediately.

HOW TO TREAT A MINOR WOUND OR CUT

A wound is a break in the skin. It may be a cut, a scratched surface, or a puncture. Bleeding helps to cleanse the wound, so infection is less apt to follow the minor wound that bleeds freely.

The extent of the wound, the amount of bleeding, and the patient's condition will tell you how severe the wound is and whether a doctor should be called or not. If the patient's pulse is weak and rapid, his color pale, and his skin moist, he needs more medical attention than you are prepared to give him. Call the doctor.

It is important to cover any wound, no matter how slight, to prevent infection. You can apply mercury antiseptic, tincture of iodine, or alcohol, before applying the dressing. Never use ointments or salves on a cut.

Apply a sterile dressing, secured firmly with a bandage or strips of adhesive tape. If the dressing slips or slides over, it becomes unsterile.

An adhesive pad makes a satisfactory dressing for small cuts or scratches. Such pads, which come in different sizes, should be kept in the home at all times. Be sure not to touch the part that is placed over the wound.

THE IDEAL FIRST AID KIT

First aid material in the average home may be scattered in kitchen, bathroom, and medicine cabinets. The best plan is to have this material kept in or near the medicine cabinet. A satisfactory kit can be made from a metal, wooden, or cardboard box of any convenient size. No special size or type is considered best; kits may range from the small pocket size to the large cabinet. The size and contents are varied to suit needs of the family.

Here are suggested items for a typical home kit:

Petroleum jelly (for lubrication and minor irritations).
Iodine or a **mercury antiseptic** (for cleansing of minor wounds).
Mineral oil (for lubrication and minor burns).
Epsom salts (for hot compresses or foot baths).

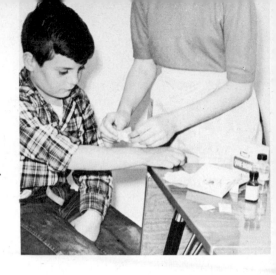

Cover any wound, no matter how slight.

Calomine lotion (a soothing lotion for skin rashes, insect bites, and itching).

Sodium bicarbonate (for stomach acidity and soothing skin irritations).

Aromatic spirits of ammonia (for quick revival for faintness, or for shock—1 t. in 1 qt. of water).

Scissors (to cut bandages, cut off tight clothing, etc.).

Tweezers (to remove slivers or other foreign bodies).

Paper cups (for giving stimulants or medication).

1-inch and 2-inch **roller bandages** (for a small dressing or to hold dressings in place).

Thin board **splints** (for splinting broken arms and legs).

Adhesive pads (for small scratches and abrasions).

Sterile gauze squares, 3″ × 3″, individually packaged (for open wounds, for dry dressings or burns).

Triangular bandages (for a sling; as a cover for a dressing).

VIOLENT EMERGENCIES

Whatever the disaster or emergency—tornado, fire, flood, epidemic, explosion, or hurricane—you may be asked to serve in shelters, emergency aid stations, hospitals, clinics, in the homes of your neighbors, or at the scene of the disaster.

If an emergency catches you unprepared, what you don't know about protecting your home and family could be costly—even fatal. Home protection is not the same in all parts of the nation. It is important that you know the means of helping in a number of situations, from minor accidents in the home to mass casualties such as a mine cave-in, fire, or tornado. Many of these disasters will bring only minor problems such as we have just discussed. You may be called upon because you have some knowledge of nursing skills or have the ability to teach others. At any rate, since we are unable to cover here all the conditions which may arise in such emergencies, the following is offered to familiarize you with the types of conditions which may arise and the suggested nursing care, treatment, and medications in each case. In some instances you may proceed on your own, but usually you will receive instruction from the person in charge.

Convulsions—Loosen clothing; protect from injury but do not restrain; turn head on side to protect tongue from being bitten.

Diarrhea—*Adult:* Take temperature, pulse, and respiration (TPR); discontinue solid food; arrange for rest and quiet. *Infant:* Take TPR; discontinue feedings; give boiled water only; arrange for rest and quiet.

Elevated temperature—Advise bed rest; keep patient quiet; give liquid diet and adequate fluids (nothing by mouth with abdominal pain); isolate if communicable disease is suspected; sponge for temperature 102.5° F. (adults—mouth) and 104° (infants or children—rectal); give ten aspirin grains until patient is seen by physician.

Nausea—Take TPR; advise rest; give liquid diet; give ½ teaspoon spirits of ammonia with 5 drops spirit of peppermint in hot water.

Animal bites—Encourage bleeding; scrub around wound with soap and water; apply sterile dressing; refer to physician immediately, as anti-rabies treatment may be indicated.

Burns—Cover the burned area with a clean, dry compress or pad of cloth. Use several layers, arranged smoothly. Cover every part of the burn. Once the bandage is on, let it alone until the physician can treat the case.

Chemical burns—Wash with large quantities of lukewarm water; apply sterile dressing. For affected eyes, irrigate with sterile water; drop clean olive oil, mineral oil, or castor oil into the eyes; bandage.

Contusions—Apply cold compresses immediately following injury; follow later, after 24 hour time lapse, with application of moist heat.

Fractures—Treat for shock; apply sterile dressing for compound fractures; apply temporary splints or immobilize with sandbags, wrapped newspapers, or pillows.

Heat exhaustion—Treat for shock; lay patient down, keep him warm, and administer stimulants; give table salt ½ teaspoon at a time with several swallows of water until as much as a tablespoon has been given.

Heatstroke or sunstroke—Remove clothes and wrap in cold wet sheets; apply icecaps to head and entire body or give cold tub bath, rubbing arms and legs to restore circulation; give cool, non-stimulating liquids if victim is conscious.

Insect bites—Apply alcohol; remove stinger if present; apply cold

It takes a level head and a sound knowledge of first aid principles to be really helpful in a situation like this tornado disaster in Massachusetts. Could you do the job?

compresses moistened with sodium bicarbonate solution or ammonia water.

Poisons—Induce vomiting repeatedly with numerous glasses of lukewarm plain water, salt water, soapy water, or milk. Treat for shock and use artificial respiration if necessary; give antidote listed on label of poison container or use the following:

For *acids:* Frequent and large amounts of water and weak solution of sodium bicarbonate, milk, olive oil, or egg white.

For *alkalies:* Vinegar solution or lemon juice, butter, olive oil, fat, mild emetic such as lukewarm water.

For *arsenic:* Milk and raw eggs.

For *iodine:* Solution of starch.

Shock—Conserve body heat—blanket over and beneath patient; keep patient comfortable but do not overheat; place patient on cot, bed, or stretcher; keep head low, if this does not interfere with breathing; give small amounts of fluid (hot tea, coffee, or broth if water is not tolerated) frequently by mouth unless there is abdominal injury or patient is unconscious.

Suffocation—Get the patient away from the cause of his condition. (It may be caused by breathing in dust, dirt, food, liquid, smoke, gas, live wire contact, or near-drowning.) Remove any objects from his mouth and explore throat with your finger for any obstruction; then apply artificial respiration at once until help comes.

In any of the mentioned conditions, remember that when mass casualty occurs there will be many and all types of casualties, or a combination of several. Obviously, your contribution to the welfare of others will depend upon the knowledge of the five essential procedures of survival care. They are (1) stop bleeding; (2) splint any fractures; (3) dress wounds; (4) maintain a free air passage; (5) handle patients properly.

With this knowledge you will be able to care for your own and others' minor injuries, thus increasing the pool of those needed to care for the critically injured.

Atomic Information . . .

The atomic bomb is a weapon of great destructive power. It is many times more powerful than the most powerful TNT bomb in its explosive capacity. The explosion is accompanied by highly penetrating, invisible rays in addition to intense heat and light. The rays are highly radioactive, capable of inflicting serious harm to those who may have been exposed.

Here are a few basic facts to help you know what to expect and do in the event of an atomic explosion:

1. You will see it before you hear it.
2. It will be brighter than a thousand suns.
3. Act fast:

• **In a building:** Drop to the floor. Crawl under protectors such as tables, beds, desks. Avoid openings, doors, and windows. If possible, press yourself against an inside partition.

• **Out of doors:** You have seconds to take cover. Get back of a tree, into a doorway, or into a gutter. *You've got one step to make it—two are too late.* Turn away from the light. Protect yourself from flying debris after ten seconds elapse.

Volunteer workers use their abilities in many ways to aid and comfort disaster victims. Here a volunteer takes a case history statement from a Flint, Michigan tornado victim.

4. In or out of doors, cover as many exposed parts of your body as possible—such as face, hands, neck—as protection against flash burns. These are caused by the release of infra-red waves, which are relatively slow in travel.

5. There is always danger of radiation sickness. If exposed to an atomic blast, report at once to your emergency medical unit.

- How does your home rate as a safe place to be?
- Is instruction in first aid and civilian defense available in your neighborhood? Have you had this instruction?
- Have any accidents happened in your home recently? Were you asked to help with first aid?
- What would you do if your baby brother began to choke?
- What would you do if you stepped on a nail and could not locate your family doctor?
- Check your medical supplies at home. Does your family maintain enough for emergencies?

17: MOTHERHOOD AND INFANT CARE

Mothers and babies have a rosier future today than they ever had before. There is a new ingredient in maternity care. Fathers and mothers and families learn together what to expect from the first moment of pregnancy until they meet their new member face to face. The United States Children's Bureau and state and local groups have worked constantly to improve mother and baby care. Mothers are learning more; clinics provide care for both mother and baby after it arrives; health insurances provide hospital care.

PRENATAL CARE

Prenatal means before birth. Prenatal care refers to the care of the mother before the arrival of the baby.

The modern mother will know something about the facts of birth, gained from talking to her physician, reading, or from attending classes in preparation for childbearing. The high birth rate in recent years has made her condition a popular one. She knows that having a baby is a perfectly natural physiological process. She intends to follow along the path several times; she wants more than this baby; she wants children.

Instructions . . .

The Maternity Center in New York City has been conducting mothers' classes for many years; in recent years, it has added classes for fathers, too. Information is available to high school classes, also. The mothers are divided into classes where all the persons have a similar background. In these classes, mothers learn about the normal process of pregnancy. They learn how to care for themselves and what to prepare for the baby; how to bathe the baby and to prepare his formula. The importance of a happy home both before and after the baby comes is explained. Mothers are urged to keep in close touch with their doctors.

Many health departments, visiting nurse associations, hospitals, and doctors throughout the country give the same kind of instruction.

SIGNS OF PREGNANCY

The absence of the menstrual period usually causes a woman to suspect that she is pregnant. However, if the menstrual cycle has frequently been irregular, then this is not always reliable. Other tests can be made by a doctor.

Sometimes, for a while, usually within the first three or four months, a woman may be bothered with nausea in the morning. This "morning sickness" disappears soon after the mother's body adjusts to the changes that occur when a new life begins to grow. Occasionally, however, the nausea is so severe as to endanger the lives of both mother and baby. This is when it helps to have a member of the household co-operate. You can take over the early morning duties of preparing breakfast for the younger members of the family, packing lunches, and seeing them off to school. If mother knows that everything is being handled smoothly, she will be more inclined to heed her doctor's advice about sleeping in a little later. A few crackers at her bedside for her to munch on before rising to a sitting position sometimes settle the stomach. If the morning sickness is severe to the point that it interrupts the whole daily routine, then her doctor will want to prescribe something for her.

There will be other symptoms, too; she may feel unusually cheerful; there may be tingling in the breasts and nipples. As the uterus enlarges with the growth of the baby, pressure on the bladder may increase.

About the fourth month, the doctor will hear the baby's heartbeat when he puts his stethoscope to the mother's abdomen, and the biggest thrill comes between the fourth and fifth month when the baby begins to move about. These movements reassure the mother that her baby is alive, and delight the other members of the family. Now is the time to tell them about the new baby.

Consulting the Doctor . . .

Any one of the signs of pregnancy is reason enough to bring a woman to her doctor. When you realize the important part the mother plays in the baby's development and future life, it is easy to see why she needs good care from the moment the baby's life is suspected.

The family physician may be the one to take care of her and deliver the baby; more than half of America's babies are brought into the world by family doctors, or general practitioners. If you live in a town or city, however, you may find that the family doctor no longer delivers babies and the about-to-be mother will be referred to another doctor with specialized experience and training—the *obstetrician*.

The doctor makes a complete physical examination of the mother; this includes: Blood tests for syphilis, anemia, and other factors; a chest X-ray to test for tuberculosis; a urine examination to determine the condition of the kidneys; a blood pressure test to determine the condition of the heart; takes her weight to use as a guide against overweight or underweight as pregnancy progresses. He also examines the pelvic organs and takes measurements to determine whether the passageway is wide enough to permit the baby to be born. This is especially important in the first pregnancy.

The doctor advises the expectant mother concerning her diet and other health habits. He explains what she must observe about herself and what she must report immediately. He will see her about every month for the first seven months, every second week during the eighth month, and every week during the ninth month. If necessary, he will see her more often. He asks for a specimen of early morning urine each time and checks her blood pressure and weight. Special treatments are given according to the condition of the patient.

The father should go to the doctor on the mother's first visit. The more the doctor knows about the family history, the better job he can do in caring for the mother and preparing for the baby.

STAGES OF PREGNANCY

The baby's life begins when a tiny male germ cell (a *spermatozoon*) unites with the female egg *(ovum)* in the mother's body. This is called conception, or fertilization. Once each month one of these female eggs is discharged from the *ovary* and starts its journey through the *ovarian tube* to the *uterus,* or womb. If, during its passage through this tube, it joins a single sperm, fertilization takes place and a new life begins. The fertilized ovum then settles itself into the wall of the uterus and begins to take in food from the well-filled blood vessels in the lining.

The new cell divides and redivides very rapidly to form different types of cells that make up the human body. The cells form the body systems; as the blood vessels develop, a circulatory system is established in the baby. Food materials from the mother's blood pass into the baby's blood at the place where the baby is attached to the wall of the uterus by a group of blood vessels. This cluster of blood vessels is called the *placenta.* As the baby grows, it swings from the placenta by the *umbilical cord.* The cord is the baby's canal for taking his food supply from his mother and sending off waste materials.

The mother supplies food for the baby's growth by watching her diet and eating the food nutrients the baby needs.

It takes about 280 days for the baby's body to grow to the point where all the body systems can function on their own. The mother's uterus lengthens and widens and stretches to accommodate the baby; gradually it pushes up into the abdomen in front of the abdominal organs, and fine "stretch-lines" appear on the outer skin of the lower abdomen. The breasts enlarge and secrete a fluid (colostrum) which will feed the baby until the milk begins.

Family Attitudes . . .

Pregnancy should be a happy time for all members of the

family. The affection each holds for one another should prevent emotional upsets that can affect the mother and baby. If there are other small children, they should be told ahead of time—but not too early. All the children should be told what the new baby can and cannot do. If the newcomer is to take over the crib that an older child is now occupying, make the shift to new quarters beforehand, lest the older youngster get the idea that he is being shoved aside. Explain he is moving because he is getting so big.

It is natural for the expectant mother to experience moody spells. When you see the symptoms approaching, give her some special attention or seek out Dad and plan some little surprise. Go for a ride, see people, do some of the things she likes and her spirits will improve.

THE MOTHER'S HEALTH AND COMPLICATIONS

Pregnancy used to be considered a "delicate" condition, but now many mothers-to-be feel better than they ever have before. Normal body changes may bring about certain normal symptoms—perhaps an unusual sleepiness, a sensitivity to odors, sometimes leg cramps, in the latter part of pregnancy.

Morning sickness you know about already. It is natural that if there is a digestive upset, it will most likely be accompanied with constipation. Plenty of fruits, vegetables, and water will help correct this condition. The doctor may have other suggestions for her; laxatives or cathartics are never taken except upon the doctor's orders.

"Heartburn"—a burning sensation which has to do with digestion, not the heart—bothers some women, especially in the last few months of pregnancy. The doctor will suggest preventive measures, or medication for relief. Varicose veins may appear in the lower legs or thighs; hemorrhoids may appear and be quite painful. These conditions can lead to serious complications and should be reported immediately.

The feet and ankles may swell a little in the latter months of pregnancy. It is helpful to elevate the legs and feet while the mother-to-be is resting or to slip a pillow under the feet at night. The doctor will want to check on her diet if this occurs and may suggest she cut down on the use of salt to help the condition.

She should keep away from anyone with contagious diseases. Any exposure to a contagious disease should be reported to the doctor immediately. If she missed German measles in childhood, she will want to avoid it now at all costs. Recent discoveries show that if an expectant mother contracts this disease during the first several months, it can affect the baby.

During the last two or three months, she may notice a shortness of breath. If this becomes too severe, the doctor should be consulted about it.

Complications of pregnancy are very rare these days. However, any warning signal should be reported to the doctor immediately, even though it may not appear very serious at the time. Typical warnings are: bleeding from the vagina, or birth canal; persistent headache or blurring of the vision in the latter half of pregnancy; an excessive weight loss or gain; swelling of the hands and face; fainting spells or dizziness; abdominal cramps or pains; severe vomiting; temperature of 100 degrees or more.

Mother-baby Relationship . . .

The growing baby depends entirely upon its mother for food. He needs the same things that she does; if her diet is well balanced, so is his. She will need to increase food intake. If she fails to provide additional essentials, they will be taken from her body tissues. For example, if the mother does not drink enough milk to provide the baby with calcium and phosphorus, her teeth may become affected.

The baby gets its food through the mother's blood. The placenta vessels collect blood from the mother's vessels; then feed the large blood vessel in the umbilical cord, and so to the baby.

The Mother's Diet . . .

The mother's diet must be sufficient to build the baby's body and keep her own in repair; must keep her system in good working order and prepared for nursing the baby; must provide energy for two lives.

Milk heads the list, but others include these everyday requirements.

1. The protective foods—milk, green and yellow vegetables, lean meats, eggs and fruit, especially citrus fruits. See the Daily Food Guide, Chapter 8.

2. Minerals, for building bones, teeth and blood—milk, whole grain cereals, fruits and vegetables.

3. Vitamins, for regulating body processes and to keep the body in good working order—fruits, red meats, dry cereals, butter, cheeses.

Coffee and tea, in moderation, are usually harmless during pregnancy, provided they are not constipating, do not disturb the sleep, and are counted with the total intake each day, when sugar and cream are used.

Some pregnant women have food cravings, such as a longing for dill pickles, strawberries, or rich foods. There is no reason why mothers should not have the foods they crave if these foods do not upset them or increase their weight too much.

Exercise . . .

Exercise improves the circulation, the appetite, and the digestion; it also helps elimination and makes the mother sleep better. How much exercise she will need during pregnancy will depend upon how much exercise she has always had. The doctor may forbid strenuous activity and encourage a daily walk in the sunshine, routine housework, perhaps a little gardening. After the seventh month, the rule is to limit exercise entirely to walking and household activities. She should stay out of crowds to avoid the risk of infection and fatigue. She should never do heavy lifting or reaching.

Sometimes a mother with several children will find it difficult to indulge in a short walk, unless you help supervise them. Arrange your activities to see that Mother has her free period; amuse the children, help with accumulated chores—offering such aid before it is asked of you.

The mother who is ordinarily nervous about traffic should give up driving during pregnancy; offer to drive her on her shopping trips and errands. You can contribute much by being kind, considerate, and thoughtful during this period.

General Hygiene . . .

Having a baby usually brings a special radiance and sense of well-being to a mother; sometimes it is this glow that gives away the secret. Feeling that she looks well helps her to feel well. The daily bath will relax her. After the eighth month, the mother should not sit down in a tub because she is more susceptible to infections in the last months. Since the sweat glands work overtime removing waste materials during pregnancy, frequent hair shampooing is beneficial. An occasional offer to set her hair or give a manicure will be pleasing to her. A pretty smock will add to her morale.

The modern mother who follows a well-balanced diet and

sees her dentist regularly need not worry about teeth damage during pregnancy. It is important to have necessary dental work done so as to remove sources of infection from the mouth.

Care of the breasts during pregnancy prepares them for the baby. They should be kept clean; the nipples should not be allowed to harden. Hard nipples are likely to crack and invite infection. Light massage of the abdomen with cocoa butter will keep the skin soft and prevent permanent stretch lines from forming.

A mother's diet and regular habits should be such as to encourage good elimination. No laxatives should ever be taken without the doctor's knowledge or recommendation. The fluid intake should be such as to permit urination of three to four pints a day; if it is any less than this, it will become concentrated and may be irritating. The bladder external opening is close to the birth canal, so an irritation in this area might spread to the vagina.

The pregnant woman should have at least eight hours of uninterrupted sleep per day. Some women need more. Many employed women work through much of their pregnancy and do most of the home tasks, too. This may be done without harm if they avoid heavy work and get additional rest.

The Unborn Baby's Growth . . .

The baby begins to take form within a few days. By the sixth week, his backbones are starting to form and he has the beginnings of eyes, head, arms, legs, and sex organs. By the eighth week, he has a big head, arms, legs, even fingers and toes, and the beginning of his vital organs—heart, lungs, digestive tract. Before he is ten weeks old, his bones start to thicken and his muscles to form so that he can move around. By the seventh month, he is strong enough to live in the outside world if he were to be born prematurely. For the rest of the time, he grows stronger and bigger, so that at the time of birth he should weigh about 7½ pounds and be about 20 inches long.

NATURAL CHILDBIRTH

It helps the mother to know what to expect when she gives birth to a first baby. Although childbirth has been commonly associated with pain, authorities believe that it need not be if the mother knows, while the baby is being born, how best to use the machinery nature has bestowed upon her. Many medical schools and hospitals today are teaching *natural childbirth* with excellent results. The mother should think of birth as a process for which she can train; she learns what her body is trying to do and how it goes about it; she practices exercises to strengthen certain muscles, she learns how to co-ordinate them, how to control her breathing, and how to relax.

The theory of natural childbirth goes along with what you have learned about mind, body, and emotion. Fear always causes tension, so it is no wonder that it is taken for granted that the labor must be a painful experience. If the fear of it were removed, then most of the pain would be removed also. The success of this method depends upon the mother's temperament and her ability to co-operate in making it work. But, since more and more women are having comparatively painless labor, perhaps the time will come when the mother will actually look forward to doing her part in bringing her baby into the world without drugs.

Labor . . .

Labor is nature's way of getting the baby born. He must be pushed out of his protected life in the uterus, through the cervix, through the bony passage of the pelvis, and on down the birth canal, out into the world. The cervix is soft and stretchy. It must open; the protective sac filled with fluid must break. The *uterine muscles* contract to supply the pressure that causes the cervix to open.

The uterine contractions come about in a natural process— one of the mysteries of nature; the mother can do nothing to hurry or delay them. It begins slowly and increases gradually; the muscles alternately contract and relax and keep the tissues from tearing.

When the cervix is stretched to its fullest extent, the abdominal muscles and the diaphragm join the muscles of the uterus to push the baby out. This is where the mother must help—if she is able; she takes a deep breath, holds it, and pushes with each contraction. The baby slips down a little farther each time, then moves back slightly as the muscles relax. She relaxes as the contractions lift so that she is ready for the next push . . . and then, the baby is born.

The placenta, which is attached to the uterine wall, is expelled after the baby is born, in an effort by the uterus to rid itself of any foreign bodies. The abdominal muscles contract along with the uterine muscles; the placenta is expelled all at once. Sometimes a part of the placenta may be retained; this might cause bleeding later on. The doctor or nurse keeps a hand firmly over the empty uterus until it feels firm and hard; this means that the muscles and the blood vessels are contracted and there is less danger of bleeding dangerously.

What You Can Do . . .

Now that you know and understand the stages of pregnancy and the birth process, you will better understand the ways in which you can help someone who is expecting a baby. Knowing what to expect and do gives you a sense of confidence. Others may not be as fortunate as you; remember it is the fear of the unknown that is frightening. This fear may be harmful to both the expectant mother and the baby. Encourage her to talk freely about her feelings, her diet, the baby's layette, her plans for the first days after he is born. Besides being helpful to her, it will give you the thrill of sharing the most satisfying, rewarding experience of life.

- How and why has mother and infant care improved in recent years?
- What is prenatal care? When should the expectant mother report to her doctor?
- Your married sister, Judy, has been having spells of upset stomach almost every morning. Her menstrual periods have not stopped. Her husband insists Judy see her doctor, but Judy says she can't be pregnant because her periods haven't stopped. What will you advise Judy to do?
- Why is it important for the father to make an occasional visit to the doctor with the expectant mother?
- Should the expectant mother's diet differ from the rest of the family's? In what ways?
- How does the baby get its food essentials?
- How would you tell eight-year-old John, the youngest member of your family, that a new baby was on the way?
- In your own words explain the process of creation and growth; what is natural childbirth?

CARE OF BABY AND MOTHER

As soon as the baby is born, he takes his first breath and makes his first sound, usually a lusty cry! He looks bluish at first, but as soon as the oxygen in his lungs enters the circulating blood, he turns pink. Sometimes, if the mother has had an anesthetic, the baby does not breathe at once; when this happens, the doctor lifts him by the heels and gives one sharp slap across the buttocks, thereby stimulating him to his first cry.

The doctor clamps, cuts, and ties the umbilical cord. The nurse is ready to receive the baby in a warm blanket. The baby's eyes are wiped and drops of 1% silver nitrate, or Opthalmic Penicillin ointment, or other safe antiseptics are put in them. This is done to avoid infection which might occur from the baby's passage through the birth canal.

After the doctor hands the tiny infant over to the nurse, he sees to the expulsion of the placenta. He makes sure the uterus is firm and that a sterile pad is placed over the vaginal opening.

The baby may weigh anywhere from 5 to 10 pounds; he is anywhere from 18½ to 21 inches long. His head looks too big for his body and he does not seem to have much of a neck. His legs are bowed and spindly; his bones are soft, his muscles weak. His eyes are usually blue at birth—they may change color later on. He has rather thin hair or none at all; his skin is covered with a cheesy sort of material; underneath, the skin is very soft. He has soft spots on the top of his head because his skull bones do not meet. He cannot direct his movements or change his position. All he can do is wave his arms, and clench his fists, kick, and cry.

The Nursery and Equipment . . .

The brand new baby will need something to sleep in, something to wear, something to be bathed in, something to eat from, and something to go riding in. Father can help to get ready for baby. You can get the room ready. Here is a list of the equipment and the clothes that the baby will need. He does not ask for luxuries; only the essentials. It provides everything that the mother—and you—needs to take care of the baby safely and easily.

FOR BATH AND CLEANING

Oval bath tub of enamelware or metal, 21 to 26 inches long	Easy to keep clean
Bath apron	White washable material
2 or 3 bath towels	Soft toweling material
3 washcloths	Different from ones the family uses

Face towels	Of soft linen
1 pound of absorbent cotton	
1 package of toothpicks	You can buy the cotton swabs already made up.
1 metal or wooden tray	About 10 × 15 inches

WHAT GOES ON THE TRAY

1 covered jar for cotton balls	
1 covered soap dish with cake of mild or castile soap	
Flat covered dish	For the day's supply of oil
Covered jar	For boiled water
Covered jar for large toothpick swabs	For cleansing the mother's nipples
4-ounce nursing bottle with nipple and cover	To give water to baby
Capped 8-ounce bottle	For the day's supply of boiled water
Covered jar	For 3 sterile nipples
Covered jar	For small cotton swabs
Bar of soap	For pincushion
Bath thermometer	Can also test water with elbow
Rectal thermometer	To take baby's temperature

BABY'S CLOTHES

Bandage to hold the cord dressing in place	Can be made of outing flannel; gauze bandage. No dressing is necessary after the cord stump comes off.
4 dozen diapers, 27 × 27 inches square	Soft, without nap, absorbent, easy to wash, inexpensive, durable.
	Diaper services now provide a supply of clean diapers and wash soiled ones.

Disposable diapers	For occasional use
6 to 12 pads 11 × 18 inches	Toweling sewed doubly makes good pads.
Rubber pad 11 × 18 inches	Or any durable water-proof material.
4 shirts—size 2	Open down the front to avoid putting over baby's head.
Rubber pants	To be used occasionally; they prevent body moisture from evaporating and are hot and uncomfortable.
6 squares 36 or 40 inches square made of baby flannel	To keep baby warm; use for top sheet.
Sacques—number depends on uses found for them.	Supply more warmth in cold weather; can be used on cold mornings in warm weather; serve as short nightgowns.
Sweaters	Provide extra warmth.
Baby bunting made of soft wool	Provides extra warmth.
Nightgowns of soft cotton material	
Dresses, as mother desires	Should be soft, easily washable

NURSERY EQUIPMENT

Nursery chest.	For the things the baby uses.
Covered 2-gallon pail	For diapers. Keep half-full of water containing 1 tablespoon of borax to each quart.
Bed or crib.	Consider the space. Temporary bed may be 30 inches long, 17 inches wide, 12 inches deep.
Mattress—firm—quilt or cotton blanket, folded to right size is acceptable.	To support the child's body; for good posture.
Cotton pillow case	To slip on over mattress.
Blanket—at least 4. Light washable wool.	For additional warmth

Baby's Bath . . .

The baby may have a daily oil bath until he is about ten days old and the navel cord is dry. It preserves body heat and protects a dry or irritated skin.

HOW TO GIVE AN OIL BATH

Steps in Procedure	Remember
1. Place bath needs within reach.	Never leave baby alone on table; always hold him with firm grip.

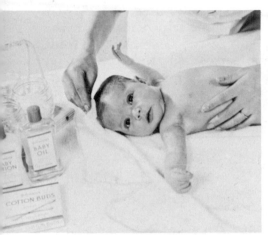 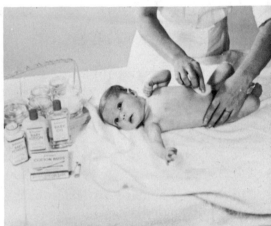

THESE AND FOLLOWING PICTURES THROUGH PAGE 323 COURTESY OF JOHNSON AND JOHNSON

Hold the baby firmly (STEP 1).   •   Use fresh cotton (STEP 7).

2. Lay baby on bath table.	You may also use the top of kitchen or bathroom sink cabinet.
3. Wash eyes, nose, ears and face as in sponge bath.	
4. Dip cotton in warmed baby oil, squeeze out excess, and clean head gently.	
5. Dry with clean cotton.	
6. Undress and wrap baby in blanket.	
7. Use fresh cotton squeezed out of oil for each part and go over body.	Wipe by light stroking (not rubbing) underarms, between fingers, buttocks, in groins and all creases.

317

Steps in Procedure

  8. Dry with clean cotton.

  9. Apply clean dressing to un-healed navel.

10. Dress baby.

A sponge bath is used if a skin lesion or wound must be protected from water, if the baby is sick, or if the room is cool. Most doctors allow the tub bath for baby as soon as the navel is healed. The shower or spray is sometimes used, if it is part of the bathinette equipment. The bathinette provides a surface on which to put the baby, with a rubber tub beneath it. It folds for storage. It is useful in a small apartment that is short on space for the baby's things. Although convenient in many ways, it is *difficult to keep clean,* so special attention must be given to cleaning it to insure the baby's health. However, the bathroom sink, if large enough, or the kitchen sink, scrubbed spotless, still is an inexpensive bathinette.

HOW TO GIVE A SPONGE BATH

The daily bath should be at a regular time, uninterrupted, unhurried.

See that the room is warm (75° to 80°) and free from drafts; water is 99°-100° F., or comfortable to your elbow. Have all materials on hand for bath and toilet according to page 314.

Steps in Procedure	**Remember**
1. Put on fresh apron.	Remove jewelry that might scratch.
2. Wash hands thoroughly.	Keep fingernails short.
3. Put on a mask if you have a cold or a sniffle.	This protects the baby.
4. Check the baby's tray.	See that everything is ready.
5. Remove covers from the soap dish, oil dish, large and small swab dishes and cotton jar.	Put the covers down inside up.
6. Undress baby except for diaper; wrap in blanket.	

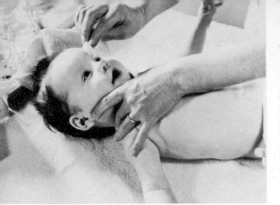
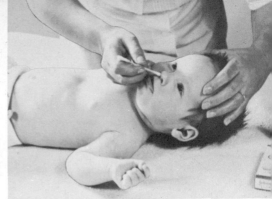

Wipe eyes with cotton (STEP 7). • Moisten and cleanse nostrils (STEP 8).

7. Hold head firmly with left hand; wipe each eye with fresh cotton squeezed out of boiled water.

Wipe from inner corner to outer corner.

8. Moisten fresh cotton applicator with baby oil and cleanse just inside each nostril.

To make applicator, twist cotton about tip of toothpick. To remove mucus, cleanse opening with twisting motion.

9. Dip fresh cotton applicator into oil lightly and wipe each outer ear and crevices behind the ear.

Do not go into the ear canal.

10. Wrap wet, squeezed out washcloth around your hand. Wash face one side at a time. Pat dry with soft towel.

11. Place arm under baby's back with hand behind the head. With free hand wet hair and wash head with soap.

Use circular motion; hold head over basin.

Care for ears (STEP 9).

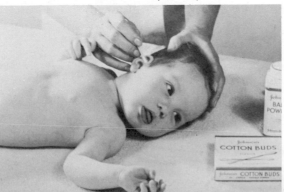

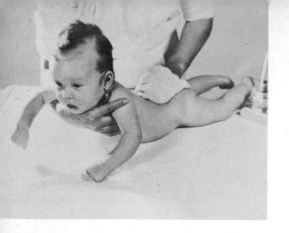

Wash the back (STEP 15).

Steps in Procedure	Remember
12. Rinse with washcloth; pat dry with towel.	
13. Remove diaper.	
14. Soap washcloth; go over body, washing all folds and creases.	Boy babies—push back foreskin; cleanse area with swab dipped in oil. Girl babies—separate labia; cleanse with cotton ball dipped in oil.
15. Turn on stomach and wash back. Rinse every part and pat dry before proceding to next.	
16. Apply clean dressing to un-healed navel and, if a boy, to circumcision.	
17. Dress baby.	Put the baby in his bed while you clean up the toilet articles. Check the baby's fingernails. Keep them short so he doesn't scratch himself.

HOW TO GIVE A TUB BATH

Steps in Procedure	Remember
1. Put on fresh apron.	
2. Wash hands thoroughly.	
3. Put a mask on over nose and mouth if you have any sign of a cold.	

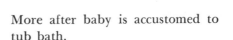

Apply soap to baby's head (STEP 9).

4. Check tray and equipment.

5. Lay small towel in tub to prevent slipping.

6. Put in about 3 inches of warm water.

   More after baby is accustomed to tub bath.

7. On table, undress baby except for diaper.

8. Cleanse eyes, nose, ears, and face as in sponge bath.

9. Apply soap to head with hand, or use washcloth.

   When baby has more hair, use liquid soap of a type that will not irritate the eyes.

10. Remove diaper.

11. Lower baby into tub, feet first, keeping head out of water.

    Slip right hand under baby's shoulders with thumb over right shoulder and fingers around right arm. Support buttocks with left hand, grasping right thigh with thumb and fingers.

12. With left hand, rinse head, letting water run well back.

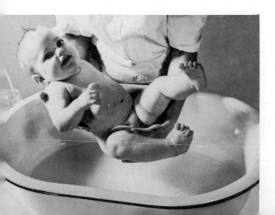

Lower baby into tub (STEP 11).

Soap and rinse front and back
(Step 13).

Steps in Procedure	Remember
13. Soap front and lower part of body. Reverse hold; soap, then rinse back with washcloth. Reverse hold, rinse front.	Never turn baby over while in tub.
14. Lift out of tub.	Using same hold as when you lifted baby into tub.
15. Lay on towel; pat dry.	Give special attention to creases.
16. Wrap in blanket and prepare for dressing.	
17. Moisten fingers from cotton ball dipped in oil and apply to all creases—around neck, armpits, arms, legs, feet.	With cotton, push back foreskin on boy babies. Cleanse the area with cotton swab dipped in oil. For girl babies, separate the labia; cleanse with cotton ball dipped in oil.

Drying the baby (Step 15).

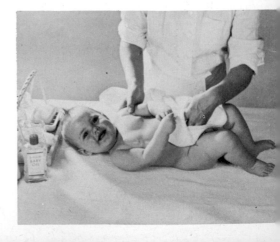

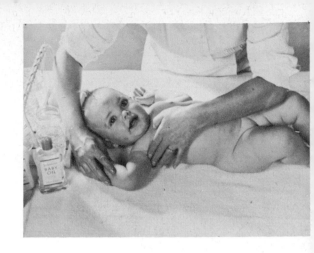

Applying baby oil (STEP 17).

18. Sprinkle baby powder on cotton ball and lightly pat over large areas of body.

19. Apply cream to any irritated part.

20. Dip cotton ball lightly in oil and apply to groins, buttocks, creases in diaper area.

21. Check nails—hands and feet. Trim if necessary.

22. Dress baby.

To bathe baby in the *bathinette,* the procedure is the same as in tub bath except baby can be laid on a hammock in the rubber tub and his soaped body bathed with spray. Preparation for dressing is done on the bathinette's lower table top.

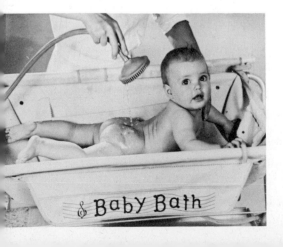

The bathinette.

Three Ways to Diaper The Baby . . .

Below, for those who are just learning the art of diapering, are three different methods for you to try.

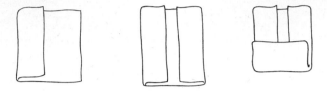

CONVENTIONAL METHOD

1. Fold one edge of diaper over, as shown.
2. Fold the other edge over.
3. Fold bottom edge up.
4. Place baby on diaper, pin at sides.

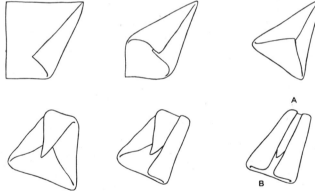

DRAWINGS COURTESY OF GEORGE WOODS, SONS, AND CO.

NURSE'S METHOD

1. Fold lower right corner part way.
2. Fold left corner to form cone.
3. Fold bottom corner in, making a triangle.
4. Fold point down (to baby's size).
5. Fold right side part way over.
6. Fold left side in same way.
7. End "A" goes to the front on a boy, end "B" to front on a girl.

A TAILORED DIAPER METHOD

1. Spread tailored diaper out flat.

2. Turn up the bottom section.

3. Flip in corners, then raise lower section.

4. Place baby on diaper, pin tabs in front. Chain-linked pins come with this diaper.

After-Delivery Care of Mother . . .

The mother will be tired. After her husband sees her for a few minutes, he should leave her. He probably feels the need of rest himself, for he has gone through an emotional strain, too. If the mother rests now, she is less likely to feel the let-down that sometimes comes after having the baby. The next few days should be happy. She sees and nurses her baby; her tummy is nice and flat again; she visits with relatives and friends.

A new mother should never be left unwatched immediately after delivery. Although this is a big responsibility and you may never be called upon to help in a home delivery, it is good to know the signs of hemorrhage, since this may occur after the mother returns home. Should she be pale, her skin clammy, and the sheet stained a bright red, get help immediately. Until help comes, put your hands on either side of her abdomen over the uterus and press down hard. This stimulates the relaxed uterine muscles to contract.

The *lochia* is the normal discharge from the uterus after the baby is born. It is made up of blood and the old lining of the uterus and lasts about three weeks. It starts out bright red, fades to a pink and finally turns yellow. If the lochia is still red after two weeks, it should be reported to the doctor.

In about six weeks the uterus is back to normal; this is hastened if the mother nurses her baby.

The *perineum* and the *vaginal opening* (pelvic outlet) are covered with a sterile pad, held in place with a binder or sanitary belt. The pad is changed whenever it is soiled; sterile water is poured over the perineum after voiding. Sometimes the patient has perineal stitches if the perineum was torn or cut during delivery, but these should be fairly well healed before the mother leaves the hospital. If the baby is delivered at home, the doctor will tell you how to care for these.

Nursing the Baby . . .

The cheapest, simplest and best way to feed baby is to breast feed. The mother's milk is free from harmful organisms and always ready. The new mother is spared the chore of making formulas. Another benefit is emotional, a sense of continuing to give life to the baby she brought into this world.

If the mother is happy, wants to nurse her baby, is not worried or overtired, it is likely that she will have an excellent milk supply. The mother's mental attitude will affect both the quality and the supply of the milk; her emotional upsets will affect the baby's digestion.

Some mothers think that nursing their baby will make them fat. There will be no weight gain during the breast feeding period if she watches her diet. Others fear that the breasts will be permanently changed. This need not be. If they are properly supported by well-fitted brassieres before the baby is born and during the months he is being nursed, then there will be no permanent sagging due to breast feeding.

Care of the Breasts . . .

The breasts contain a thin, watery fluid called colostrum, until about the third day after delivery. The baby is put to breast for the first time from eight to twelve hours after he is born. Nursing helps to stimulate the flow of milk. The colostrum is the beginning food, having a laxative effect; then comes the nourishing mother's milk. This helps protect the baby from infections. The breasts become full and hard; the baby relieves this condition when he is fed.

A good nursing brassiere helps to support the breasts. Sometimes they become so full that there is more milk than the baby needs and it may become painful. Perhaps the doctor might suggest pumping with a special bulb and glass cup but this stimulates the secretion of milk. If the baby nurses well and empties the breasts each time, the supply of milk usually regulates itself. The mother's diet affects both the quality and quantity of her milk.

The nipples should be protected from cracks which might be a likely entrance for infection. Wash before and after each nursing; protect from rough clothing; have the mother release the baby's jaws before drawing the nipple from his mouth; put the whole nipple in his mouth so his jaws close beyond its base.

Sometimes when the nipples become dried and crack, they need protection during the nursing procedure. A nursing shield is a glass, cup-shaped affair, with a rubber nipple fitted on the end of it. You put the shield over the outer edge of the mother's nipple.

Feeding Schedule . . .

The usual baby feeding schedule is every four hours. It usually begins at 6:00 A.M. but can begin any time so long as the feedings are at four hour intervals. After the third week, the 2:00 A.M. feeding may be omitted. The baby nurses twenty minutes—ten minutes at each breast.

Just like all time tables, the feeding schedule may be changed—on the baby's firm "demand." In demand feeding, the baby is fed only when he is hungry and when he says so; he works out his own schedule.

Try to time the bath so that the baby may feed immediately afterwards. The mother should feel rested, since baby's eating habits respond to the feeling in her body. She will be more comfortable sitting up with her back and arm supported. An armchair will be best, with a pillow supporting her arm. Be sure she is warm enough and clear of drafts. *Wash both her hands and your hands* before you give her the baby.

EQUIPMENT:

- Jar of sterile water.
- Jar of large cotton applicators.

Steps in Procedure	Remember
1. Cleanse the nipple and the area around it with a moistened applicator.	To protect the baby and the nipple from infection. Start with the nipple and work outward.
2. Put the baby on the mother's arm which rests on the pillow.	Rest his head in the bend of her arm, with his head slightly raised. He is less likely to swallow air in this position.
3. Raise the breast and direct the nipple into the baby's mouth.	Be sure he has the nipple and is in a comfortable position. Don't be in a hurry for he knows instinctively if you are upset.
4. When he has nursed for 10 minutes, change him to the other breast and repeat the above procedure for 10 minutes more.	

Steps in Procedure	Remember
5. Press the baby's lower jaw gently away from the nipple.	To release his hold on the nipple and to prevent injuring it.
6. Remove the baby from the breast.	
7. Cleanse the nipples with moistened applicators.	Use a separate applicator for each breast.
8. Hold the baby over your shoulder and "bubble" him. Pat his back gently or rub with a circular motion.	Place clean diaper over shoulder first. Bubbling releases air bubbles and prevents him from spitting up milk; makes him comfortable

Bottle Feeding . . .

If it happens that the mother has less milk than the baby needs, the mother is encouraged to nurse him oftener to build up the supply, and he may be bottle fed additional feedings—the amount the doctor decides.

It might be necessary to put baby on a formula immediately. Besides an inadequate milk supply, illness might make it inadvisable for the mother to nurse. Drugs are now given that dry up the breasts without much discomfort.

Baby's Formula . . .

Although the basis of most formulas is milk, the doctor will prescribe the kind that is best for the individual. The kinds of milk used are evaporated or liquid modified milk, powdered milk, and fresh bottle milk. Even though you use pasteurized fresh milk from the bottle, it should be boiled for two reasons: (1) Greater safety; (2) easier to digest. Cooking is one means of modifying cow's milk so that small, soft curds are formed in the stomach, more like those resulting from breast milk. The disadvantages of boiling are: (1) Changes the flavor; (2) makes milk constipating; (3) destroys vitamin C.

How to Make the Formula . . .

The doctor will prescribe the formula to use. Never use the formula equipment for anything else; store it in a clean place. Plan to make the formula when the mother and baby will not need you, when the kitchen is free, and when you have the time to proceed uninterrupted.

EQUIPMENT:

- Sterilizer with rack or deep kettle.
- Six 8-ounce and two 4-ounce bottles, complete with nipples and caps.
- One 32-ounce measuring pitcher.
- Set of measuring spoons.
- Long-handled mixing spoon or stirring rod.
- Funnel-strainer.
- Pair long-handled tongs.
- Can opener.
- Table knife (for leveling powdered milk or sugar).
- Dinner plate (to serve as sterile tray).
- Nipple jar with perforated lid for sterilizing nipples.

To Sterilize the Equipment . . .

In this process, the nursing bottles and articles are sterilized first. Sterile ingredients are used to make the formula, which is then placed in the sterile bottles. Do not contaminate bottles with your hands or unsterile objects. To sterilize *plastic bottles,* follow the directions on the plastic bottle wrap.

1. Clean all equipment.
2. Put freshly washed bottles in sterilizer, placing them upside down in rack. If using large kettle, place towel in bottom, then place bottles in upside down.
3. Add one quart of water and bring to boil.
4. Put the nipples and caps in jar with perforated lid; place jar upside down in the center.
5. Between the bottle put the spoons, can opener, strainer, funnel, *with tongs in last with handles up.*
6. Put cover on sterilizer or kettle and boil for 5 minutes Start counting time when steam comes from sterilizer.
7. Remove rack of bottles from sterilizer. Outside of bottles may be touched with fingers but not top edges.
8. Place other articles from the sterilizer on a sterile plate or on the lid of the sterilizer ready for use.

To Prepare the Formula . . .

1. Put a mask over your nose and mouth if you have any infection.

2. Wash your hands.

3. Put water in pan on to boil; fill water bottles.

4. Open the can or the bottle of milk with the can opener.

5. Measure the required amount of milk into the measuring pitcher.

6. Add the rest of the ingredients—level the spoonfuls with the knife.

7. Stir the formula with the long-handled spoon.

8. Fill the bottles, using the funnel and strainer.

9. Pick up the nipples one at a time, snap on the bottle; cover with cap. With certain types of bottles the nipples fit on the bottle, tips down; the cap and cover screw over top.

10. Put the bottles on the plate and store in refrigerator immediately.

To Prepare a Bottle of Milk or Water for Feeding . . .

1. Remove the cap and place nipple in position.

2. Stand the bottle in a deep pan of warm water or use an electric bottle warmer.

3. Shake a few drops on the inside of your wrist to test the temperature and the size of the nipple hole. Should be warm; should drop from nipple. Discard nipples with holes too large.

Care of Bottle and Nipples . . .

1. After use, remove the nipple; empty the bottle; rinse it well with warm water. Fill with cool water and put aside on tray in safe place.

2. Wash the nipples and the caps inside and out with brush, removing every bit of milk.

3. Drop the nipples in a dry jar.

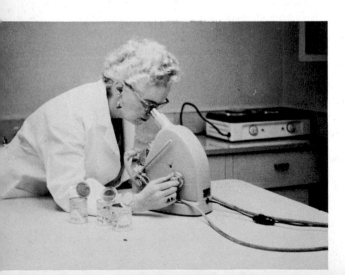

Food experts with the finest equipment and modern research techniques work full time to learn and prepare what is best for the baby's diet.

LIBBY, MCNEILL AND LIBBY

Adding Other Foods . . .

The doctor will add other foods very soon. The baby's diet for the first year will include the following:

2 or 3 weeks	Cod liver oil; vitamin concentrates.
1 month	Orange juice.
2 months	Prune juice, tomato juice, apple juice.
3 months	Cereals, banana flakes.
4 months	Strained spinach, carrots, string beans, peas, beets, butter, cottage cheese, egg yolk, scraped ripe banana, Zweiback to chew on.
6 months	Pineapple juice, apple sauce, stewed prunes, apricots, peaches, whole egg.
7-8 months	Baked potato, scraped liver or beef, custard.
9 months	Crisp bacon.
10 months	Ground lamb, beef, chicken; mashed vegetables.
12 months	White fish, raw carrots, lettuce, celery.

The vegetables are strained at first; later they may be coarser. Canned vegetables, fruits, custards and other foods are well prepared and convenient to use. Give him very small amounts of new foods at first. Cover him with a bib and never mind the mess. Encourage him to feed himself as soon as he can.

Baby's Laundry . . .

Diapers should be plentiful enough so that they need to be washed only once a day. Use a mild soap, being extra careful to rinse every bit of soap out because the baby's skin is very easily irritated. Hang the diapers in the sun if you can. Use without ironing.

Squares of cotton placed inside the diaper prevent some staining; after the baby's bowel elimination becomes regular, you will know about when to line the diaper.

Other clothing that is wet with the baby's urine should be washed with mild soap and rinsed thoroughly. Dry outdoors whenever possible.

New Mother's Diet . . .

Most mothers are ready for a regular diet after they are rested. Of course, if your mother or other patient is in hospital confinement, you will have little to do those first few days except prepare things at home—and it is well to think about giving her a nourishing diet. A balanced diet, with additional protein, vitamins, and minerals, is usually best. Her food must supply her own needs and still give the baby enough nourishment to develop and grow. She will need plenty of fluid. The daily diet should include at least the following:

> 1 quart of milk a day (skimmed if mother is overweight)
> 1 egg
> ¼ pound lean meat, fish or poultry
> ½ cup of navy, kidney, lima beans or peas
> 2 to 4 servings of vegetables
> 4 servings of fruits—2 of them citrus
> 1 serving of potato
> 4 slices of whole wheat or cracked wheat bread or substitute
> 3 tablespoons butter or fortified margarine

Weight . . .

Due to a number of factors, the mother usually loses from ten to as many as twenty pounds after her baby is born. For a short time all of her organs have been more active than usual causing fluid loss through the skin, kidneys, bowels, uterus, and breasts. The nursing mother loses more than the mother that does not nurse her baby. She will most likely be back to her normal weight within six weeks if care is given to diet and the exercise program the doctor precribes.

Exercises . . .

The doctor will prescribe exercises to suit the needs of the patient; however, there are certain standard ones which it will be helpful for you to know. The mother is encouraged to lie on her abdomen for at least two hours every day to bring the uterus forward into its normal position. Ten days after delivery (some doctors prefer this before) she is instructed to take the knee-chest position (patient is on floor with knees and chest resting on floor, knees slightly apart) for approximately ten minutes both morning and evening to bring the uterus up into normal position, slightly tilted forward. She will keep up with the exercise routine until she goes to see the doctor for her next check-up.

Elimination . . .

The mother may be constipated for several days after the baby is born, and she may also have difficulty in urinating. There are several possible reasons for this, such as fatigue, or a decrease in bladder tone. Perineal stitches also make voiding painful, and pressure on the abdominal and bladder muscles during labor and delivery may cause slight, temporary paralysis. An anesthetic often disturbs the voiding processes temporarily. Usually, the diet will regulate these normal functions within a few days. The doctor may order an enema to stimulate the bowels. Sometimes hemorrhoids appear after delivery; rectal suppositories or cold packs are usually prescribed to help this condition.

Natural birth may avoid the worst of the above problems, since muscle control is the main factor involved.

After Pains . . .

For the first few days after delivery, the mother may have abdominal cramps; this is caused by the uterine muscles contracting in an effort to return to normal and expel the lochia. Breast feeding also often starts "after-pains"; they decrease as the uterus muscle tone returns.

Check-up . . .

Before the mother leaves the hospital, she should be advised to make an appointment with her doctor for her six weeks check-up. He will examine her pelvis, check her weight, her blood pressure, and her general condition. If the family doctor has delivered the baby, he will want to see the baby sooner; any questions the mother has will be answered at this time.

WHEN BABY COMES HOME

When a newborn baby comes to your house, be prepared for many new and interesting experiences. Each baby is an individual, with his own special looks, personality—and, yes—mischief. The theme song of having a new baby in the home is: Enjoy yourself! Relax and watch the phases of this young life unfold. If you can enjoy and appreciate each new development, you will appreciate even more your active part in it.

Rest . . .

The tiny baby will sleep away most hours of the day. Ordinarily if he is comfortably fed, dry, has regular feeding habits and is put into a good bed—he sleeps. If any of these essentials are disturbed, he may fuss; many mothers and older brothers and sisters fall into the habit of rocking baby at such times. But if rocking becomes associated with sleep, you will find baby soon demands it.

Elimination . . .

Before the baby is very old, his habits of elimination will be established. Be matter-of-fact about changing diapers, letting him know it is the correct thing; this will help later when toilet training time comes. Don't give the impression that changing diapers is an unpleasant duty and that there is something unpleasant about elimination.

Food . . .

A healthy baby looks forward to his food eagerly. If he refuses to nurse or take his bottle, something is wrong. He may have other disturbing symptoms: Spitting up, vomiting, an unusual amount of gas, or muscle spasms. A cough or nasal discharge may block his nose and interfere with nursing. Any such departure from normal calls for the doctor's care.

Baby's Cry . . .

The normal body temperature for a newborn baby is 98° to 99° F. His temperature must be taken by rectum. It may rise if he is too warm, does not get enough water, or has an infection or some other body disturbance.

Crying is the only means by which the baby can call for help. It does not always mean that he is hungry. He may be too hot or cold. You must regulate his temperature by his clothing, blankets and the temperature of the room. Hunger cries are healthy, lusty cries. If he tries to put his fingers into his mouth or makes sucking noises, this is a sign, too, that he is hungry.

Cries after feedings may mean there is still some gas that escaped the bubbling, or his formula may not be right and may need adjusting.

And, of course, the baby cries when he is wet. The acid content of the urine is irritating to tender skin. When you change the diaper, look for signs, such as liquid content or color, which will show whether the diet needs adjusting.

• What do you understand by labor? At what stage would you call the doctor?

• You are called to stay with your sister when she comes home from the hospital with her baby. The baby is four days old. What will you do about formula?

• It's baby's bathtime; you have a sore throat, but there is no one else available to give baby his bath. What should you do?

• Why do you test baby's bottle on your wrist? What would you do if the milk is too hot?

• What is the difference between cow's milk and mother's milk?

• Why do you boil cow's milk before using it in the formula?

18: THE CHILD

The younger members of your family are the future citizens of our country. You have a responsibility toward helping them adjust and meet the problems that are likely to arise. If you don't have younger brothers and sisters at home, you may serve as a helper or baby sitter—or you may be looking to the future, knowing that the study of child care will some day help you in the care of your own family.

THE WELL CHILD

We begin with the well child because it is hoped that your experience will largely be concerned with children in good health. Childhood habits and training also explain many grown-up actions.

The Younger Member and You . . .

Every child has a personality of his own, and yet you and all others he knows will have an effect on his personality.

The parents, family, teachers, doctors, nurses, dentists, and nutritionists are all concerned with his health; but there are other needs that persist all his life. In addition to good physical care, all children need to feel that they are loved; they belong; they amount to something.

These factors may be classified as follows:

1. **Security**—supplied by his parents' love, his family world, his playmates, the feeling that he belongs and has a place of his own.

2. **Health**—protected by food, clothing, a home, rest, play, and health care.

3. **Satisfaction**—that comes from learning to use his body and mind in work and play.

Home is the child's first world. Little by little this enlarges to include the neighborhood, the church, the school, and social activities. He meets more and more people with whom he must get along. This is how he makes friends, learns to share, to take responsibility. He meets people that look different from him, people whose skin is a different color from his, people who act differently. How he accepts these differences depends largely upon the seeds of behavior and attitudes set up in his own home. Here the child in the large family sometimes has the advantage over the only child. The child who knows he is liked by his parents, brothers, and sisters is the child who is emotionally free to like others. The family in which the youngsters are treated democratically is the family from which come friendly, unprejudiced attitudes and relationships with outsiders.

Parents, family ties, family income, physical and mental makeup all affect a child's development. Some children develop more rapidly than others. You should be familiar with what to expect from a child of a certain age group, yet it is not wise to judge him simply by his age. Rapid growth may make him clumsy for a while. He may start more slowly in school—and catch up later. He may have talented parents, yet be just average himself. Try to accept him for what he is, rather than for what you want him to be. Give him a chance to develop *in his own way*. He will surprise you!

MILESTONES IN NORMAL BEHAVIOR PATTERNS

One of the most important factors in understanding chil

Before the second birthday, the child rides in a stroller . . .

dren is knowing the way in which they grow. You probably know vaguely how a child should behave, and what he can or cannot do, but, actually, if given some thought, you will realize your ideas about normal development may be a bit hazy.

Remember, a child grows up in several ways. Milestones represent much more than the mere activities that are named on the following pages, for the activities are the outward sign of the inner development in matters of responsibility and independence. The child does not progress by sudden jumps and the maturing processes do not always follow logical order. For instance, a boy may be able to dry his hands before he can wash them. A girl may be able to sew before she can thread a needle. Children may read before they write, and write before they can spell. Though the child's progress may appear to be hit-and-miss to you, it is likely to be the logical way, so far as the youngster is concerned.

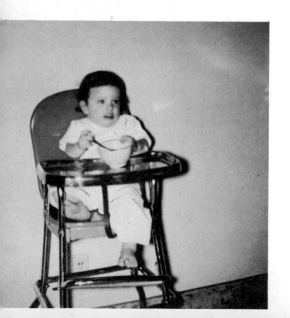

. . . eats with a spoon without too much spilling . . .

. . . gets about the yard fairly well . . .

Let us look now at some milestones along the way to growing up. *Before the second birthday,* the child:

1. Crawls upstairs without help, gets about the house and yard with only occasional problems. Gives up baby carriage to ride in a stroller, or walk.

2. Eats with spoon from bowl or cup, without help or too much spilling. Chooses between suitable foods and substances unfit for eating.

3. Performs useful things, such as "helping the baby" and bringing named objects from nearby places. Opens and closes doors, climbs up on chairs to reach, removes simple obstacles from path. Uses basket to carry things.

4. "Helps" with undressing by removing socks and shoes. Uses short sentences, and has vocabulary of twenty-five words or more. Names familiar objects for practical purposes.

. . . and helps a younger child.

339

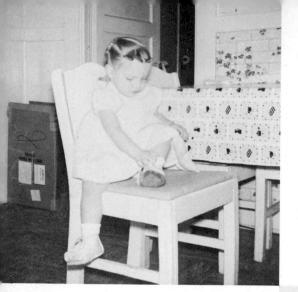

NORMAL BEHAVIOR PATTERNS

Before the second birthday, the child helps with undressing . . .

. . . and amuses himself in the yard . . .

. . . without constant supervision.

Before the third birthday, the child enjoys more advanced playthings, like a rocking horse . . .

Before the third birthday, the child:

1. Occupies self without "looking after" at own play such as drawing with crayons, building with blocks, dressing dolls, looking at pictures. Uses blunt-end scissors in cutting paper and cloth; is not purposefully destructive.

2. Uses fork without much spilling, and eats solid food that does not require cutting. Can get drink of water unassisted, turning water tap on and off. Dries own hands if washed.

3. Gives simple accounts of own experiences and tells stories that can be understood. By action or speech makes known desire to go to toilet—seldom has daytime "accidents."

4. Avoids simple hazards. "Comes in out of the rain." Is careful about falling when on stairs and high places, avoids sharp edges, broken glass, etc., and should keep out of the streets. Takes wrapper off candy.

. . . or a doll, and begins to understand the danger of playing in the street.

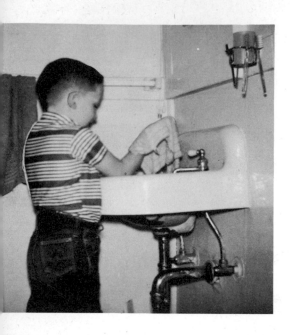

Before the fourth birthday, the child washes his hands acceptably.

Before the fourth birthday, the child:

1. Washes hands acceptably without help, to the point that he can dry them without soiling the towel. Puts on and buttons clothes, but may need help otherwise in dressing. Few daytime "accidents."

2. Walks downstairs without help, one step at a time. Runs, skips, marches, and shows other simple rhythm.

3. Takes part in such group activities as simple games; joins in simple tea parties and activities requiring no skill. Performs for others if encouraged.

4. "Helps" in small ways about the house, such as running short errands, picking things up, feeding pets, dusting.

Before the fifth birthday, the child:

1. Dresses self except for tying laces, ribbons or ties. Does all own buttoning, but clothing is laid out. May need help with muffler or overshoes, especially with difficult, close-fitting clothes.

2. Washes face, except ears, acceptably and dries his face without help. Goes to toilet alone without help; brushes teeth without supervision; unfastens own clothes; no daytime "accidents."

3. Goes about neighborhood unattended; may be restricted as to areas or "deadlines" so he can be found easily, but should

Before the fifth birthday, the child makes simple but recognizable drawings . . .

be on his own within his limits. Plays in small groups, such games as tag, jump-rope, hopscotch, marbles, etc.

4. Draws with pencil and crayon simple but recognizable forms of man, house, animal, and landscape.

. . . and plays more adventurously; he may be given some freedom to go about the neighborhood.

Before the sixth birthday, the child plays group games . . .

Now let us look at the milestones he should be passing from here on his way to his twelfth birthday. *Before the sixth birthday,* the child:

1. Takes care of himself unsupervised, outside his own yard; manages roller skates, sled, wagon, scooter, and other play vehicles.

2. Plays simple games with others that require taking turns, observing rules, attaining goals, without undue squabbling.

3. Goes to school unattended. He may go with friends, but no one is in direct charge of him. Learns to print simple words and his first name without copying.

4. Is trusted with small amounts of money to make clearly stated purchases. He carries out directions in returning purchases, but he may not be able to make change.

. . . and manages simple play vehicles.

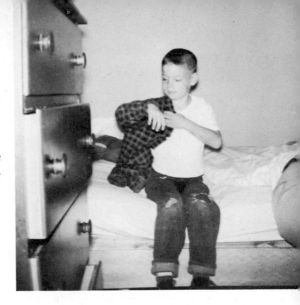

Before the seventh birthday, the child goes to bedroom alone, undresses . . .

Before the seventh birthday, the child:

1. Uses knife at table. At play, cuts, folds, pastes. Takes care of a doll quite well. Sews crudely if needle is threaded. Cannot tie knot. Enjoys making simple figures in clay.

2. Writes (not prints) legibly with pencil a dozen or more simple words, correctly spelled. Does so at own desire, or from dictation, but does not need to copy.

3. Takes bath unassisted. Needs help in preparing tub, washing ears, drying hair, and touching up.

4. Performs bedtime operations without help; goes to bedroom alone, undresses, attends to toilet, turns out light according to routine. May be tucked in as a matter of sentiment, but requires no assistance.

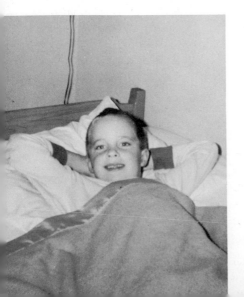

. . . completes his preparations and puts himself to bed without assistance.

Before the eighth birthday, the child reads a clock . . .

Before the eighth birthday, the child:

1. Uses table knife for cutting meat. He may need help with tough or difficult pieces such as around bones.

2. Reads ordinary clock or watch correctly to nearest quarter hour, and actually uses clock for practical purposes. Answers telephone.

3. Brushes and combs hair acceptably without help or going over when dressing, going out, or receiving company.

4. Boys prefer activities that do not require much organized skill, such as sandlot baseball or basketball, follow-the-leader, hide-and-seek, hiking, and bicycle riding. Girls prefer playing house, school, nurse-doctor, and other imitations of home and social affairs.

. . . answers the telephone helpfully . . .

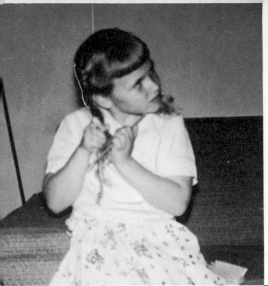

. . . brushes and combs her
hair acceptably.

Boys like loosely organized activities.

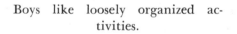

Girls imitate home and social
affairs.

Before the ninth birthday, the child makes use of tools . . .

Before the ninth birthday, the child:

1. Makes some use of tools such as hammer, saw, or screw driver; uses household and sewing utensils; handles simple garden implements successfully; writes legibly in longhand.

2. Helps with such routine household tasks as dusting, sweeping, setting table, washing dishes, making beds, raking lawn. Assumes responsibility for share of household chores.

3. Reads independently comic strips, movie and TV titles, simple stories, elementary news items for own entertainment or information.

4. Takes bath acceptably without any help; undresses, prepares tub or shower, washes and dries self (except hair), without need of touching up.

. . . and no longer needs help preparing a bath.

BEFORE TENTH BIRTHDAY

Before the tenth birthday, the child may go to many parts of the community alone, and has few restricted play areas . . .

Before tenth birthday, the child:

1. Looks after all his own needs at table; helps himself, handles such items as baked potatoes, boiled eggs, difficult cuts of meat.

2. Buys useful articles and exercises some choice in making purchases. Is responsible for safety of articles, money, and correct change. Does this independently or can be relied upon to follow directions.

3. Goes about home and community freely, alone or with friends. There may be forbidden areas, but the restrictions do not confine the child's activities to his block neighborhood.

4. Runs useful errands; is trusted as a messenger, or to carry out orders to and from not-too-distant points, with clear instructions.

. . . at the table he tends to his own needs.

Before the eleventh birthday, the child writes occasional letters . . .

Before the eleventh birthday, the youngster:

1. Writes occasional letters to friends or relatives on own initiative, or following mild suggestions. Does so without help except perhaps in spelling unfamiliar words.

2. Uses telephone for practical purposes; looks up number, makes call, and carries on sensible, purposeful conversation.

3. Does occasional or brief work on own initiative about the house or neighborhood, such as housework, helping in care of children, or running errands.

4. Responds to magazine, radio, TV, or other advertising by mailing coupons, requesting samples, sending for literature, and ordering from catalogues. May keep up a collecting hobby.

. . . uses the telephone for his own purposes . . . responds to advertising.

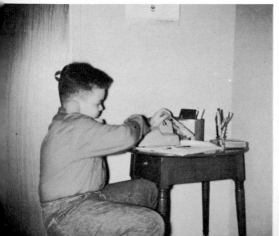

Before the twelfth birthday, the child reads for information or enjoyment . . . cleans hair thoroughly . . .

Before the twelfth birthday, the youngster:

1. Makes useful articles or does easy repair work. Cooks
or sews in small way; does a little gardening; raises pets; writes
brief stories; produces fairly mature artwork.

2. Is sometimes left alone at home or at work for an hour
or so, and is successful in looking after his needs and those of
younger children left in his care. Takes interest in competitive
skills.

3. Reads for practical information or own enjoyment stories or news items in papers, magazine articles, library book
stories.

4. Is responsible for a thorough job at cleaning hair, but
may need reminding to do so.

. . . and may be left at home
alone, when occupied.

THE CHILD IS AN INDIVIDUAL—SICK OR WELL

A young child is full of curiosity of what goes on about him; it is normal that he should want to investigate. He may be too young to recognize danger and must rely upon grownups' word for some things. As far as possible, he should know why some things are forbidden. He has the right to explanations— truthful, reasonable answers to his questions.

A child wants to feel that he is "somebody." Every time he does something new, he gains maturity. If he helps some- one, he realizes that people depend on him. A word of praise tells him that you recognize and appreciate his worth. Let him choose what to do, when convenient; let him choose the book you read at bedtime. He will respond to suggestions such as, "When shall we read your story—before dinner or after your bath? You choose the time."

Play teaches *very young* children and gives them a chance to use up extra energy; it also tires them. They need both ac- tive and quiet play. Give a child toys he can handle easily and safely. Select washable, non-toxic toys for the very young; small children love to throw things on the floor and put them in their mouths. As a child becomes older, he finds he can direct his fingers and can use colored crayons. He likes fat crayons that make wide marks. A child's play gives him a chance to express feelings that he cannot put into words. The things he makes sometimes tell much of his feelings. Find out what kind of games and stories he likes and learn to tell a story well. Use words that suit the child's age and give him your whole attention while talking to him.

School Problems . . .

A child really begins to manage his life when he starts to school. It is natural that by moving into this world, prob- lems arise. He is trying to handle affairs which sometimes grown-ups do not understand. He is moving into an unfamiliar world with new faces; he must follow new rules. He must struggle between following his own wishes and those of others. If you appreciate this struggle, you can help him to help him- self. Make him feel safe and loved and show him how every- one has similar problems, by talking about them. It is some- times easier for him to sulk, cry, or throw a tantrum when things do not go the way he wants them; you must be careful that these tricks do not get by you. They are attempts to make him feel better inside. Help the child to substitute more desirable ways of behavior, always remembering what he is trying to accomplish. If he fails by attempting a task that is too difficult, help him find a satisfactory substitute.

HABITS AND TRAINING

Food Habits . . .

Eating is fun for the hungry child. Fast growing, *active, happy* youngsters are always hungry. Lack of success, loneliness, will make them resist food. A child's diet at any age should be enough to keep his body growing properly. The protein requirement increases with age. See Chapters 7 and 8. The most important protein foods in his diet are meat and milk and eggs. A quart of milk a day supplies most of the young child's protein requirement. Proteins build muscle and bone. Most of his energy comes from carbohydrates—cereals, macaroni, bread, potatoes. The amount of carbohydrates needed in the diet depends upon the individual child; an active child will need more than a quiet one. Sick children, as a rule, need less carbohydrates. Some fats are necessary to help the body use vitamins and to make food taste better. The above foods, plus green and yellow vegetables, usually supply enough vitamins and minerals except vitamin D.

Vitamin D is needed by growing children to make strong bones and teeth. The amount supplied in his food may be inadequate so he should have it added to the diet in some other way. Growing children usually need cod liver oil or vitamin D in all but the summer season and sometimes, even then. The amount of water a child needs varies with the weather, the climate, and his activity. Usually from three to five glasses per day are required. Be sure that sick children get enough water, because they will not often ask for it or may be unable to handle a drinking glass.

Allergic children cannot eat certain foods. They may lose the food immediately after it is swallowed, or hives (rash) may appear on the skin a little while later. If the food disagrees with the child, the doctor should be consulted about omitting it from the diet. Of course, there are times when refusal of foods has nothing to do with the food itself. It may be a way of getting attention or it may be in imitation of older family members.

Mealtimes should be pleasant occasions that the child enjoys. A tired or sleepy child cannot always do a meal justice; emotional upsets affect him as they do grown-ups. Take it for granted that a child in good spirits will eat what you give him and never let him know you are concerned about whether he will eat it or not. Do not make him the center of attention at the table, yet make him feel he belongs. Encourage him to eat a little of everything. When he has had all the time he needs, remove his plate or tray even though he has not eaten; *do not talk about it*. He will probably be hungry enough at his next meal to make up for any underfeeding.

Make him comfortable in his highchair or at the family table. It is better for him to eat with you. Give the small learner unbreakable utensils; do not expect too much of a child who is learning to feed himself. Protect his clothes with a bib, and the floor with newspapers. Encourage him to feed himself, even though it does take extra time and sometimes is messy.

Bright-colored bowls and dishes encourage small children to eat. Give a child plenty of time for his meal but not too much —about half an hour. If the child dawdles make helpful suggestions to speed him along. *Don't nag.*

Protect the bed beneath the *sick child's* tray; tell him not to worry if he spills something, for you know it is hard to eat in bed. A child in bed can feed himself if he is well enough; help him with the hard parts, such as cutting meat and buttering bread.

Rest . . .

Children from age *two to six* should sleep half the time. Two-year-olds usually sleep from 1 to 2 hours at naptime; the nap gradually decreases as the child grows older but should be encouraged until he starts school. Four- to five-year-olds should have a rest period even though they do not nap; it is especially good for the child who becomes overstimulated. A child should be put to bed in a quiet room. Although it is always desirable for him to have a room alone, it is not always possible. If two or more children share the same room, a definite schedule for all must be established. Tell the youngest that everyone sleeps more at his age. Ask older children to support you in this honest claim. Children should be lightly but warmly covered. The room should be well ventilated. See that all wants are attended to—take him to the toilet, give him a drink of water, give him his favorite cuddly toy if he wants it. Sometimes a child may be afraid of the dark; a low night light may be kept in the room and withdrawn as he matures. Over-excitement just before bedtime will keep him from going to sleep; avoid it.

If possible, always give necessary treatments some time before you get a sick child ready for the night. A bedtime story and a little extra affection will not make him feel so much alone. Always reassure a sick child that you will be ready to come if he should awaken and need you.

Toilet Training . . .

The healthy child usually falls into a good bowel routine. Regular diet and regular meals encourage regular elimination. Here again, he is an individual; his own rate of digestion and absorption of food will determine his time of elimination. It is important that this time be treated as a pleasant, relaxed time, and not as a time for struggle or threats. Familiarize him with a smaller toilet seat over the adult seat that can be removed later. He may be started on this routine as early as six months, atlhough it usually comes about seven to ten months of age.

By the third year most children have learned to control the bladder. When a child is about 15 months old his bladder is large enough to hold urine for about 2 hours. He can be encouraged to urinate when he is on the toilet seat for his bowel movement. Gradually he learns to tell his mother before his diaper is wet. He can wear panties as soon as he has gained some control. By degrees, he will learn to go to the toilet before he goes to bed at night; at naptime and after he gets up; when he comes in from play; before and after meals. This is the time to help him establish the habit of washing his hands after he goes to the toilet. When he has learned to use the toilet during the day, then possibly he can be awakened and put on the toilet at night. Of course, if he struggles, cries or cannot fully awaken, he needs more time and this may be put off for a while. Generally he will wake and ask to go, because he doesn't like a wet bed. Usually by the time he reaches his third birthday, he will be sleeping dry.

If a child is unable to control the bladder by the time he is 4 or 4½, something is wrong. It may be a physical or emotional disturbance. Take him up each night before the time he wets the bed; cut down on his liquids just before bedtime. If it does not result in improvement, you will naturally ask the help of the family doctor.

Health Habits . . .

All just discussed is part of helping the child develop health habits. In addition, from the time he begins to have real control over his actions, he should be taught to care for his body. He should become accustomed to brushing his teeth, the daily bath, and appreciating clean clothes. The things he uses should be his size so he can handle them. Being dirty comes naturally to a child; don't be alarmed when he wants to stay dirty. Admiration helps him understand "clean"; he does not think of cleanliness as a part of health or social custom.

Thumbsucking . . .

When a child past babyhood starts sucking his thumb again, it may be his way of getting certain satisfactions that he should be having in normal ways. More satisfactions and fewer tensions in his everyday life may solve the problem. The idea is not to take the comfort away but to remove the strain. He may need to be around other children; he may need something interesting to play with. Don't scold, just see that there are activities for him to do.

Most experts agree that thumbsucking probably doesn't change the shape of the jaw or mouth unless it persists after the second teeth appear. In the large majority of cases it is over before then.

THE SHUT-IN

By now you know what to expect from children of various ages and know that each child is an individual personality. You give time to understanding the child and winning his confidence, but it is worth it. Children respond to being treated as persons. Never let a child down; do not make promises you cannot keep. The child who is sick may be hard to handle if he has had some unpleasant experiences; if he has been spoiled, he will demand extra attention, but he won't respect you unless you ask cooperation and self-help from him.

The Long Illness . . .

Children have many of the same diseases that adults do. There are some differences in treatment and in the effects of the treatment. Take the rheumatic fever patient: The adult person does not find it too difficult to be quiet; a child has to give up the things that come natural to his age—running, jumping, playing. The older person has many of his experiences behind him; the child is just beginning his. It is harder for the child to be marked off as different from others; he wants to be a part of his group.

You can understand how a severe illness may affect children. For this reason, social and welfare workers, occupational and recreational therapists are constantly searching for ways in which to help the disabled child to lead a near-normal life.

Treating Him At Home . . .

When he is home, arrangements may be made through the school principal for a home teacher to call on him several times a week. A schedule of work is set up so that he can keep pace with his classmates and fit right in when the time to return to school comes. Friends from the classroom may be invited in at specific times if the doctor allows it.

CHILDHOOD DISEASES

Children usually begin to contract communicable diseases after they enter school or when they start to play with other children.

Because most of the childhood diseases make it necessary for the child to stay indoors for a certain period, and there is need for precaution against spreading the disease, problems arise when two or more children share the same bed or room. Local laws vary on this. If the other children in the family have not been exposed to the disease, they should be separated. Or if children have had contact with the sick member, they are kept out of school.

If a child gets a communicable disease, he should be isolated from other people until there is no danger of passing it on. There is a difference between isolation and quarantine: Isolation means separating the person who has the communicable disease from others in the home until there is no danger of passing the disease to someone else; quarantine means that no one is allowed to enter or leave the place where the person with the disease is located. Because you may have to take care of such children at home, you will find information about typical childhood diseases on the following pages.

Chickenpox . . .

Chickenpox is caused by a virus. It usually begins with a

slight fever and loss of appetite. Then a rash appears on the face or the body and then spreads to the arms and legs. Victims break out in small, raised, rose-pink spots which change to blisters. In some cases, there are so few of them that they almost escape notice. The blisters are filled with a clear fluid; they gradually dry, crust, and fall off after one to three weeks. The child is usually isolated until all the crusts have fallen off.

The chickenpox virus is in the nose and throat, in the blisters and under the crusts. It takes from fourteen to sixteen days from the time of exposure for chickenpox to develop. Usually the child is not very sick and begins to feel well after one to three days. The disease is sometimes confused with a mild case of smallpox because the rashes are somewhat alike. But smallpox usually begins with more violent symptoms. The blisters are mostly on the face, the legs, and arms, are deeper in the skin and have a pearl-like luster.

Nursing aid is mainly isolation, normal diet, and the usual comfort care. Try to keep the child from scratching the eruptions; your doctor will probably prescribe a medication to relieve itching. Keep the child amused and occupied until the isolation period is over.

Mumps . . .

Mumps is another virus disease. It affects the salivary glands, usually the *parotids*, which are located one in front of each ear. Children under two seldom have mumps and adults rarely have this disease. It takes closer contact to transmit mumps than most other communicable diseases. The incubation period is from two to three weeks.

Usually the first sign of mumps is the swelling of the parotid glands; sometimes only one of the glands is affected. Occasionally, before the swelling begins, there is a slight fever and sometimes an earache, sore throat, or vomiting. When these symptoms are mild, outside of discomfort when opening the mouth, the child may not feel sick at all. After two or three days, the swelling begins to go down, and usually disappears by the tenth day. Isolation from ten days to two weeks is usually long enough.

Children seldom have complications, but grown persons may. In men, mumps may cause inflammation of the testicles; in women, the ovaries, the breasts, or the external genitals may be affected. Convalescent serum will prevent mumps if the serum is given a few days after the person has been exposed.

The nursing care is isolation, heat applications to the swollen glands to relieve pain, a diet that does not require chewing. Acid foods during the painful stage cause the glands to work, therefore adding pain. Modern treatment allows the child up, with adequate rest periods. Adults are encouraged to remain in bed to eliminate complications.

Whooping Cough . . .

Whooping cough is a serious, highly contagious disease. More than 95% of the cases occur among children under five years of age. Very young infants are susceptible to it, but children over ten rarely have it. Usually it breaks out in the spring and early summer. The child has attacks of coughing and makes a crowing sound (the whoop) with each indrawn breath, as he coughs. A child can be immunized against whooping cough with injections of vaccine. All infants and children should be immunized because whooping cough can be very serious.

It takes about seven to fourteen days for whooping cough to develop. It begins with bronchitis and a slight temperature; the cough grows worse, leading to spasms. The first stage lasts about a week; the severe coughing stage from two to three weeks. It takes about two or three more weeks for the entire cough to disappear. Whooping cough can last from six weeks to several months if complications appear. The most serious and most common of these is pneumonia, it is apt to be fatal. Children also often have nosebleed, brought on by the coughing spasms. Keep their throats cleared of phlegm at night to avoid choking.

The isolation period should last through the coughing period. Medications are given to quiet the coughing spells. The child is kept indoors, although bed rest is not necessary unless he has complications. If vomiting occurs, small feedings are desirable.

Measles . . .

Measles is caused by a virus which is present in the nose, the mouth, the throat, the eyes, and in their discharges. It is highly contagious yet may not be recognized immediately because the symptoms resemble those of a cold in the beginning. The incubation period is from ten to fourteen days. Serum prepared from blood of persons convalescing from the measles will prevent the disease from developing. It works, however, only when given before the symptoms appear; if given later, although the serum does not prevent the disease, the attack will be mild.

Isolation should last until the discharges from the nose, throat, and eyes have disappeared and the temperature is normal. The eyes should be protected from the light by using an eye shade or turning the bed so that the patient's back will be to the window. Burn all discharges from the infected areas. Keep him in bed until all discharges have disappeared and the temperature is normal. When his temperature is elevated, the diet consists mostly of liquids tolerated; the amounts are increased and solid foods added as the fever subsides.

German Measles . . .

German measles is also caused by a virus but the disease is mild and lasts only a few days. It may be called the "three day measles." The symptoms are like measles symptoms but not nearly so severe and spots never appear inside the mouth. The rash appears on the face, then quickly spreads over the body; it disappears just as rapidly. In two to four days it has completely gone.

Isolation is usually very brief or not carried out at all because the infectious stage is so short. Diet is usually normal.

Rheumatic Fever . . .

Rheumatic fever, although not a communicable disease, is both a killer and a crippler. Except from accidents, more young children die of rheumatic fever than of any other cause; it is also responsible for a large part of adult heart disease. Usually, it begins in children between the ages of five and ten, but adults have it, too. One attack may do little damage, but it has a way of attacking again and again.

Rheumtic fever, a chronic disease, causes inflammation of the heart and the tissues that line the joints. The joints recover, but the damage to the heart may be permanent. The first attack may not harm the heart, but two-thirds of the victims do have permanent heart damage. The damage can be serious enough to make the person an invalid.

Rheumatic fever occurs more often in the cold, wet seasons. It seldom happens in a warm climate. Its exact cause is not known but in nearly all cases it has been found to have been preceded by an attack of respiratory *streptococcal* infection. However, people do have rheumatic fever with no preceding infection. Some people are more susceptible to the disease than others. If a person has had rheumatic fever, an attack of streptococcus infection will nearly always bring it on again.

There is no proof that a person inherits rheumatic fever, although, as with other diseases, he may inherit the tendency. Malnutrition makes one more susceptible; many victims live in crowded quarters; others live in damp, drafty homes. Although a person who has rheumatic fever cannot pass it on to anyone else, other people about him may give him a harmful infection, thereby bringing on a fresh attack of rheumatic fever.

Rheumatic fever begins suddenly, usually after a cold or sore throat. The patient complains of aching in the arms and legs and has a low-grade fever, which increases rapidly. Then the joints begin to swell and become extremely painful. The pain may begin in one joint and progress to others, or it may affect several joints at a time. It usually lasts from a few days to a week in each joint and gradually subsides. The joints are completely normal after the attack.

Children may complain of many signs that go unnoticed. Various aches and pains are put off with the idea that they are "growing pains." Jerky, nervous movements, frequent nose bleed, loss of appetite and weight, tiredness—these may all be the danger signs of rheumatic fever in your young brothers and sisters. They may go unheeded, because they are connected with other possible disturbances, too.

In treatment of rheumatic fever, bed rest is the main requirement; this protects the heart and guards against another attack. Aspirin and other medications may be ordered to relieve pain.

The disease is still present after the outer symptoms disappear; remember that bed rest is important until all tests have shown negative. A certain blood test will tell how active it is. A person who has rheumatic fever should have periodic heart examinations to check on any heart signs, even if there were no signs of heart involvement during the attack.

You must remember that all people in the home who have slight colds or other infections must be kept away from the rheumatic patient so he will not become reinfected, thereby bringing on another attack. He must be kept warm and out of drafts. His diet is normal. It will take considerable thought to keep a child quiet and amused. The doctor will tell you what the patient can safely do without endangering his heart. Co-operation on the part of the patient is very important; explain that staying in bed now will give him his chance to recover and do what he wants to do later on in life. Keep him occupied but quiet. Protect him from falling out of bed by tying sheets to side of bed.

Tests show that some of the sulfa drugs and penicillin help to prevent second attacks of rheumatic fever. When your patient is taking these drugs, he should be given plenty of fluids, since they need water to do their work and to be flushed from the body.

HEART DISEASE

Many of those who have rheumatic fever do not have heart disease; many others do. How does heart disease affect a child's life? The following classifications of people with heart disease, prepared by the American Heart Association, show what they can safely do:

1. Patients who can take part in activity—such children can go to school and do anything that other children do.

2. Patients who are allowed ordinary activities but not strenuous ones—children can go to school but must not take part in competitive sports, such as races, football, basketball, or tennis.

3. Patients who must be moderate about ordinary activities and must avoid strenuous ones—children can go to school but should be given extra time for such things as climbing stairs.

4. Patients who definitely must limit even ordinary activities—children must learn not to run and should never be allowed to become overtired; they should also have definite rest periods.

5. Patients who should have complete rest—children may be allowed to sit up in chair; or they may have to stay in bed.

The need for medical supervision is constant, but you should help the child with a heart disease to be as much like other children as possible. Teach him to learn to live within the limits of his own disability. If he seems bewildered, give him assurance and affection. Do little things to show that you love him—a smile, a greeting, a caress—these mean much to the restless child. If he is receiving special school instruction, sit with him while he works, and read to him. Give him the feeling that he is not going to be left out or slighted just because he can't do all the things he used to do. An occasional friend in for a quiet game will help his morale, too.

SKIN DISEASES

IMPETIGO

Impetigo is caused by a very infectious organism. Blisters form and ooze pus; then scabs or crusts appear on the infected spots. The organisms, carried on clothing and other objects, spread rapidly. School children pass impetigo from one to another. Isolation and instructions are important to help people with impetigo to keep from spreading it. The usual treatment is the application of solutions of oil to soften the crusts which are then removed; an antibiotic cream is then applied.

SCABIES OR "7-YEAR ITCH"

Scabies are tiny parasites that burrow under the outer layer of skin. A month or so after they enter the body, the skin begins to itch, especially in the warmer body parts—under arms, around the waist, in the groin. Red spots with tiny blisters appear and tiny blisters or depressions appear, mainly between the fingers and toes. The parasites get into personal clothing and bed clothing, so special precautions are necessary to keep scabies from spreading. Boiling the clothes or ironing kills the parasites. The usual recommended treatment is a hot bath to open up the infected spots followed by the application of a prescribed medication, usually some form of sulphur preparation. Most of the medications containing sulphur stain the clothing, so it is advisable to wear an old pair of pajamas that can be bleached later. The ointment is kept on for twenty-four hours and all bed clothing and personal garments are kept clean.

RINGWORM

Ringworm is a fungus infection and may appear on many parts of the body, but most often, the infection attacks the scalp, the areas about the fingernail beds, the groin and feet. It may have its start at the site of a single hair, then gradually increase into a circular lesion or roughened area up to an inch or two across the diameter. The base of the hair is literally eaten up by the fungi spores. The skin becomes scaly and inflamed. It may be itchy, especially if the victim received the original contact from an animal. The fungi may be transmitted by various means but there are many different types and special laboratory tests are necessary in order for direct treatment to be effective. The cure of the lesions requires a long period of application of some fungicidal substance, such as tincture of iodine or an ointment containing undecylinic acid (Desenex).

THE SPASTIC CHILD

Spastic paralysis is paralysis of a whole arm or leg, or both, or half of the body. Muscle movements are not entirely gone but the child has no control over them. It is caused by a birth injury that causes a change to the brain. The affected muscles are tense. When the child begins to walk, the muscles become stiff and noticeable. The muscles on the inside of the legs are stronger than those on the outside; therefore the spastic person walks with a swinging, cross-legged walk or gait.

Primary medical care is preventing contracture of the muscles. Splints are used and the process of muscle re-education begins. He progresses slowly to the sitting up, crawling, and walking stage. It does no good to hurry him, for it only makes him more tense and less able to move. Some spastic children may be mentally deficient, but the majority are normal or superior. The mentally normal child can be taught to use his limbs.

The Crippled Children's Service provides the individual care he needs to create opportunities comparable to those of normal children, for those who cannot pay for specialized care for their youngsters. Such aid is necessary; the intelligent child feels helpless because his body will not always do what he wants of it. He feels insecure; he is unattractive to look at; he can't do many things that other children do. He may have a speech defect and his uncoordinated muscles make it impossible for him to write well if at all.

His ambitions may be much greater than anything he will ever be able to do. It is important to help the spastic child

Co-ordination develops through occupational activity as these cerebral palsy victims thread and stack spools.

AMERICAN OCCUPATIONAL THERAPY ASSN.

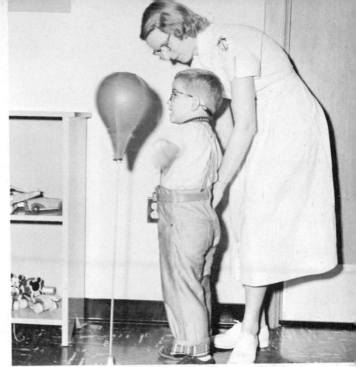

A therapist trains a 5-year-old boy before he can be fitted with artificial arms. AMERICAN OCCUPATIONAL THERAPY ASSN.

find the things he *can* do satisfactorily. He must be shown how to face reality and make the most of life in spite of his handicap. In short, he learns to live with his handicap as do other physically handicapped children. See Chapter 14.

- What do you understand by the term "normal child"?
- What do we mean by the milestones of a child's growth? How much importance should be placed on them? Are they always right?
- What will a child's play tell you about him?
- Do you have a smaller sister in your family who doesn't like to eat at mealtime? What can you do about this?
- When should a child begin his regular health habits?
- Why does a child have difficulties when first starting to school? What can you do to help him over this period?
- What are the most common childhood diseases?
- What special precautions should be taken when your little brother gets the measles? Why are these necessary?
- Why are mumps so serious for adults?
- Give a short summary of what you understand about rheumatic fever and some important steps in nursing care.
- Do you know a spastic person who is in your age group? Make it a point to appreciate his inner brightness and capabilities.

WORDS YOU SHOULD KNOW

Absorbent—soaks up liquid like a sponge.

Acute—sharp, as pain; acting keenly on the senses.

Adolescence—the period from the end of childhood (12-13) to the beginning of adulthood (18-21).

Alkali—a soluble salt, or any substance having the marked basic characteristics of a salt, such as sharp or bitter taste and ability to neutralize acids.

Allergy—excessive sensitivity to any specific substance that is harmless to most people.

Amenorrhea—abnormal absence of menstrual discharge.

Anatomy—the structure of an animal or plant; or the study of that structure.

Antibody—a substance produced by the body cells to fight the germs of a specific disease.

Antidote—a substance which neutralizes poisons and their effects.

Antitoxin—a substance produced in the body which counteracts body poisons. Normally produced in the blood and other body fluids, antitoxin may be artificially prepared.

Artery—one of the vessels carrying blood from the heart through the body.

Asphyxia—too little oxygen or too much carbon dioxide in the blood, as from suffocation or drowning, causing death or suspended animation.

Astringent—agent which checks secretion of mucous membranes or contracts and hardens tissues, limiting secretions.

Axilla—underarm.

Bacillus—a rod shaped bacterium; loosely, any bacterium, especially if disease-producing.

Bacterium—a tiny organism, consisting of a single cell. Some are useful; others cause communicable disease.

Bile—fluid secreted by the liver; important as a digestive juice.

Bones—see chart on page 42 listing all bones.

Buccal—pertaining to the cheeks or the cavity of the mouth.

Capillary—a tiny thin-walled blood vessel, through which food nutrients are absorbed by the tissues.

Carrier—a person who has in his body the germs of a communicable disease, although he may show no signs of it himself.

Cerebral—pertaining to the brain.

Chronic—continuing for a long time, as a disease or illness.

Clavicle—the collar bone; situated between the breastbone and shoulder blade.

Coccyx—last four bones of the spine, below and working with the sacrum. (See definition later.)

Colloid—any substance, like gelatin, that diffuses but does not dissolve in water.

Colostrum—secretions from the lactiferous (milk-bearing) glands before the onset of true milk.

Communicable disease—any disease caused by a living germ or virus, no matter how it may be transmitted from the sick to the well; an infectious disease.

Conception—the act of becoming pregnant; the fertilization of the egg or ovum.

Congestion—localized inflammation or "overfullness" of blood vessels, sometimes resulting in infection.

Conjunctiva—mucous membrane which lines the eyelids and is reflected on eyeballs.

Contagious disease—a disease which may be transmitted by contact with someone who has the disease.

Contaminated—containing germs, viruses, or other agents capable of causing disease.

Convalescence—a period of gradual recovery from illness, beginning with the disappearance of the symptoms.

Cornea—clear, transparent, glasslike portion of the eyeball.

Cranium—the eight bones of the head comprising the skull.

Croup—an illness marked by difficult breathing, throat muscle spasms, hoarse coughing, and sometimes by the formation of a false membrane in the air passages.

Cyanosis—slightly blue-gray skin discoloration, caused by deficiency of oxygen in the blood.

Cystoscopy—visual examination of the bladder with an instrument called a cystoscope.

Decubitus ulcer—bedsore.

Diagnosis—the act of recognizing disease from its symptoms; also, the decision reached.

Diaphragm—a partition of muscles and sinews between the cavity of the chest and the abdomen.

Disease—see index for specific diseases.

Disinfect—to free from infection, especially by destroying disease germs; frequently done by use of heat or chemicals.

Distention—enlargement; swelling; dilation.

Douche—a stream of water or vapor directed against a part of the body or into a body cavity. This method is sometimes used in giving a bath.

Duodenum—the first part of the small intestine, between the stomach and the middle division or jejunum.

Dysmenorrhea—difficult and painful menstruation.

Dyspnea—difficult or labored breathing.

WORDS YOU SHOULD KNOW

Embryo—organism in earliest stages within the mother's body.

Endemic disease—a disease constantly occurring among a particular class of people, or in a given locality.

Enzyme—any of a class of complex organic substances that accelerate specific chemical transformations in plants and animals, as in the digestion of food.

Epidemic—sudden temporary increase in the occurrence of a communicable disease, not limited to any particular class of people or small locality.

Epiglottis—a thin plate of stretchy, yellow cartilage which forms the upper part of the larynx and protects the glottis during swallowing.

Esophagus—tube that carries food from the pharynx to the stomach; the gullet.

Eustachian tube—auditory tube from middle ear to the upper pharynx which equalizes pressure on both sides of the ear drum.

Fahrenheit—scale for measuring temperature in which the boiling point of water is 212° and the freezing point 32° above zero.

Fallopian tube—in female mammals, one of two tubes which conduct the egg from the ovary to the uterus.

Feces—excretion of the bowels.

Fetus—the child in the mother's womb, especially from the third month until birth.

Flatulence—the presence of gas in the stomach and intestines.

Fractured bone—broken or cracked bone; broken cartilage sometimes is also referred to as fractured.

Gamma globulin—a substance in the blood, rich in antibodies, helping to protect against disease.

Gastric—pertaining to, or situated near, the stomach.

Germ—a tiny, living organism; especially, any of the disease-causing bacteria.

Globulin (see gamma globulin)

Glottis—space between the two vocal cords in the larynx.

Hemorrhage—discharge of blood from the blood vessels, caused by injury; often used in reference to excessive bleeding.

Hemorrhoid—painful swelling about the anus, caused by dilation of blood vessels and nerves.

Ileum—last part of the small intestine, between the jejunum and large intestine.

Illness—see index for specific illnesses.

Immunity—power of resisting infection or disease; may be resistance to infection in general (nonspecific), or to a particular disease (specific).

Immunization—process or treatment by which a person acquires resistance to disease.

Incubation of disease—time between entry of disease germs into the body and appearance of first symptoms.

Infection—condition caused by living, disease-producing organism (germ, virus) entering the body and multiplying.

Inflammation—reaction of body tissues to injury, characterized by redness, swelling, pain, and heat.

Isolation—separation of an infected person from others during the time when the disease is communicable.

Jejunum—second or middle division of the small intestine, between the duodenum and the ileum.

Lacteal—milky or pertaining to milk.

Larynx—the voice organ.

Lymph—nearly colorless, coagulable fluid, composed chiefly of blood plasma and colorless corpuscles; contained in lymphatic vessels, which stores, absorbs, or stops toxins.

Malnutrition—faulty or imperfect nutrition.

Masticate—to chew.

Mucous membrane—thin tissue lining the throat, nose, and other cavities and tubes of the body which have external openings.

Mucus—sticky, slimy secretion produced by and protecting the mucous membranes.

Neuralgia—acute pain along the course of a nerve; also, the ailment causing such pain.

Nutrition—the sum of the processes by which the body absorbs and uses food substances.

Organs—see index for specific organs.

Otitis media—an inflammation of the middle ear.

Ovaries—in female mammals, a pair of glandular organs in which the eggs are produced.

Palate—the roof of the mouth.

Paralysis—loss of muscle function or sensation.

Pediatrician—doctor who specializes in treating children.

Pediculosis—infestation with lice.

Peristalsis—the wormlike, wave motion of the intestines, caused by muscle contractions, which moves the contents onward.

Pharynx—food-carrying tube between the mouth cavity and the esophagus; situated back of the nose, mouth, and larynx.

Physiology—science dealing with the function of living organisms and their parts.

Placenta—the structure by which the fetus or embryo is nourished, in humans and some other mammals; located on wall of uterus; fetus is attached to it by the umbilical cord.

Plasma—the fluid part of blood, lymph, or milk.

WORDS YOU SHOULD KNOW

Pleura—delicate, watery membrane that lines the thorax and folds back over the lungs, in mammals.

Pneumonia—inflammation of the lungs.

Prenatal—before birth.

Ptyalin—enzyme found in saliva.

Quarantine—restriction to a certain building or area; placed upon a person who has been exposed to a communicable disease, so that he will not spread it to others. Usually applied outside a hospital.

Rectum—the end of the large intestine.

Resuscitation—artificial respiration or breathing aid.

Roseola—any rose-colored rash.

Sacrum—bone made up of five united vertebrae, at the low end of the spine.

Schick test—a test for susceptibility to diphtheria.

Serum—the watery portion of an animal fluid remaining after coagulation.
Blood serum: contains specific immune bodies, as antitoxins.
Convalescent serum: serum obtained from the blood of a person who has recently recovered from a specific disease; such blood will contain bodies immune to the disease from which the person was suffering.

Sinus—a hollow or cavity; specifically, a cavity in a bone of the skull which communicates with the nostrils and contains air.

Sordes—foul matter, especially the dirt and crusts that form on the teeth and lips during some diseases. Common after long spells of mild fever.

Spermatozoa—mature male germ cells which fertilize the egg of the female.

Sternum—flat, oblong front chest bone of humans; sometimes called the breastbone.

Streptococcus—a germ belonging to the cocci family of bacteria, of which several species are extremely harmful in causing various diseases.

Subcutaneous—under the skin.

Suppository—a medicinal preparation applied by inserting it into certain body openings.

Susceptible—not resistant to a specific disease; able to catch a disease or likely to be severely affected by it.

Tepid—moderately warm; lukewarm.

Tetanus—a painful, often fatal, infectious disease characterized by spasms of the voluntary muscles, particularly along the base of neck and spine. Commonly called "lockjaw."

Thermometer—an instrument for measuring temperature.

Thoracic—pertaining to the thorax; in humans this is roughly the chest area.

Tourniquet—any instrument used to control hemorrhage.

Toxin—a poisonous substance produced in a vegetable or animal organism.

Toxoid—a weakened toxin used to immunize a person, as against diphtheria; the poisonous effects are destroyed, but the toxoid is still strong enough to induce the formation of antibodies.

Umbilicus—naval; scar on the abdomen where the umbilical cord was attached.

Vaccinate—to inoculate with any substance (called a vaccine) that prevents or lessens the effects of a disease.

Vein—a vessel carrying blood from the body tissues to the heart.

Virus—any of a group of disease-causing agents, so small they cannot be seen under an ordinary microscope nor caught in a filter.

BIBLIOGRAPHY

Books, listed by author or source . . .

American Cancer Society, Inc., *A Cancer Source Book for Nurses,* New York, N.Y., 1956.

American National Red Cross, *Textbook on Red Cross Home Nursing,* The Blakiston Co., Philadelphia, Pa., 1950.

Cole, W. H., and Puestow, Charles B., *First Aid: Surgical and Medical* 5th ed., Appleton Century Crofts, Inc., New York, N.Y., 1960.

Dakin, Florence, and Thompson, Ella M., *Simplified Nursing,* 5th ed., J. P. Lippincott Co., Philadelphia, Pa., 1951.

Day, Sister Mary Agnita, *Basic Science in Nursing Arts,* 2nd ed., C. V. Mosby Co., St. Louis, Mo., 1947.

Hansen, Helen F., *A Review of Nursing,* 8th ed., W. B. Saunders Co., Philadelphia, Pa., 1951.

Harmer, Bertha, and Henderson, Virginia, *Textbook of the Principles and Practice of Nursing,* The Macmillan Co., New York, N.Y., 1942.

Hawley, Estelle E.; Garden, Grace; and Munves, Elizabeth, *The Art and Science of Nutrition,* 4th ed., C. V. Mosby Co., St. Louis, Mo., 1955.

Hull, Edgar, and Perrodin, Cecelia, *Medical Nursing,* 5th ed., F. A. Davis Co., Philadelphia, Pa., 1956.

Kimber, Diana; Gray, Carolyn; and Stackpole, Caroline, *Textbook of Anatomy and Physiology,* 11th ed., The Macmillan Co., New York, N.Y., 1952.

Leake, Mary, *Manual of Simple Nursing Procedures,* 2nd ed., W. B. Saunders Co., Philadelphia, Pa., 1956.

Lilly and Company, *A Pocket Reference for Diabetics,* Indianapolis, Ind., 1957.

Minkoff, Anna B., *A Community-based Home Care Plan* (Progress in Nursing Service), Nursing Outlook, New York, N.Y., 1957.

Rothweiller, Ella, and White, Jean, *The Art and Science of Nursing,* 4th ed., F. A. Davis Co., Philadelphia, Pa., 1956.

Schering Corporation, *Latest Reports on Therapy with Meticorten,* Bloomfield, N.J., 1957.

Shepard, Katherine, *Textbook of Attendant or Practical Nursing,* The Macmillan Co., New York, N.Y., 1948.

Upjohn Company, *Vitamin Manual,* Kalamazoo, Mich., 1957.

Williams, Jesse F., *Personal Hygiene Applied,* 8th ed., W. B. Saunders Co. Philadelphia, Pa., 1946.

Williams, Jesse F., and Brownell, Clifford Lee, *The Administration of Health Education and Physical Education,* 3rd ed., W. B. Saunders Co., Philadelphia, Pa., 1949.

Woodward, Henry L., and Gardner, Bernice, *Obstetrical Management and Nursing,* 6th ed., F. A. Davis Co., Philadelphia, Pa., 1959.

Periodicals, listed by author or source . . .

American Heart Association (two pamphlets), *Heart Disease Caused by Coronary Arteriosclerosis,* New York, N.Y., 1956, and *What You Should Know about Rheumatic Fever,* 1956. (Both distributed by Delaware State Board of Health, Dover, Del.).

John Hancock Mutual Life Insurance Company, Health Education Service, *Diversions for the Sick,* Boston, Mass., 1954.

Lederle Laboratories Division, American Cyanid Co., *What Is an Antibiotic?* 1957.

Metropolitan Life Insurance Company, *Respiratory Diseases,* New York, N.Y., 1954.

National League for Nursing (three pamphlets), *The College Way to a Nursing Career,* Committee on Careers, New York, N.Y., 1956; *Nursing Has a Future for You,* Committee on Careers, N.Y., 1956, and *Preparing Tomorrow's Nurses* (by Elizabeth Ogg), Public Affairs Pamphlet No. 185, Public Affairs Committee, New York, N.Y., 1952.

National Tuberculosis Association, *Tuberculosis: Basic Facts in Basic English,* 1956. (Distributed by Delaware State Board of Health, Dover, Del.).

Pet Milk Company, Research Division, *A Guide for Prenatal Care,* St. Louis, Mo., 1956.

Schering Corporation, *Modern Methods of Allergy Management,* Bloomfield, N.J., 1958.

Thompson, Harry E., *Climate and Rheumatic Diseases,* Arizona Medicine, Vol. 8, No. 4, April, 1951.

United States Department of Agriculture (two pamphlets), *Essentials of an Adequate Diet,* Home Economics Research Report No. 3, 1957, and *Family Fare,* Home and Garden Bulletin No. 1, 1955.

INDEX